A Guide to Neuropsychological Testing for Health Care Professionals

Eric R. Arzubi, MD, is a second-year resident in psychiatry at the Yale School of Medicine. He is working toward completing a fellowship in child and adolescent psychiatry and hopes to work with school-age children who struggle with mental illness and comorbid learning dysfunctions.

Dr. Arzubi graduated with a BS from the Georgetown University School of Foreign Service in 1991. He worked as a journalist in Buenos Aires, Argentina, reporting for Bloomberg Business News and, after 2 years, moved to New York City to pursue a career in finance. After 6 years as a Latin American bond trader, he was ultimately promoted to Vice President at Morgan Stanley.

Feeling unfulfilled with life on Wall Street, he turned his focus to his true passion: medicine. He completed his premed requirements at Columbia University and graduated from the Yale School of Medicine in 2008. During his time at the Yale School of Medicine, Dr. Arzubi was a 3-year member of the School's Education Policy and Curriculum Committee. Also, during that time, he was a 3-year member of the School's Committee of the American Academy of Child and Adolescent Psychiatry. He was an active member and a student leader of the Donald J. Cohen Medical Student Fellowship in Child Psychiatry for 5 years. In 2008, Dr. Arzubi was named a Leadership Fellow of the Connecticut Health Foundation; the goal of the Fellowship is to train future leaders to tackle racial and ethnic disparities in health care.

Dr. Arzubi was drawn to child and adolescent psychiatry through his part-time work tutoring children in grades K–12. He and his wife, Ela, owned and managed a learning center in Westport, CT, called Raging Knowledge, from 2000 to 2009.

Elisa Mambrino, PhD, is a psychologist licensed in Connecticut and New York. Her clinical training, experience, and interests focus on individualized psychological, psychoeducational, and neuropsychological assessment, primarily with children, adolescents, and young adults. Dr. Mambrino was a Marie Kessel Postdoctoral Fellow in the Department of Psychiatry at Columbia University College of Physicians and Surgeons. She also completed a Postdoctoral Fellowship at the Yale University School of Medicine's Child Study Center. In 2003, Dr. Mambrino received her PhD from Columbia University's Teachers College in School Psychology, a program accredited by the American Psychological Association (APA). She completed an APA-accredited, pre-doctoral internship in Clinical Neuropsychology and Rehabilitation Psychology at Mount Sinai Hospital and Mount Sinai School of Medicine in Manhattan. In her career as part of a multidisciplinary treatment team, Dr. Mambrino has performed individualized neuropsychological assessments in a variety of hospital settings: outpatient clinics, day hospital, day treatment, locked inpatient psychiatric units, as well as inpatient spinal cord and brain injury rehabilitation settings.

A Guide to Neuropsychological Testing for Health Care Professionals

ERIC R. ARZUBI, MD

ELISA MAMBRINO, PhD

Editors

SPRINGER PUBLISHING COMPANY

New York

Springer Publishing Company, LLC
11 West 42nd Street
New York, NY 10036
www.springerpub.com

Acquisitions Editor: Philip Laughlin
Production Editor: Pamela Lankas
Cover Design: David Levy
Composition: International Graphic Services

Ebook ISBN: 978-0-8261-4416-4

10 11 12 13 14 / 5 4 3 2 1

The author and the publisher of this Work have made every effort to use sources believed to be reliable to provide information that is accurate and compatible with the standards generally accepted at the time of publication. Because medical science is continually advancing, our knowledge base continues to expand. Therefore, as new information becomes available, changes in procedures become necessary. We recommend that the reader always consult current research and specific institutional policies before performing any clinical procedure. The author and publisher shall not be liable for any special, consequential, or exemplary damages resulting, in whole or in part, from the readers' use of, or reliance on, the information contained in this book. The publisher has no responsibility for the persistence or accuracy of URLs for external or third-party Internet Web sites referred to in this publication and does not guarantee that any content on such Web sites is, or will remain, accurate or appropriate.

Library of Congress Cataloging-in-Publication Data

A guide to neuropsychological testing for health care professionals / Eric R. Arzubi, Elisa Mambrino, editors.
    p. cm.
Includes bibliographical references and index.
ISBN 978-0-8261-4415-7 (alk. paper)
1. Neuropsychological tests. I. Arzubi, Eric R. II. Mambrino, Elisa.
RC386.6.N48G845 2010
616.8'0475—dc22
                        2010006466

Printed in the United States of America by Bang Printing

This book is dedicated to my wife, Ela, and my two girls, Katya and Nathalia. They have been lovingly patient and supportive during my ongoing work on this volume and throughout my medical training. Moreover, I am forever grateful to my mentors at the Yale Child Study Center, especially Jim Leckman and Andres Martin. Their wisdom and guidance were instrumental in my decision to pursue a career in child and adolescent psychiatry, and in developing the confidence to take on this rewarding project. Thank you also to the Yale Department of Psychiatry, which afforded me the time to work on this book through the Clinical and Academic Skills Enhancement (CASE) initiative.

—***Eric Arzubi***

I wish to dedicate my work on this book to my family—young and old, near and far—for all their support and love.

—***Elisa Mambrino***

Contents

Contributors

Lois M. Black, PhD
Oregon Health & Science University
Beaverton, OR

Mark A. Blais, PsyD
Massachusetts General Hospital
Boston, MA
Harvard University
Boston, MA

Ellen B. Braaten, PhD
Massachusetts General Hospital
Boston, MA
Harvard University
Boston, MA

Christine L. Castillo, PhD
Children's Medical Center
Dallas, TX
University of Texas Southwestern Medical Center
Dallas, TX

Melody Nichols Dilk, PhD, JD
Forensics Psychological Consultants of Indiana
Indianapolis, IN

Dario J. Englot, PhD
Yale University
New Haven, CT

Catherine A. Fiorello, PhD
Temple University
Philadelphia, PA

Robert T. Fraser, PhD
University of Washington
Seattle, WA

Joy Goldberg, PhD
Phoenix Children's Hospital
Phoenix, AZ

Gerald Goldstein, PhD
VA Pittsburgh Healthcare System
Pittsburgh, PA
University of Pittsburgh
Pittsburgh, PA

Ashley A. Gorman, PhD
Morris Psychology Group
Parsippany, NJ

Lynn Grush, MD
Massachusetts General Hospital
Boston, MA
Harvard University
Boston, MA

James B. Hale, PhD
Philadelphia College of Osteopathic Medicine
Philadelphia, PA

Thomas A. Hammeke, PhD
Medical College of Wisconsin
Milwaukee, WI

Mary R. Hibbard, PhD
New York University
New York, NY

Erica K. Johnson, PhD
Western Washington University
Bellingham, WA

David E. Layman, PhD
Mount Sinai School of Medicine
New York, NY

Robert F. Newby, PhD
Medical College of Wisconsin
Milwaukee, WI

Ellen O'Donnell, PhD
Massachusetts General Hospital
Boston, MA
Harvard University
Boston, MA

Martha Pierce, PhD
New York Univeristy
New York, NY

Molly Colvin Putnam, PhD
Massachusetts General Hospital
Boston, MA
Harvard University
Boston, MA

Ara J. Schmitt, PhD
Duquesne University
Pittsburgh, PA

Marisa Spann, PhD
Yale University
New Haven, CT

Robert K. Stewart, Jr., PhD
Mount Sinai School of Medicine
New York, NY

Ayame Takahashi, MD
Southern Illinois University
Springfield, IL

Rajesh R. Tampi, MD
Masonicare Behavioral Health
Wallingford, CT
Yale University
New Haven, CT

Rebecca Thompson, MEd
Temple University
Philadelphia, PA

Jay M. Uomoto, PhD
Veterans Administration Puget Sound Health Care System
Seattle, WA

Wilfred G. van Gorp, PhD
Columbia University
New York, NY

Nadia Webb, PsyD
Children's Hospital of New Orleans
New Orleans, LA

Brian Willoughby, PhD
Massachusetts General Hospital
Boston, MA
Harvard University
Boston, MA

David L. Wodrich, PhD
Arizona State University
Tempe, AZ

Kristina F. Zdanys, MD
New York University
New York, NY

Preface

Effective clinical work requires dedicated professionals who are willing to collaborate and share their talents with others in the pursuit of a common goal. The same can be said about the publication of this book, which I hope will be both educational and practical. This book demystifies the field of neuropsychology and renders neuropsychologists and their reports more accessible. In fact, the opening chapter, "What is Neuropsychology?" by Gerald Goldstein, PhD, eloquently answers many of the most basic questions for the reader right away. The remaining chapters open many different windows to this specialty and celebrate its growing use among clinicians, lawyers, and teachers. Physicians- and psychologists-in-training who are interested in brain–behavior relationships should read this book. Today's practicing clinicians who find reading neuropsychological reports challenging will find this material enlightening and may even find that they can make better use of future neuropsychological consults. School-based practitioners will find at least four chapters that provide very practical answers to important clinical and legal questions surrounding the assessment and treatment of children requiring special education services, as well as chapters that are full of illustrative case examples. *A Guide to Neuropsychological Testing for Health Care Professionals* is not meant to be a textbook. It is designed to be a practical and user-friendly book authored by some of the country's most respected clinicians and professionals, all of whom regularly employ and make use of the rich set of tools made available by neuropsychology.

Neuropsychology focuses on understanding the complex relationship between the brain and human behavior. Although psychiatry and neurology can claim to make attempts at the same, neuropsychology, a subspecialty of psychology, is a field that makes this task its primary goal. In fact, psychiatrists and neurologists, among other clinicians, often rely on the specialized knowledge and skills of neuropsychologists to appreciate the subtleties and nuances of brain–behavior dynamics.

I am a 40-year-old psychiatrist-in-training with a strong interest in knowing a lot more about neuropsychology. From 2001 to 2009, my wife, Ela, and I owned and managed a learning center, called Raging Knowledge, dedicated to supporting children in grades K–12 who were struggling in school. Our work with nearly a thousand families and their children uncovered my passion for child and adolescent psychiatry, and it inspired a particular interest in understanding the relationship between emotional–behavioral problems and learning dysfunctions. It turns out that neuropsychology provides essential tools for the assessment and treatment of children who have comorbid psychopathology and learning problems.

Early in my work with our students, I encountered the daunting 20-page "neuropsych" report, a document that was generated by a local psychologist, or perhaps an out-of-state nationally acclaimed expert, following hours and hours of exhaustive interviewing and testing of a patient. Now, let me mention that on good days, I consider myself to be a smart guy, however, trying to read through some of these reports quickly made me challenge that notion. I was frustrated; I found the reports to be dense, data-packed, and loaded with psychological jargon that only specialists could understand.

As a result, I reached out to the authors of these reports and learned an important lesson: Communication and collaboration is fundamental to successful clinical work. The wonderful psychologists on the other end of the phone, or across a small table at a local diner, introduced me to the world of neuropsychology and the field's powerful ability to inform families, clinicians, and other caring professionals about a certain family member, client, or patient. With neuropsychological testing, geriatric psychiatrists can successfully track subtle cognitive changes in their patients, while neurologists depend on neuropsychologists to better understand the effects of traumatic brain injuries in their patients.

Although discussing individual cases was very helpful, I wanted to know more about neuropsychology and how to read reports. Specifically, I wanted to understand how these extensive psychological work-ups could help me teach my students more effectively. About 50% of children with attention-deficit/hyperactivity disorder (ADHD) also struggle with comorbid learning disorders. I hoped that the detailed diagnostic testing could uncover whether the source of academic problems was due to the ADHD or an underlying reading disability. I was fortunate to come across two very practical books, *Straight Talk About Psychological Testing for Kids*, by Ellen Braaten, PhD, and Gretchen Felopulos, PhD, and *Children's Psychological Testing: A Guide for Non-psychologists*, by David Wodrich, PhD. The authors, two of whom have written chapters for this book, gave me a much deeper understanding of neuropsychology, and a greater appreciation for the rich information revealed by well-written neuropsychological reports.

As I met other medical professionals, including pediatricians, neurologists, and child psychiatrists, I discovered that many of them also struggled to understand much more beyond the "Recommendations" section of neuropsychological reports that they read. It also appeared that neuropsychological reports were increasingly surfacing in nonclinical settings, creating challenges for professionals such as special education lawyers and school teachers who were unable to take full advantage of the wealth of important diagnostic and intervention information contained in these documents.

That's when I thought to create this volume—*A Guide to Neuropsychological Testing for Health Care Professionals*. There are many different specialists who rely on neuropsychological testing to inform their work, including pediatricians, child and adolescent psychiatrists, social workers, special education lawyers, forensic psychiatrists, neurologists, adult psychiatrists, geriatric psychiatrists, school psychologists, clinical psychologists, speech and language therapists, rehabilitation psychologists, and psychotherapists, among others. Although it seemed like a good idea to me, I was hoping a present-day practicing neuropsychologist would agree that writing a book aimed at reintroducing neuropsychology to this broad collection of practitioners and professionals would truly be a good idea.

Elisa Mambrino, PhD, a neuropsychologist, loved the idea and generously agreed to join me in this endeavor. In fact, she identified many of the specialists listed above as important consumers of neuropsychological consultations. Philip Laughlin, our primary editor at Springer Publishing Company, came up with the idea for splitting the book into two broad sections based on the lifespan. Finally, our distinguished contributing authors did the heavy lifting, so to speak—in drafting informative, practical, and readable chapters that should help readers understand the importance of neuropsychological testing in a variety of settings.

—Eric R. Arzubi, MD

REFERENCES

Braaten, E., & Felopulos, G. (2004). *Straight talk about psychological testing for kids.* New York: Guilford Press.

Wodrich, D. L. (1997). *Children's psychological testing: A guide for nonpsychologists.* Baltimore, MD: Paul H. Brookes.

Acknowledgments

All the individuals mentioned here, as well as unnamed others, were instrumental in helping the contributing authors, my coeditor, and me to create this book. We transformed conversations into ideas, ideas into pages of text, and pages of text into a book that contributes to a continuing dialectic on aspects of neuropsychological testing's utility. The multidisciplinary training of my coeditor and Yale colleague, Dr. Eric Arzubi, as well as his prior experience on Wall Street and as a journalist, primed him to ask sensible questions about neuropsychological testing and inspired his quest for answers that culminated in this volume. We offer our thanks and appreciation to our chapter authors, whose talent and diligent efforts over many months made this book come to life.

I wish to acknowledge Philip Laughlin, Senior Editor at Springer Publishing Company, for all of his instrumental guidance and patience in helping us launch this book. Senior Vice President, Sheri W. Sussman, guided us through the later stages with aplomb and a steady hand. I am grateful to them both. The sharp eye of Assistant Editor, Kerry Vegliando, was invaluable in helping with innumerable details, large and small.

To those chapter authors who provided some of my clinical training and/or were faculty members at hospitals where I received some of my professional training, I thank you for contributing to my initiation into the guild that provides specialty training in neuropsychological testing in particular, and into the helping professions in general.

—Elisa Mambrino, PhD

Introduction

This book is devoted to neuropsychological assessment, which is a specialty practiced by licensed psychologists who possess the requisite predoctoral, doctoral, and postdoctoral level education, training, and clinical experience in neuropsychology. Across the lifespan, neuropsychological testing is an invaluable tool for teasing apart factors that contribute to patients' brain and behavior relationships across a variety of contexts, including learning disabilities that meet diagnostic criteria, subclinical learning differences, traumatic brain injury, neuropsychiatric disorders with accompanying chronic cognitive deficits, and acquired or congenital neurological conditions. Because cognition and emotion are intertwined, neuropsychological data sheds light on the ways in which patterns of cognitive strengths and weaknesses impinge on emotional states, psychodynamic aspects of personality functioning, family dynamics, as well as psychosocial functioning with peers at school and in the community. A neuropsychological evaluation can help answer various differential diagnostic or forensic referral questions, and provide a platform for planning academic, psychotherapeutic, psychosocial, and vocational and rehabilitation interventions.

Our purpose in creating this edited work on neuropsychological testing is to showcase the richness of this specialty and its practical use in diagnosis and intervention planning. This book is not intended as a comprehensive text; instead, our collection of chapters is a testament to ways in which neuropsychological testing often works hand in hand with diverse disciplines, including clinical psychology, school psychology, neurorehabilitation psychology, vocational rehabilitation, psychoanalytic psychotherapy, speech and language pathology, neurology, child and adolescent psychiatry, geriatric psychiatry, brain injury litigation, and education law. Finally, we constructed the book so as to include a lifespan perspective on the ways in which neuropsychological assessment helps assess and plan interventions to treat patients from preschool children to older adults. Although neuropsychology is a rarified specialty, which is chosen and practiced by only some licensed psychologists, this discipline is invaluable to a wide variety of patients and their families, as well as practitioners and professionals in separate but related disciplines that work side by side in multidisciplinary care settings, from hospitals to community clinics to schools.

Several of our chapter authors possess multidisciplinary training in addition to being licensed psychologists with specialty expertise in neuropsychology. They are uniquely suited to discuss the many ways in which neuropsychology works collaboratively with other specialties, such as clinical psychology, educational psychology, psychoanalytic psychotherapy, speech and language pathology, forensic neuropsychology, and education law. Our authors, most of whom have experience in a multidisciplinary clinical milieu and or have multidisciplinary training, are keenly aware and sensitive to issues related to respect for scope of practice between and among disciplines, making sure that complementary specialties are just that.

Although the thrust of our book celebrates this diversity, the content of the chapters in this book emphasizes that clear boundaries between and among the professions that touch upon neuropsychology are essential for the responsible treatment of patients. By law, practice guidelines and licensure laws for each profession exist to protect the public, as well as professionals in neighboring but distinct disciplines, assuring that separate disciplines remain clearly defined in terms of scope of practice.

TRAINING AND PRACTICE IN NEUROPSYCHOLOGY: AN INTRODUCTION TO THE GUILD

Our book emphasizes that neuropsychologists are first and perhaps foremost doctoral-level psychologists whose scope of practice is highly regulated and governed by the laws of the state in which the psychologist is licensed. Specializing in neuropsychology requires a license plus specialty training. In general, specialty boards—not licensing boards—set specific standards for training guidelines in neuropsychology. Psychologists who specialize in neuropsychology tailored their doctoral education and clinical training to gain sufficient experience in neuropsychology. Typically, they possess vertical training that shows a thread of experience in neuropsychology beginning in predoctoral education, training, and/or clinical experience, and continuing through predoctoral training and postdoctoral experience. Subspecialization within neuropsychology is also an option, which is why we devote chapters to pediatric neuropsychology, neurorehabilitation psychology and vocational rehabilitation.

Besides meeting the requirements for doctoral-level course work and licensure, clinical and research experience in neuropsychology is obtained in medical hospitals, neurorehabilitation settings, and/or psychiatric hospitals. For example, in my own training as part of a multidisciplinary treatment team, I performed individualized neuropsychological assessments in a variety of hospital settings: outpatient clinics, day hospitals, day treatment centers, locked inpatient psychiatric units, as well as inpatient spinal cord and brain injury rehabilitation settings and outpatient rehabilitation.

The book's chapters discuss integrated neuropsychological evaluations, which typically means that the testing includes, but is not necessarily limited to, assessment (not listed here in any particular order) of intellectual functioning, various types of attention, memory, language, motor skills, academic achievement, as well as emotional and personality functioning, self-report measures, and behavior ratings. In addition, the neuropsychologist collects background data from the patient and the family, including any previous testing of any given type, the patient's medical history, family medical history, school records, work history, psychosocial history, which all provide context for the neuropsychological test data.

Clinical Supervisors as Master Craftsmen

Guilds originated in ancient societies, such as China, India, Greece, and Rome. Modern day guilds are very much with us, although we seldom think of professional organizations as such. Many professional organizations have a structure that resembles that of a guild, whether or not they retain the word in their respective titles: The American Psychological Association, the American Medical Association, and the American Bar Association.

Even now, in the 21st century, specialty training in neuropsychology is still based on a tradition of one-to-one and small-group training that is somewhat akin to apprenticeship and eventually membership in a time-honored guild. In neuropsychology, the trainee learns the art and science of neuropsychological assessment through years of apprenticeship in the form of intense supervision led by experienced licensed psychologists who possess training that meets criteria for the specialty of neuropsychology. In this sense, neuropsychologists are professionals who are not mass produced. Quite the contrary, their training and experience is in many ways hand crafted, yet systematically done in such a way that is compatible with criteria set out by specialty boards and the "inspirational" Houston Conference Guidelines describing requirements for specialty training in clinical neuropsychology.

OUTLINE OF THE BOOK

Part of the inspiration for this book was an appreciation for the extent to which neuropsychology, as a specialty, is useful to so many other specialty domains, within psychology, psychiatry, speech and language specialists, and the legal profession. In spite of its tremendous utility to individuals ranging in age from preschoolers to senior adults, neuropsychology is not as well understood or utilized as a specialty, as perhaps it could be. In this spirit, we divided the book into chapters that fit into the following three sections, described below.

Part I: Introduction to Neuropsychology

In chapter 1, neuropsychologist Dr. Gerald Goldstein, founding editor of *Neuropsychology Review*, provides a brief history of neuropsychology as a discipline and discusses some of the basics of the craft. Chapter 2, by Dr. Thomas A. Hammeke, the current president of the American Psychological Association's Division 40 on Neuropsychology, and Dr. Robert F. Newby, echoes a sentiment that helped provide the very impetus for this book: Professionals, patients, and families sometimes tend to know relatively little about the discipline of neuropsychology. Drs. Hammeke and Newby, both neuropsychologists, discuss what a neuropsychologist's formal training involves and what specialized services a neuropsychologist is uniquely qualified to provide.

Part II: Neuropsychological Testing for Children and Adolescents

In the section on neuropsychology and specialties within psychology, we discuss ways in which neuropsychological testing can be utilized with individuals who range in age from toddlers to older adolescents on the verge of young adulthood—and by various specialties in psychology-related helping professions.

Pediatric neuropsychologist Dr. Nadia Webb, author of chapter 3, provides an introduction to pediatric neuropsychology as a subdiscipline, anchored in developmental aspects of brain and behavioral functioning.

In chapter 4, Dr. Lois M. Black, a neuropsychologist, provides a compelling discussion of a psychodynamic-neuropsychological approach to the evaluation of toddlers and illustrates her chapter with case studies of preschool children. Her chapter helps shed light on the interplay of cognitive, emotional, and personality functioning that integrates the neuropsychological profile with psychodynamic factors emergent in the child and the family, as well as the importance of early diagnosis especially in very young children. She also highlights the neuropsychological evaluation's key role in providing a basis for psychoeducation to help parents utilize recommendations made in the report and adopt them in everyday life, as they respond to the preschool child as an individual with an already unique pattern of strengths, weaknesses, and needs.

For school-age children, adolescents, and young adult psychotherapy patients, Martha Pierce, PhD, and Ayame Takahashi, MD, a psychoanalytic social worker and a child psychiatrist, respectively, illuminate learning disabilities from the point of view of psychoanalytic psychotherapy and neuropsychiatry in chapter 5. With neuropsychological assessment as a means of assisting early diagnosis, Drs. Pierce and Takahashi draw upon their respective psychoanalytic training to provide the reader with some background on Freudian theory and neuropsychiatry. Their case studies illustrate how therapists utilize neuropsychological testing to inform their conceptualization of the patient's psychodynamic functioning, as well as the utility of test data for treatment planning.

Neuropsychology coupled with child psychiatry is the subject of chapter 6, by psychiatrist Lynn Grush, MD, and neuropsychologists Dr. Ellen B. Braaten and Dr. Brian Willoughby. The authors explain that pediatric neuropsychology and child psychiatry both evolved from adult clinical disciplines and bring a developmental perspective to the understanding of the relationship between brain activity and behavior. Good communication between these disciplines increases informed clinical collaboration and the effectiveness of the care both specialties provide. The chapter describes the domains typically assessed as part of a neuropsychological evaluation, some commonly used measures within each domain, along with guidance on how neuropsychological test data can help inform diagnostic impressions in the field of child psychiatry.

In chapter 7, Dr. Ellen B. Braaten and Dr. Ellen O'Donnell, both neuropsychologists, discuss the cognitive and behavioral problems of the developing child as related to the child's neurological status. They explain how a pediatric neuropsychological evaluation can be useful for some of the more common pediatric medical conditions, such as early developmental problems, epilepsy, pediatric multiple sclerosis, and juvenile diabetes. The authors provide two case studies of adolescents, to illuminate how the pediatric neuropsychologist plays a key role in providing care as part of a multidisciplinary treatment team.

In chapter 8, neuropsychologist Dr. Christine L. Castillo discusses the complementary though distinct disciplines of clinical neuropsychology and speech-language therapy, also known as speech-language pathology. She discusses the boundary lines between neuropsychology and speech-language therapy, as established by the respective training guidelines, tenets of professional ethics and standards, as well as state law and clinical practice issues that help distinguish between these two disciplines. Although only neuropsychologists are qualified to conduct a neuropsychological evaluation, both neuropsychologists and speech-language pathologists rely on neuropsychological test data to deliver comprehensive care related to information on the ways in which a person's individual strengths and weaknesses in expressive and/or receptive language may influence daily functioning in other domains, such as memory and learning. Dr. Castillo provides two case studies, one on the neuropsychological evaluation of a toddler and one on a young adult, to help illustrate how the results of such an evaluation can be used in treatment planning and intervention in the realm of speech-language therapy goals and objectives.

Chapter 9 addresses the use of neuropsychological testing and aspects of school psychology. Neuropsychologist Dr. David L. Wodrich, Dr. Ara J. Schmitt, and neuropsychologist Dr. Joy Goldberg discuss neuropsychological test use in primary and secondary schools and provide concrete examples of the application of those techniques among children with and without obvious brain impairment. They highlight important issues related to policies (e.g., No Child Left Behind and Response to Intervention [RTI]) and traditions in today's schools that may influence the use of neuropsychological assessments. The authors discuss background issues related to neuropsychological test use in school-based settings, evaluation of developmental learning disabilities in reading and math, the RTI option for the diagnosis of specific learning disability (SLD), and neuropsychological evaluation of congenital and acquired disorders in school-age children.

Neuropsychologist Dr. James B. Hale, licensed psychologist Dr. Catherine A. Fiorello, and Rebecca Thompson, MEd, a doctoral candidate, bring us chapter 10, which discusses comprehensive school-based practice issues related to integrating neuropsychological principles with RTI. The authors describe a convergence of neuropsychological (e.g., Lurian) and the cognitive-psychometric (e.g., Cattell-Horn-Caroll) theories, advocating evidence for both approaches. RTI and School Neuropsychology (SNP) approaches to school-based assessment and intervention are also discussed. Also included in this chapter is the Cognitive Hypothesis Testing model, which provides a scientific method approach for integrating cognitive and neuropsychological assessment for children who do not respond to standard interventions.

In chapter 11, Dr. Melody Nichols Dilk provides a multidisciplinary point of view on neuropsychology and special education law. Her chapter addresses responsibilities and functions of neuropsychologists from an integrated perspective based upon her roles as a pediatric neuropsychologist, attorney, and administrative law judge presiding over special education due process hearings. She addresses aspects of special education law relevant to neuropsychological services and how neuropsychology can facilitate effective and efficient implementation of laws ensuring free appropriate public education to children and young people with disabilities.

Part III: Neuropsychological Testing for Adults

Well beyond childhood and adolescence, development continues in one way or another across the lifespan and into the realm of advancing age. Focusing on neuropsychological testing for adults and seniors, chapters in this section discuss severe and persistent mental illness in adults, brain injury, adults with learning disabilities, adult neurorehabilitation outpatients who are returning to work, and neurological conditions in older adults.

Neuropsychologists Dr. Ashley A. Gorman and Dr. Wilfred G. van Gorp discuss the role of adult neuropsychological testing in the context of severe and persistent mental illness, including unipolar depression, bipolar disorder, obsessive-compulsive disorder and schizophrenia. In chapter 12, Drs. Gorman and van Gorp are careful to describe what neuropsychological assessment is and provide caveats as to what it is not. They discuss topics related to adult psychiatric patients, recent research, and the utility of neuropsychological testing for referral questions concerning diagnosis and treatment planning.

In chapter 13, psychiatrists Dr. Molly Colvin Putnam and Dr. Mark A. Blais, focus on the intersection of neuropsychology and the practice of psychiatry specializing in adults, with the purpose of helping psychiatrists become more familiar and comfortable with the many benefits of neuropsychological assessment. The authors characterize neuropsychology as a dynamic, rapidly evolving clinical discipline with significant potential to improve psychiatric care through the comprehensive assessments of cognitive functioning. Ironically, the adoption of neuropsychological assessment in routine clinical care has lagged behind that of other diagnostic procedures. From the vantage point of their roles as neuropsychologists on a multidisciplinary treatment team, the authors provide case studies of patients ranging in age from young adult to geriatric adult, to illustrate issues that present in adult attention-deficit/hyperactivity disorder, neurodevelopmental and learning disabilities, schizophrenia spectrum illnesses, bipolar affective disorder, dementia, and depression.

Dario J. Englot, MPhil, a medical student, and neuropsychologist Dr. Marisa Spann, provide a practical guide for neurologists on how to best utilize neuropsychology referrals and consultations. In chapter 14, these authors express the opinion that, even among neurologists who have adequate resources available in their geographical area, neuropsychology referrals are sometimes under- or inappropriately utilized because of a less than optimal understanding of the potential benefits of the referral and difficulty other professionals sometimes have in interpreting the neuropsychology report. These authors provide the reader with a practical Why-Who-When-and-How roadmap, describing the benefits of a neuropsychological evaluation, which neurological patients should be referred, the best time to refer them, and the important information one should include in the referral. From the neurologist's point of view, the authors help identify salient aspects of the neuropsychological report as well as provide some guidance on ways that neurologists in clinical practice can utilize that information.

Chapter 15 focuses on neuropsychology and rehabilitation psychology, as it describes the roles and functions of those licensed psychologists who, by prior training and clinical experience, practice neurorehabilitation psychology. Specialists in this field themselves, Dr. Mary R. Hibbard, Dr. David E. Layman, and Dr. Robert K. Stewart, Jr., describe neurorehabilitation psychology as a subspecialty that emerged over the past 3 decades, combining the theoretical underpinnings of clinical neuropsychology with rehabilitation psychology. The chapter highlights the ways in which neurorehabilitation psychologists address the complex treatment needs of individuals and families coping with the many cognitive, emotional and behavioral challenges resulting from either a brain injury or other neurological conditions. The authors introduce a conceptual model, called the ABCs of Neurorehabilitation Issues and Interventions. They illustrate use of the ABC model via three narrative case studies describing neurorehabilitation patients who range in age from young adult to older adult.

In chapter 16, Dr. Robert T. Fraser, Dr. Erica K. Johnson, and Dr. Jay M. Uomoto discuss the role of the outpatient rehabilitation neuropsychologist specializing in vocational planning or vocational rehabilitation for patients with physical disabilities, sensory disabilities, trauma or neurological insult, and/or disease process. Proficiency in producing vocationally oriented neuropsychological evaluations requires specific training and experience on the part of the neuropsychologist, ideally obtained as a member or coordinator of an outpatient rehabilitation team. Dr. Fraser and Dr. Johnson are rehabilitation psychologists and certified rehabilitation counselors (CRC) practicing in neurological vocational rehabilitation. Dr. Uomoto is a licensed psychologist practicing in rehabilitation psychology and neuropsychology. Their chapter provides a thoughtful review of considerations for the neuropsychologist practicing in the vocational rehabilitation arena. The authors emphasize the importance of clear communication between the neuropsychologist and referral source, and between the neuropsychologist, patient/family and referral source, in terms of results as well as practical recommendations designed to help those patients who can return to some form of work.

In keeping with our lifespan perspective, our final chapter is devoted to neuropsychological testing with older adults. In chapter 17, Drs. Kristina F. Zdanys and Rajesh R. Tampi, who specialize in geriatric psychiatry, explain the many ways in which neuropsychological testing is beneficial in the assessment of geriatric patients who exhibit symptoms of cognitive decline. The authors explain that diagnosis of cognitive impairment in the elderly is often complicated by comorbid medical conditions, medications, affective symptoms, and demographic features. An illustatrative case study takes the reader step-by-step through a sample neuropsychological report, generously provided by neuropsychologist Dr. Keith Hawkins. This exercise helps show that, as part of a comprehensive evaluation by a host of other professionals— psychiatrists, psychologists, medical doctors, radiologists, family resource specialists, and social workers—the neuropsychological evaluation can help establish a baseline, monitor pattern of decline, aid in diagnosis, assess for safety, and provide a basis for clinical management in geriatric psychiatry patients.

NEUROPSYCHOLOGICAL TESTING IN AN EVER-CHANGING WORLD

Response to Intervention and No Child Left Behind

The reauthorization of the Federal Individuals with Disabilities Education Act (IDEA) became law in December 2004. The reauthorization granted States and school districts more options to use in evaluating students with specific learning disabilities (SLD).

IDEA allows the use of Response to Intervention, the discrepancy model, or both to identify learning disabilities. Although some of our authors comment on RTI and related issues, these chapters reflect the authors' own viewpoints and are not intended to represent any definitive position or a representative sample of the many wide-ranging opinions that exist on RTI or other education-related legislation, such as No Child Left Behind (NCLB).

Managed Care's New Horizons

No discussion of neuropsychological testing would be quite complete without some mention of managed care. As of this writing, health care in the United States was undergoing significant policy changes. Only time will tell how any managed care system, private or otherwise, will respectfully pay neuropsychologists for their services or adequately reimburse patients for an integrated neuropsychological evaluation. It is my hope that this book gives some indication of just how important neuropsychological testing is and the importance of making it accessible to individuals of all ages and from all walks of life, allowing them to benefit from its many practical insights into brain–behavior relationships played out in everyday life.

—Elisa Mambrino, PhD

Introduction to Neuropsychology

1

What Is Neuropsychology?

GERALD GOLDSTEIN

DEFINITIONS

Neuropsychology is a broad term covering a wide area of clinical and scientific activity. However, a basic subdivision can be made between the experimental and clinical aspects of the field. Experimental neuropsychology, sometimes described by the word *neuropsychology* alone, is a basic science involving the discovery of relationships among nervous system structure, function, and behavior. Probably, most of the work in the area is researched with animals, and involves laboratory, or sometimes field studies, usually of brain function, but sometimes involving the spinal cord and peripheral nerves. Clinical neuropsychology is a health care profession that specializes in assessment and treatment of patients with brain disorders. All of its work involves humans. Experimental neuropsychologists may work in health care settings and clinical neuropsychologists may do scientific research, but their missions are quite different. This chapter will be restricted to a consideration of clinical neuropsychology, but in doing so will support the view that the two fields interact. Clinical neuropsychologists acquire information from their experimental colleagues for use in their practices, and, in turn, experimental neuropsychologists may have areas of interest that concern clinical phenomena. Thus, for example, an experimental neuropsychologist may do research involving development of an animal model for stroke, and clinical neuropsychologists may apply the information obtained from this research in their own practices.

Several brief, formal definitions of clinical neuropsychology have been proposed—all of them stating that it is a branch of psychology that specializes in the assessment and treatment of patients with brain damage or dysfunction, and that neuropsychology is concerned with uncovering relationships between brain function and behavior. The clinical neuropsychologist has particular expertise in how various brain disorders, or brain damage located in different parts of the brain, alter behavior. Typically, this expertise is expressed through the use of neuropsychological tests. Thus, Ralph Reitan, a founder of clinical neuropsychology, has said informally that a neuropsychological test is a test that is sensitive to the condition of the brain. In contemporary practice, such tests must meet acceptable psychometric standards, and become validated using brain tissue samples from patients with some form of a well-diagnosed brain disorder.

Formal Definitions

Professional clinical neuropsychology is represented by two societies: the National Academy of Neuropsychology (NAN) and the Division of Clinical Neuropsychology (Division 40) of the American Psychological Association. There is also an International Neuropsychological Society (INS), which is an interdisciplinary international group for both experimental and clinical neuropsychologists, and the American Academy of Clinical Neuropsychology (AACN), an organization associated with the American Board of Clinical Neuropsychology (ABCN), and the branch of the American Board of Professional Psychology (ABPP) that confers Diplomate status to clinical neuropsychologists. NAN and Division 40 have provided slightly different definitions (Barth et al., 2003), and the Houston Conference, a national meeting on specialty education and training in clinical neuropsychology (Hannay, 1998) has presented yet another definition. The Houston Conference definition is the most concise and is cited here:

> A clinical neuropsychologist is a professional psychologist trained in the science of brain behavior relationships. The clinical neuropsychologist

specializes in the application of assessment and intervention principles based on the scientific study of human behavior across the lifespan as it relates to normal and abnormal functioning of the central nervous system. (1998, p. 161)

The other definitions go into more detail concerning training, supervision, licensure, and role of board certification. Virtually all practicing clinical neuropsychologists in the United States are licensed psychologists in their states; however, only a minority has obtained Board certification. Most practicing clinical neuropsychologists are Members or Fellows of NAN or APA Division 40. Active membership in one of these organizations and possession of a license provide reasonable assurance that clinical neuropsychology is within the scope of practice of the psychologist.

HISTORICAL BACKGROUND

One helpful way of describing and defining clinical neuropsychology is to review its history, tracing its roots and identifying its founders and major contributors. Discussion about who pioneered the development of clinical neuropsychology and what were its beginning activities, and consideration of its course and development, may provide important insights regarding the nature of the profession as it exists today. One opinion is that clinical neuropsychology represents a confluence of the behavioral neurology of Central Europe and England practiced during the nineteenth and early twentieth centuries and the psychometric tradition developed primarily in the United States. The field owes a great debt to the European *diagram-makers* who conceptualized aphasia and related neurobehavioral disorders in terms of localization theory that, in general, postulated that the brain functioned through establishment of regionally localized centers connected by specific pathways. The examinational procedures used during that period eventually merged into what we now call neuropsychological tests. That step was accomplished largely in the United States by converting these clinical examinational methods into psychological tests through the use of the now widely accepted standardization procedures, creation of quantitative scoring systems, and consideration of psychometric procedures including scaling, validity, and reliability studies. Thus, for example, the examinational observations by Paul Broca and Carl Wernicke of patients with aphasia evolved into the Boston Diagnostic Aphasia Examination (Goodglass & Kaplan, 1983).

There was another theoretical framework different from diagram-making that held the view that the brain functioned as a total entity that we would now characterize as working on a systems basis. This view, supported by the animal studies of Karl Lashley involving his theories of *equipotentiality* and *mass action* and by the clinical and theoretical writings of Hughlings Jackson, and later by Kurt Goldstein (1939), appears to have led to the contemporary neuropsychological assessment of complex higher functions such as abstract reasoning and problem solving ability. Contemporary clinical neuropsychological assessment can be viewed as representing a merger of the strict localization and mass action theories such that we now have tests for aphasia and other specific disorders that assess individual functions in detail, and tests of reasoning, such as the Wisconsin Card Sorting Test (Heaton, Chelune, Talley, Kay, & Curtiss, 1993), which evaluate complex brain functions and associated cognitive abilities.

This history is captured in the work of individuals and associated groups who constitute the founders of the field. On the localization theory side we have the behavioral neurologists such as Broca, Wernicke, Kleist, and Liepmann, who during the late-nineteenth and early-twentieth centuries did pioneering work in the major syndromes of aphasia, apraxia, and agnosia (see Heilman & Valenstein, 2003, for detailed reviews). Their early work merges quite clearly into the modern behavioral neurology of Norman Geschwind (1984), and the neuropsychology of Edith Kaplan, Harold Goodglass, Nelson Butters, and numerous other members of what is described as the *Boston Group*; a group of neurologists and neuropsychologists associated with the Boston VA Hospital and Boston University who made major contributions to behavioral neurology and clinical neuropsychology. Arthur Benton may also be viewed as having his roots in this group since he maintained an interest in specific syndromes, such as finger agnosia, and individual functions such as facial recognition. Contemporary neuropsychologists oriented toward localization theory tend to be occupied in their practices mainly by patients with aphasia and other relatively specific neurobehavioral syndromes. For example, Goodglass and Kaplan spent most of their careers in a specialized clinical center for stroke patients with aphasia.

Henry Head and Hughlings Jackson are probably the most well known of the early representatives of mass action theory, and clearly form a bridge with Kurt Goldstein and Martin Scheerer, who constructed what now would appear to be the first battery of neuropsychological tests of complex cognitive functions (K. Goldstein & Scheerer, 1941). Shortly after publication of their monograph, Ward Halstead published his book, *Brain and Intelligence* (1947), which contained a description of a large number of tests of cognitive abilities. Several of these tests were organized into a factor-analyzed battery. They consisted largely of measures of complex functions such as problem solving, attention, and spatial skills. Ralph Reitan was a student of Halstead and developed what is now known as the Halstead-Reitan Neuropsychological Test Battery over a period of many years (Reitan & Wolfson, 1993).

During the 1940s and early 1950s, there appears to have been a marked change in the field involving the introduction of the Goldstein-Scheerer and Halstead-Reitan procedures, which provided materials for specialized assessment of individuals with brain disorders. Goldstein and Scheerer never wished to pursue psychometric development of their tests for philosophical reasons, but others took on that task (Reitan & Wolfson, 1993). Quantification and psychometric development of the Halstead-Reitan Battery has been extensive and continues to this day. Arthur Benton published several of his tests of specific abilities in a manual in 1983 (Benton, des Hamsher, Varney, & Spreen, 1983), and quantified aphasia tests were published by Goodglass and Kaplan (1983), and Kertesz (1979).

At the time that this work was taking place in Western Europe and the United States, what can be described as a parallel development was taking place in Russia under the leadership of A. R. Luria. However, his work was largely unknown outside of Russia because his books had not been translated, and he did not publish any tests. However, he had developed an elaborate theory of brain function and method of assessment that is now widely recognized as a major contribution (Luria, 1973). The inaccessibility of Luria's work has largely broken down because of several events including the translation of his books into English, the publication of several of his test procedures in the form of a manual and kit by Anne-Lise Christensen (1975), and the writings of Elkhonon Goldberg (2001), one of Luria's students who came to the United States. Additionally, Charles Golden and collaborators using material contained in the Christensen kit developed a standardized procedure based on the test items in the kit. It is now known as the Luria-Nebraska Neuropsychological Battery (Golden, Purisch, & Hammeke, 1985). Luria's work has now been incorporated in numerous ways into Western clinical neuropsychology.

This very brief history has traced a progression beginning with clinical examiners, mainly neurologists, through an intermediate period during which objective test procedures were developed but not necessarily quantified, to the present era in which a vast majority, if not all, practicing clinical neuropsychologists place some reliance on quantitative tests that have at least adequate psychometric properties. Kurt Goldstein, Martin Scheerer, Arthur Benton, Ward Halstead, and Ralph Reitan are generally viewed as the leaders of this movement, with some adding Alexander Luria to the list as well. The major contributions of Harold Goodglass, Edith Kaplan, and Nelson Butters are also widely recognized. The proliferation of neuropsychological tests is probably best exemplified in the succeeding editions of Lezak's increasingly large volumes describing the currently existing neuropsychological tests (Lezak, Howieson, & Loring, 2004). New tests continue to appear, with recent developments including several computer-administered and scored tests and test batteries (Kaminski, Groff, & Glutting, 2008).

WHAT CONSTITUTES A NEUROPSYCHOLOGICAL ASSESSMENT?

Another way of defining clinical neuropsychology is through discussion of what constitutes neuropsychological assessment. Such information may be of particular interest to patients referred for neuropsychological testing and who may want to know what such testing entails. In general terms, neuropsychological testing is an evaluation of cognitive, perceptual, and motor abilities. It has some overlap with intelligence testing and an intelligence test is often given as part of the procedure; however it is substantially more detailed in its evaluation of cognitive function than an intelligence test.

Although there are numerous neuropsychological tests (Lezak, Howieson, & Loring, 2004) and testing systems (Goldstein & Incagnoli, 1997), they are similar in that they evaluate a number of abilities that may be divided into several domains. A brief description of these domains and representative types of tests include:

Attention: Attention is the ability to maintain concentration on a stimulus of interest. It is often evaluated in a situation in which the individual must attend to a selected stimulus while filtering out distractions. Repeating digits or responding selectively to a designated target are commonly used tests of attention. Neuropsychological tests of attention vary greatly in complexity ranging from immediate repetition of stimuli to complex decision-making procedures with multiple contingencies. Varying degrees of distraction are involved, and contingencies may range from simple requirements (e.g., press a button when you see the letter X), to complex (e.g., press a button when you see the letter X only if it is preceded by the letter C), to even more complex (e.g., press a button when you see the letter X only if the letter R appeared two letters before it). Some tests of attention blend with tests of working memory, which involves temporary recall of material during the performance of a task (e.g., remembering a phone number just read when engaged in dialing it).

Memory: The ability to recall information or to learn new information is typically assessed with tests in the memory domain. Memory for verbal or nonverbal material, length of time between stimulus presentation, and recall are generally considered. Memory tests are included in the major batteries, but there is also a large number of individual tests of various aspects of memory, notably the Wechsler Memory Scale (1987) and the California Verbal Learning Test (Delis, Kramer, Kaplan, & Ober, 2000).

Abstract Reasoning and Problem Solving (Executive Function): This domain includes the ability to develop concepts or abstractions and find solutions to problems that require some form of reasoning ability. Conceptual flexibility and capacity to spontaneously form concepts based upon experience with test stimuli are often assessed. Executive function is a broader concept that sometimes involves regulation of motor activity or capacity for productivity. The Wisconsin Card Sorting Test, a nonverbal abstract reasoning test, is probably the most commonly used test in this domain.

Spatial-Constructional Abilities: This domain involves the ability to represent spatial relations and to construct objects in space. Abilities to analyze spatial material and to produce constructions in three-dimensional space are often assessed. The Block Design subtest from the

Wechsler intelligence scales (Wechsler, 2008) is a commonly used spatial-constructional test.

Language: The domain of language includes various communicative forms. It involves the modalities of oral speech, auditory comprehension, writing, reading, and calculation. Within neuropsychology, detailed evaluations are accomplished with aphasia tests, such as the Boston Diagnostic Aphasia Examination, but most neuropsychological assessments evaluate basic language skills, or provide screening tests for aphasia.

Perceptual and Motor Skills: This domain includes abilities in visual, auditory, and tactile perception, and in skilled movement. Typical tests might involve visual identification of objects, recognition of stimuli by touch, and various tasks involving motor speed and dexterity.

Effort: Although not a domain, most neuropsychologists evaluate effort or the individual's motivation to do as well as possible on the tests. The term is commonly used as a euphemism for malingering, but it is also applicable to other bases for not trying as hard as possible to do one's best. Several methods have been devised to make this evaluation including construction of separate tests such as the Victoria Symptom Validity Test (Slick, Hopp, Strauss, & Spellacy, 1996), developing special scores from commonly used neuropsychological tests (Allen, Caron, & Goldstein, 2006), and evaluating patterns of retesting under varying circumstances such as settlement of litigation (Reitan & Wolfson, 1997).

A neuropsychological evaluation may be specialized or comprehensive. Specialized evaluations include only one or a limited number of domains, assessed in extensive detail. Comprehensive evaluations involve most or all of the domains. Based on theoretical preference, practice demands, or referral population, some neuropsychologists do essentially all specialized evaluations while others do only comprehensive evaluations. This distinction relates to the use of what are termed *fixed* or *flexible* neuropsychological test batteries to which we will now turn our attention.

FIXED VERSUS FLEXIBLE BATTERIES

Within neuropsychological assessment there are some clinicians who always give the same tests to all patients, regardless of the referral question. Indeed, the neuropsychologist may not want to know what the referral question is because of the preference to interpret the test score on a *blind* basis without knowledge of the diagnosis or any other background information about the patient except for age, gender, handedness, and educational level. The tradition of conducting neuropsychological assessment in this manner was initiated with the Halstead-Reitan Battery, and its application remains relatively limited to users of that procedure. The procedure for test selection, administration, and scoring is so structured that the battery may be administered and scored by a trained technician. The only real choice of tests relates to whether the client is a young child, in the intermediate age range (8–14 years old), or an adult. This procedure has been characterized as the *fixed battery* approach to neuropsychological assessment, with some critics suggesting that it not an appropriate description (Lezak, Howieson, & Loring, 2004). Other critics have taken issue with the approach itself indicating that it is not the most productive way to do neuropsychological testing (Goodglass, 1986). In any event, the two most widely used fixed batteries in neuropsychological assessment are the Halstead-Reitan and Luria-Nebraska batteries. It may be noted that some clinicians, particularly in the case of the Halstead-Reitan Battery, use only some of the tests, often adding to them other tests not included in the battery. These individuals would not be viewed as users of the fixed battery approach, since such use requires that all of the tests need to be administered. There have been changes in the Halstead-Reitan Battery over the years, but most authorities would agree that there has been a stable core battery that has persisted since its beginning.

The *flexible battery* approach means most simply that the choice of tests is made by the clinician based upon patient characteristics and the reason for referral. *Blind* interpretation cannot be used with this approach since the clinician must know the client's history in order to choose the tests. It is sometimes possible for technicians to do the testing if the tests used are restricted to those having manuals with ideally verbatim instructions. In some cases, technicians may be trained to administer other procedures, or to modify standard procedures as needed. Some clinicians take something of a compromise position in which several relatively fixed batteries may be used for different populations. For example, there may be a set series of procedures for patients being evaluated for Alzheimer's disease, and a different set for patients who had suffered a head injury. Some advocates of the flexible battery approach limit their test repertoire to standardized, published tests, whereas others may use clinical procedures, or improvised examination, in combination with standard tests.

An apparently interminable source of debate among clinical neuropsychologists involves the relative usefulness of *fixed* and *flexible* batteries. It is widely covered in the literature (Incagnoli, Goldstein, & Golden, 1986) and will not be pursued here. From the standpoint of patient expectations, however, it may be noted that some patients referred for neuropsychological testing may sit in a doctor's office setting and be questioned and tested by a psychologist, whereas others will have their assessment in a more laboratory-like setting, in which the tests are administered in a standard way by a technician. Patients taking a computerized assessment may take most, if not all of the tests while viewing a computer screen. In many settings the client is interviewed at the beginning of the session before being turned over to the technician for the testing. Often, posttesting interviews are done primarily to answer questions, and a follow-up interview may be done with the client, and sometimes a family member, after the neuropsychologist has had a chance to review the test results.

THE NEUROPSYCHOLOGICAL REPORT

The product of a neuropsychological assessment is a report presenting a consultation regarding the findings. In health care settings the report typically becomes a part of the clinical record, and may be integrated by the attending physician with other historical and diagnostic material. A neuropsychological report written by a professional clinician contains the results of the tests and an interpretation of the scores, but probably most often it also contains a history of varying length, a set of conclusions about diagnosis and predicted course, and recommendations that may include further evaluations, treatment, or case management. It is probably worthwhile to mention a distinction between a freestanding and what we would characterize as a targeted report. In some settings the neuropsychological report is the only clinical information available to whoever made the referral. If that is the case, it is often preferable to write a freestanding report that covers details of the clinical history, other examinational findings, diagnoses, and related material generally found in clinical records. Whereas in other cases in which the referring agent has access to the records, the neuropsychologist has an understanding that material of that type is contained elsewhere and need not be in the neuropsychological test report. In those cases, or cases in which the neuropsychologist produces reports on a *blind* basis, the history section is minimal or nonexistent. Although the written descriptions of Ralph Reitan's teaching cases contain pertinent histories, it is understood that he did not have knowledge of these histories before writing the report, nor did he personally interview the patient before that time.

An outline for organizing a report that we have found useful follows:

1. *Background and History*: This section can be brief or lengthy depending on considerations raised above. At a minimum it should contain demographic information including gender, age, handedness, years of education, and occupation. Sometimes employment status is useful to include.

2. *Psychometric Results*: It has been our practice to present the actual quantitative test results, although doing so has been a source of controversy. We believe the referring agent is entitled to the information. The actual scores may be presented in the form of a uniform rating scale to assist in interpretation of the results (Heaton, Miller, Taylor, & Grant, 2004; Reitan, 1993; Russell, Neuringer, & Goldstein, 1970).

3. *Level of Impairment*: A statement should be made regarding whether the findings overall are consistent or not consistent with the presence of brain dysfunction. Some form of quantitative impairment index should be provided, including rating level of performance even for protocols in the normal range. Alternatives include Halstead's original impairment index, Reitan's General Neuropsychological Deficit Scale (GNDS), Russell, Neuringer, and Goldstein's Average Impairment Rating, equivalent indices from the Halstead-Russell Neuropsychological Evaluation System (HRNES; Russell, 2004), or Heaton et al.'s mean T score of the tests administered as part of their Expanded Halstead-Reitan Battery (2004). It is often useful to provide a verbal equivalent such as *mildly, moderately, severely, or very severely* impaired.

4. *Pattern of Impairment*: Information should be provided about the test profile indicating the pattern of preserved and impaired abilities. For example, the patient may have significantly impaired language skills and normal spatial-constructional abilities.

There can be a specific deficit, such as inability to recognize forms by touch, with otherwise normal function. All abilities can be significantly impaired. Sometimes a pattern is identified that is consistent with some particular syndrome or disorder. For example, if verbal intelligence (Verbal IQ) is substantially lower than performance intelligence (Performance IQ) the presence of brain damage mainly to the left cerebral hemisphere is suggested. The pattern of abilities is sometimes quite important for rehabilitation planning because it provides an indication of what tasks the patient is likely or unlikely to perform successfully.

5. *Neurological Correlates*: There should be a statement about brain–behavior relationships providing information about how the test results may be related to brain function. There are several dimensions to this analysis. Usually location is considered first, with an interpretation made regarding whether the major dysfunction is generalized, relatively restricted to the left or right cerebral hemisphere, or restricted further to a particular region within a hemisphere, such as the frontal lobe. An inference is then generally made about whether the damage is of recent origin and still acute, static and stabilized for some time, or present since birth, or developmental. At more advanced levels of interpretation, the neuropsychologist may indicate that the test findings are consistent with a specific disorder. For example, the report may indicate that the test findings are consistent with multiple sclerosis or a recent major left hemisphere stroke.

6. *Course and Outcome*: The report may comment on prognosis and outcome based upon the test results and knowledge about the disorder the patient is thought to have. Some disorders are stable, some slowly progressive, and some rapidly progressive. In some disorders recovery may be anticipated, whereas in others there is no hope of recovery with the treatments currently available. Sometimes it is pertinent to suggest how the outcome may be altered by treatment and rehabilitation. Sometimes specific rehabilitation strategies and methods may be suggested.

7. *Effort*: Particularly when there are litigation or compensation issues involved, neuropsychological reports typically provide an estimate of whether the client was making her or his best effort to do as well as possible on the tests. Effort problems are im-

portant issues that should be addressed, and they may range from poor attention to frank malingering. Several tests are now available to assess effort or symptom validity, and other methods involving analysis of the neuropsychological tests themselves, or of change in performance on retesting, may also be used.

8. *Special Issues*: In litigation in particular, the neuropsychologist is often asked to give an opinion about some matter relevant to the case. Perhaps most often, attorneys may raise questions about effort and malingering. In the case of injury claims, there is often a question about whether deficits noted on the test may have existed before the injury. Other issues that arise may involve involuntary commitment, capacity to manage funds, and related matters.

CLINICAL NEUROPSYCHOLOGY AND CLINICAL PSYCHOLOGY

Professional, practicing clinical neuropsychologists are psychologists with doctoral degrees. In the United States, they typically obtain their degrees from programs accredited in clinical psychology by the American Psychological Association (APA). They must have licenses to practice, and some have Board certification from a Board that confers Diplomate status to clinical neuropsychologists that pass its examination. Most current clinical neuropsychologists have training as clinical psychologists, but their practices differ substantially from those of the typical clinical psychologist. In 1996, the APA determined that clinical neuropsychology was a specialty area separate from clinical psychology. The major distinction was the expertise required by clinical neuropsychologists in neuroscience, particularly with regard to brain–behavior relationships. Clinical psychologists may use some of the same tests as clinical neuropsychologists, such as the Wechsler intelligence scales, but clinical neuropsychologists are specifically trained to make neurobiological inferences in their interpretation of these tests. For example, the neuropsychologists may, depending upon the context provided by other tests, interpret Block Design subtest performance in terms of function of the right parietal lobe.

As psychologists, clinical neuropsychologists typically have a background in counseling and psychotherapy, personality, psychometrics, and general psychological assessment, and the research literature in such areas as learning, perception, motivation, memory, cognition, and social behavior. Therefore these two components of psychology have a common core, just as physicians have a common core of medical knowledge in addition to their specialties. Although we generally think of clinical neuropsychologists as administering assessments, some of them manage active treatment practices, particularly involving psychotherapy, counseling, or rehabilitation for brain-damaged patients. Some neuropsychologists are involved with programs that treat patients with alcoholism or schizophrenia. In several settings there is an alliance among psychiatrists, clinical psychologists, and neuropsychologists devoted to cognitively oriented treatment for schizophrenia (Green, Satz, Ganzell, & Vaclav, 1992).

Referral patterns differ between clinical psychologists and clinical neuropsychologists. Self-referrals would appear to be made most often for psychotherapy, generally targeting clinical psychologists. Other professionals are most often responsible for making referrals to clinical neuropsychologists. Within medicine, the bulk of referrals come from neurologists and psychiatrists; sometimes referrals are made by general practitioners or other specialists. Attorneys are another major source of referrals for clinical neuropsychologists. The most common of these referrals are for brain injury in vehicular or industrial accidents, exposure to toxic or infectious agents that may have damaged the brain, and medical malpractice. Sometimes a referral deals with a problematic matter in which the patient may have a neurological disorder or a functional psychiatric difficulty. A classic example is what was at one time called *pseudodementia* in which it is unclear whether usually elderly clients have a senile dementia or are depressed, resulting in behaviors that produce the appearance of dementia. Neuropsychologists can be helpful in these cases with regard to documenting the presence or absence of objectively determined cognitive deficits. Both clinical psychologists and neuropsychologists can manage such referrals, but the neuropsychologist may be better equipped to evaluate the status of the client's brain function. It is not unusual to have patients of this type referred for neuropsychological testing.

CLINICAL NEUROPSYCHOLOGY AND OTHER SPECIALTIES

As a specialty within psychology, clinical neuropsychology has a unique relationship with some medical specialties. As we have indicated, the basic science of neuropsychology is multidisciplinary, involving numerous specialized areas including neurology, neurosurgery, psychiatry, physiatry, and neuroimaging as well as the basic sciences of molecular biology, genetics, and biochemistry. Thus, many neuropsychological researchers are not clinical psychologists, but may be experimental psychologists, neurochemists, geneticists, and professionals from numerous other disciplines. In recent years, neuroradiology has made a major impact on the field because of the appearance of the computed tomography (CT) scan, magnetic resonance imaging (MRI), positron emission tomography (PET), and advanced cerebral blood flow methods. This new technology has created an extensive literature in which behavioral measures are associated with the use of these measures. Perhaps most significantly for clinical neuropsychology, *online* procedures have been developed in which neuropsychological tests may be taken while the client is undergoing an imaging procedure. Brain function can now be observed while the behavior is taking place. A technique called functional magnetic resonance imaging (fMRI) was specifically developed for that purpose.

These considerations have numerous implications for clinical neuropsychology. First, clinical neuropsychologists have formed an alliance with neurologists and neurosurgeons comparable to the one between clinical psychologists and psychiatrists. In hospitals, clinical neuropsychologists are often found in neurology or neurosurgery services and have their clinics there. They have academic appointments in Departments of Neurology of numerous medical schools, and may direct laboratories there. In some centers, neuropsychologists form part of the team that does online imaging, generally with the task of designing and implementing the behavioral assessment. It is now common to see a neuropsychologist performing behavioral testing while the client is lying under a magnet obtaining an fMRI scan. Sometimes, neuropsychologists may administer behavioral testing during epilepsy surgery.

There appears to be a new relationship with psychiatry since the *biological revolution* that brought forward the view that much of serious mental illness is a brain disorder associated with various neurochemical changes in particular parts of the brain. We are now familiar with the *dopamine hypothesis* and other, more recent theories concerning the neurobiology of schizophrenia, and the growing evidence for a genetic etiology. Similar developments occurred in the area of autism. In the past, when psychiatrists made referrals to neuropsychologists the request made most of the time was to rule out brain damage. Psychiatrists still make referrals to neuropsychologists, but rarely, if ever, for that reason. Currently, there is more interest in obtaining a cognitive profile to assess adaptive functioning and implement rehabilitation planning. There is a great deal of interest in the relationship between cognitive function and social functioning. Repeated neuropsychological testing is used to evaluate medication effects when there is some question of change in cognitive function. Neuropsychological tests may also be given online to psychiatric patients to identify patterns and areas of abnormal brain activity. In the field of autism, there has been extensive use of neuropsychological testing for purposes of ascertaining unique characteristics of cognitive function and for online assessment of brain–behavior relations.

A major reason for formation of the alliance with psychiatry is the growing belief that cognitive function is a major consideration for serious psychiatric disorders such as schizophrenia and autism. It is not only probably associated with the development of these disorders, but its status appears to have important implications for course and outcome. Changes in cognitive function may be positive following initiation of appropriate medication or negative during periods of stress. Specific cognitive tests can help to identify particular dysfunctional regions or systems in the brain. For example, there is an extensive literature on the relationship between perseverative errors on the Wisconsin Card Sorting Test and reduced blood flow in a portion of the frontal lobes of patients with schizophrenia. Clinically, neuropsychological assessment may be useful for patients with serious mental illness in rehabilitation planning and treatment monitoring.

CLINICAL NEUROPSYCHOLOGY AND EDUCATION

There is a branch of clinical neuropsychology devoted to the assessment of educational difficulties and is often used in combination with teachers' observations and tests of academic achievement. The basic point is that some children, who are disabled with regard to learning to read, write, spell, do arithmetic, or acquire related academic skills, often have neuropsychological deficits. Beginning with studies of mental retardation, this field extended to learning disability and other disorders that impede academic progress such as attention-deficit/hyperactivity disorder (ADHD). Initially a controversial area, there now seems to be a widespread acceptance of the view that brain function is relevant to educational activity, and that neuropsychological tests can be helpful in detecting the basis of educational difficulties in terms of brain function or cognitive profile. Until recently, this area was limited to school children, but research has convincingly demonstrated that learning disability, as well as ADHD, may persist into adulthood (Katz, Goldstein, & Beers, 2001). Thus, it is not uncommon to refer a client, child or adult, who is having significant educational difficulties for a neuropsychological assessment. A large literature has emerged specifically dealing with neuropsychological aspects of learning disability focusing on the relationships between assessment results and the characteristics of the learning difficulty. For many years, neuropsychologists and behavioral neurologists have been concerned with such conditions as acquired alexia and agraphia, usually associated with stroke, because they were symptoms of localized brain disease. Currently, there is interest in the developmental types of these disorders as they are first observed in school-age children.

Clinical neuropsychology has made a substantial contribution to identifying subtypes of learning disability based on neuropsychological profiles. In addition to an extensive journal literature, an entire book has been devoted to this topic containing chapters on children with reading, spelling, and arithmetic disabilities as well as methodological approaches to identifying subtypes such as use of cluster analysis (Rourke, 1985). The identification of subtypes can be helpful in remedial educational planning because they are hopefully associated with the cognitive basis for the disability. For example, some poor readers have particular difficulty with transforming graphic symbols to sounds, while others have their main difficulty in oral reading. These subtypes have been found to have differing patterns of neuropsychological test performance. It is therefore often helpful to do a comprehensive neuropsychological assessment of individuals with significant learning disability in an effort to identify the cognitive basis of the disability and to formulate a remediation plan.

FORENSIC APPLICATIONS OF CLINICAL NEUROPSYCHOLOGY

Many clinical neuropsychologists in private practice receive the bulk of referrals from attorneys, insurance companies, or the judicial system. It is common to have two neuropsychologists on a case, one representing the complainant or prosecution, and the other representing the defense. Thus, the assessment is often an adversarial procedure and skilled clinicians typically have extensive knowledge of, and experience with, legal procedure and testimony as an expert witness in some cases or an advocate of the claimant or defendant in others. There is an extensive literature in forensic neuropsychology, and *The Clinical Neuropsychologist*, a professional journal, now devotes a section to forensic applications. Attorneys and insurance companies that deal with disability claims frequently make referrals to clinical neuropsychologists when the case involves impairment of brain function. The typical case is one in which the client was in an accident involving an alleged head injury and is therefore seeking redress in some form or compensation for permanent disability from an insurance company. In some cases, the assessment is done as an independent medical evaluation (IME) in which the neuropsychologist provides an opinion about the presence, nature, and extent of disability. Capacity for employment or independent living are often major issues. Neuropsychologists may participate in competency hearings or deliberations concerning capacity to stand trial.

In engaging the services of a neuropsychologist in forensic matters, there are several matters to be considered. First, the procedures used should meet the *Daubert Standard* issued by the U. S. Supreme Court, which requires, among other things, that the theory and techniques used in the assessment are generally accepted by a relevant scientific community. For neuropsychology, this has been interpreted to mean that tests used by expert witnesses or conclusions drawn from them need to be scientifically credible as evidenced by publication in refereed journals. The Halstead-Reitan Battery appears to be neuropsychology's best example of a set of comprehensive procedures that meet Daubert Standard requirements based on extensive research. A second matter is the qualifications of the neuropsychologist. If a case comes to trial, it is almost a certainty that the neuropsychologist will be questioned about credentials and competency to serve as an expert witness. The neuropsychologist should be a licensed psychologist holding a doctoral degree. Perhaps Diplomate status is the most satisfactory indicator of competency, but only a minority of neuropsychologists are Diplomates. Other qualifications that may be used are Fellowship in the Division of Clinical Neuropsychology of the American Psychological Association or the National Academy of Neuropsychology, membership in honorary societies, years of experience, publications, and related academic achievements.

It is now essentially mandatory in forensic matters that the neuropsychologist provide an explicit evaluation of effort. In court, there is often questioning about whether the client was exerting her or his best effort in taking the test, or frankly malingering. Three methods have been described to make this evaluation. Special tests have been published that have the sole purpose of evaluating effort, symptom validity, or malingering. They are now commonly administered in combination with the neuropsychological tests. It is also possible to infer low effort from indices derived from the neuropsychological tests themselves. These indices have been developed through research with coached malingerers, or involve the production of scores that are poorer than those obtained from the tests of severely brain damaged patients. Sometimes the occurrences of highly unlikely scores are helpful. For example, it is very unusual to be able to recite more numbers backward than forward. Within the appropriate context, this phenomenon may be an indicator of malingering. When retesting is available, a third method involves noting changes in the test scores relative to outcome of the case. The basic research finding is that patients in litigation produce substantially more inconsistent scores on retesting than do individuals not in litigation. Head-injured individuals in litigation tend to produce poorer test performance on retesting while those not in litigation produce improved scores. Testing for effort is now commonly used in disability evaluations in which the client is seeking compensation or a pension for illness or injury associated with work or an accident.

CLINICAL NEUROPSYCHOLOGY IN DIFFERENT AGE GROUPS

Neuropsychological testing is appropriate for children, adults, and elderly adults, but the specific tests used may differ, and there are distinct scientific literatures. Neuropsychological assessment, as we generally understand it, may be administered starting at age 5 and can be accomplished in some form with very elderly or ill individuals. Some of the comprehensive batteries and individual tests have been standardized for children, and some tests have been specifically designed for children. The Halstead-Reitan Battery has a young children's version (age 5–7) and an intermediate version (age 8–15). The young children's battery contains modified versions of several of the tests contained in the adult battery, plus several additional tests designed just for young children. The intermediate battery consists mainly of the adult tests in modified form. As appropriate, the Wechsler Intelligence Scale for Children (WISC) instead of the adult WAIS is used.

Child clinical neuropsychology has essentially become a subspecialty within clinical neuropsychology with its own journals, books, and required clinical skills. Rather than the disorders of adulthood such as multiple sclerosis, stroke, and Alzheimer's disease, the emphasis is on conditions that appear in childhood, notably developmental disorders. Children may also acquire traumatic head injuries, brain cancer, and various infectious illnesses involving the brain. Competence in this area requires substantial knowledge about brain development, the consequences of perinatal difficulties in the mother or child, and the clinical skills involved in working with children and parents. A major consideration is that assessment results occur within the context of a growing brain, and significant events such as neuronal growth and synaptic pruning are still occurring. Effects of localized damage and recovery may be different in children from what is seen in adults. Lifelong disorders such as autism are first discovered in early childhood, and the neuropsychologist may be helpful in planning treatment and management. As indicated previously, neuropsychological assessment is often useful in characterization of learning disabilities, and the neuropsychologist may provide important consultation to teachers and remedial education specialists.

Elderly individuals who are not suffering from a dementing illness are generally capable of cooperating for standard adult neuropsychological tests. They may show the expected consequences of normal aging, but are quite testable. Of great current interest is the problem of mild cognitive impairment (MCI) that involves memory and other cognitive difficulties that are present, but not substantially disabling (Lopez et al., 2006). Some of these individuals develop Alzheimer's disease over time, whereas others do not. Research efforts are underway to predict which eventuality will occur. There is a substantial neuropsychological literature concerning normal aging that substantially supplements the work originally done with intelligence tests. Assessment difficulties arise in individuals with dementia. Often, these people cannot cooperate for standard tests and special tests need to be developed. Some of them are derived from the standard neuropsychological tests such as the Severe Impairment Battery that evaluates specific cognitive abilities such as memory and visual-spatial abilities in individuals with severe dementia. The other method commonly used involves rating scales akin to a mental status examination. The Mini-Mental State Examination (Folstein, Folstein, & McHugh, 1975) and the Mattis *Dementia Rating Scale* (Mattis, 1988) are the most commonly used procedures. These instruments are brief, containing items that assess attention, orientation, and language with one or two items.

TREATMENT AND REHABILITATION

Part of the definition of a clinical neuropsychologist indicates an involvement with treatment and rehabilitation. This area has various aspects and there is a great deal of diversity regarding the therapeutic activities of clinical neuropsychologists. Therapeutic activities vary and range from believing that clinical neuropsychologists should do assessment and make recommendations to rehabilitation specialists, physicians and other therapists who do the actual treatment, to the firm belief that neuropsychologists should be directly involved in treatment on an everyday basis. Some of the pioneers of the field, notably Kurt Goldstein and Alexander Luria, wrote extensively about both assessment and treatment. Luria was actively involved in rehabilitation of brain-damaged patients, and Goldstein had a long career as a psychotherapist. More recently, some neuropsychologists have followed this pattern of doing both activities, while others have placed more emphasis on assessment or treatment.

Those interested in treatment have established a field now known as cognitive or neuropsychological rehabilitation. Its emphasis is on restoration of function following brain damage. It was pioneered by Leonard Diller, Yehuda Ben-Yishay, and associates at the Rusk Institute in New York City who published several seminal papers involving rehabilitation-related assessment of patients with spatial-constructional deficits associated with right cerebral hemisphere stroke (e.g., Ben-Yishay, Diller, Gerstman, & Gordon, 1970). Thereafter, head-injury patients and individuals with multiple sclerosis, and slowly progressive dementing disorders were involved in cognitive rehabilitation studies and subsequent applications. The thrust of this work was on rehabilitation of specific domain disorders including attention, memory, visual-spatial abilities, and reasoning and problem solving. Many of the training programs developed have been manualized and are available, often in the form of computer-based packages.

Most recently, cognitive rehabilitation methods have been applied to patients with schizophrenia. Earlier work in this area involved teaching how to perform better on the Wisconsin Card Sorting Test as a means of improving abstract reasoning and problem solving. Now there are multicomponent programs available that provide training in such areas as attention, memory, and social cognition. Another development has been creation of an interface with behavior therapy such that contingency management and multiple baseline design programs have been used to train behaviors in specific areas such as eating, continence, and attentional deficits. It is currently common for a neuropsychologist to coordinate programs at rehabilitation hospitals and clinics at which cognitive rehabilitation has been added to the other rehabilitation specialties. Thus, in addition to speech and language therapy rehabilitation, facilities may offer programs in memory training or maintenance of attention and associated reduction of impulsivity. In the area of autism, there are programs devoted to such relevant matters as improvement of divided attention.

SCIENTIFIC CONSIDERATIONS

The definition of clinical neuropsychology involves what clinical neuropsychology is, what neuropsychologists are, and what they do. We have reviewed the matter of qualifications and activities, and now we will comment briefly on the substance of the field itself. This substance has a scientific basis and a large scholarly literature. This literature has several components, one of which is the study of relationships between brain function and behavior in various disease entities. The diseases are mainly neurological illnesses, but several psychiatric disorders are now of interest to researchers in clinical neuropsychology. Scanning the table of contents of a recent issue of a clinical neuropsychology journal we found articles on traumatic brain injury, stroke, schizophrenia, MCI, and damage to the right hemisphere. This list seems to be reasonably representative, but we would add that there is also major interest in dementia, alcoholism and other substance-related disorders, multiple sclerosis, developmental disorders, and epilepsy. Neuropsychologists working with collaborators in other disciplines are concerned with identifying behavioral patterns associated with these disorders. For example, what is the neuropsychological profile associated with multiple sclerosis? There is a longstanding interest in differences between the two cerebral hemispheres, particularly with regard to cognitive differences. These differences were originally studied with stroke patients or other individuals who had clearly unilateral brain damage, but more recently the capability emerged of studying them with functional neuroimaging procedures.

An interfacing component has to do with studies of the behavioral domains. What is the neuropsychology of language, memory, reasoning and problem solving, attention, perception, visual–spatial functions and skilled movement? In the area of memory, for example, neuropsychology has taken findings from early experimental psychology and sought brain processes associated with various aspects of memory. These studies were accomplished in humans, studying patients with severe amnesia as subjects, and more recently with online investigation using neuroimaging while the individual performs memory tasks. These investigations have been accompanied by corresponding animal model studies. For example, we have a reasonably good understanding of the relationship between working memory and associated brain activity. Historically, there have been many years of investigation involving the relationship between abstract reasoning and problem solving and the frontal lobes, and between visual-spatial function and the right cerebral hemisphere.

There is a component of neuropsychological research that studies normal individuals for the purpose of seeking relationships between various behaviors and brain structure or function. For example, studies have been done of facial recognition and perception of affect using fMRI in normal subjects. Recently a study was published on language comprehension in normal children using fMRI (Prat, Keller, & Just, 2007). As a form of basic science investigation that we hope has implications for abnormal function, the aim of this research was to further our understanding of how the healthy brain mediates various behaviors. Recently, for example, there has been evidence that different patterns appear on fMRI associated with the same behaviors in individuals with autism and normal subjects (Mason, Williams, Kana, Minshew, & Just, 2008).

Another important component of clinical neuropsychological research involves psychometrics concerning the development of neuropsychological tests. This area includes the development of new tests and test batteries; studies of various forms of validity and reliability of existing tests; relationships among tests determined by factor analysis; normative studies in various groups; and construction of new scoring and scaling methods. New tests are always appearing and there should be demonstrations of their unique contributions, their discriminative validity accomplished through comparing various groups, and their psychometric characteristics including validity, reliability, norm development and scoring system. For example, a new battery called the Repeatable Battery for the Assessment of Neuropsychological Status (RBANS; Randolph, 1998) was reported to be particularly useful for detecting Alzheimer's disease; the repeatability of the various subtests made it particularly good for use in clinical trials. Various methods and sets of data have been reported for different scoring and scaling systems for the Halstead-Reitan Battery. New tests of effort and malingering have been developed that are particularly helpful with forensic and compensation cases (Larrabee, 2007). Factor analytic studies have been accomplished in a variety of applications to elicit the structure of various test systems, and for practical purposes, to reduce redundancy. Cluster analytic studies have been done to identify subtypes with various clinical populations using test scores as the variables placed in these analyses (Goldstein, 1994).

Clinical neuropsychology has been guided to a substantial extent by extraordinarily extensive research regarding the use of particular procedures. Research done with the Halstead-Reitan battery under the leadership of Ralph Reitan is likely the most extensive of these procedures. The first study was reported in Reitan's (1955) paper, "An Investigation of the Validity of Halstead's Measures of Biological Intelligence," and this research continues until the present time. These studies provide extraordinarily thorough evidence of the construct and predictive validity of the Halstead-Reitan Battery. In 1970, a formalized, objective system for interpretation of this battery, in the form of taxonomic keys, was presented by Russell, Neuringer, and Goldstein (1970). Other procedures associated with extensive validity research include the Wechsler Intelligence Scales, the California Verbal Learning Test, and the Luria-Nebraska Neuropsychological Battery.

In addition to the development of new tests, neuropsychologists have produced manuals and kits for rehabilitation procedures. For example, there is the Attention Process Training of Sohlberg and Mateer (2001), and the "Captain's Log" series produced by Brain Train that contains a large number of modules for cognitive training (Tarnowski, 1988). These manualized, often computerized procedures, are now in use at numerous rehabilitation hospitals and clinics in various applications. They address a large number of behaviors and skills, including such areas as memory, working memory, attention, impulsivity, reasoning, and listening. There is great interest in the effectiveness of these programs and researchers grapple with the question about whether success with the program itself generalizes to life in the community. A client may do well at these programs, but that does not necessarily assure improvement in community functioning. Also, regarding treatment, some neuropsychologists work with investigators of new medications in clinical trials. The particular problem here is practice effects that may compromise the repeatability of the tests; there have been several efforts made to develop tests that are repeatable.

A recently emerging area of interest has been the influence of cultural and socioethnic factors on neuropsychological tests (Nell, 2004). Article titles such as "Executive Ability and Physical Performance in Urban Black Older Adults" (Schneider & Lichtenberg, 2008) and "Neuropsychological Profile of Brazilian Older Adults With Heterogeneous Educational Backgrounds" (Yassuda et al., 2009) seem to be appearing in increasing numbers. Additionally, there are increasing numbers of neuropsychological studies of general medical disorders notably hepatitis C, HIV, and nutritional disorders.

SUMMARY

We have attempted to characterize clinical neuropsychology in terms of what a clinical neuropsychologist is with regard to personal, educational, and experiential qualifications, what she or he does, and what constitutes the substance of the field. Professionally, it is no longer a branch of clinical psychology, but is a separate specialty area based on a concern with relationships between brain function and behavior. It utilizes specialized tests that have scientifically demonstrated sensitivity to the condition of the brain. There are numerous such tests and different neuropsychologists use different tests or test batteries. Some use a fixed battery in which all of the tests are administered in the same way to all patients, and some use individual tests selected on the basis of a patient's history and the associated referral question. Neuropsychological assessment is frequently used in clinical, forensic, and educational applications. The field also has a treatment component that features various methods of cognitive rehabilitation and participation in clinical trials.

The essential basis for the practice of clinical neuropsychology is an extensive research literature with new developments continually emerging and published in several specialized journals and books, as well as in the more general psychological and neurobiological literature as appropriate. This scientific basis contains work on neuropsychological status in various neurological disorders, psychiatric illness, some general medical diseases, and developmental disorders. Neuropsychological assessments may be administered to both children and adults. Thus, the clinical neuropsychologist must have expertise in the neurobehavioral aspects of such disorders as traumatic brain injury, stroke, brain cancer, multiple sclerosis, and Alzheimer's disease in addition to developmental disorders such as a learning disability, ADHD, and autism.

Clinical neuropsychology has developed and validated specialized tests that are sensitive to these conditions and are sometimes helpful in making diagnoses, particularly in cases that present diagnostic difficulties. In current neuroscience, neuropsychological tests are not viewed as procedures that establish diagnoses, but rather as contributing to an understanding of functioning and differentiating areas of preserved and impaired abilities. They are often used productively in conjunction with various neuroimaging techniques to identify brain systems associated with various aspects of behavior in both normal and pathological conditions. Relevant research has also promoted sensitivity to the influence of cultural and socioethnic influences on tests, and it is now unlikely that a neuropsychological assessment will lead to the conclusion that a client is brain damaged when in fact performance is limited by, for example, having to take the tests in the client's second language, or by cultural attitudes toward testing. Contemporary neuropsychologists are sensitive to the problems associated with reduced effort and malingering, and now make efforts to elicit the client's best performance, or at least to evaluate whether poor effort or malingering influenced test performance. Clients are now often advised to make their best effort because voluntarily reduced effort or frank malingering is likely to be detected and may be counterproductive to achieving the client's goals.

Clinical neuropsychologists may be active in educational and forensic settings. They have expertise in identifying patterns of cognitive intactness and weakness that are associated with various forms of learning disabilities, often providing useful information for educational placement and remedial instruction. In forensics, clinical neuropsychologists may serve as expert witnesses or advocates for a client engaged in litigation. They may testify with regard to such matters as consequences of head injury, toxic exposure, or medical malpractice. They often are asked to comment on dissimulation and now make extensive use of the effort, symptom validity, and malingering procedures we have mentioned.

Individuals experiencing cognitive difficulties may have the choice of being referred to a psychiatrist, a neurologist, a clinical psychologist, or a clinical neuropsychologist, perhaps after being evaluated by a primary care clinician. It is somewhat unusual for an individual to make a self-referral to a clinical neuropsychologist without at least going through a primary care evaluation. More often a referral is made by a physician who has evaluated the individual neurologically or psychiatrically—the physician may make the referral to a clinical psychologist or neuropsychologist. The basis for the decision may simply be the unavailability of, or lack of knowledge about clinical neuropsychologists. Assuming availability and knowledge, there are several considerations. If the referring agent is not a neurologist, referral for neuropsychological assessment may be made in association with referral to a neurologist, or the neurologist can make the referral after seeing the patient. Psychiatrists may wish to conduct the neurological examination themselves, having the ability to order neuroimaging and other laboratory procedures. Referral to a clinical psychologist should ideally be made when there is no strong suspicion of a neurological disorder, but the client could benefit from a personality evaluation and, possibly, psychotherapy in some form. If the clinical psychologist identifies possible neurocognitive dysfunction, she or he may refer the client to a neuropsychologist. Ideally, most clinical neuropsychologists prefer to see patients who have had neurological evaluations and neuroimaging procedures.

In educational settings, typically there aren't significant medical problems, but teachers may wish to refer students for neuropsychological assessment if they are having significant learning difficulties: This is especially true if they are not well characterized by the standard psychoeducational tests. The report of the neuropsychologist should contain information concerning the student's cognitive profile, a description of how the profile characteristics might be associated with the learning disability, and recommendations for accommodation or remediation. For example, it might be found that the student has a reading difficulty because of a visual–spatial deficit that impairs the perception of letters. Appropriate specific training might help remediate this difficulty while traditional phonics training might not be of much value.

Attorneys often recommend neuropsychological assessment for their clients when there is claimed cognitive loss that may be the responsibility of the defendant. The defendant and supporting counsel may also obtain the services of a neuropsychologist as an advocate. The judge may request a neuropsychologist as an expert witness or friend of the court (amicus curiae). Neuropsychologists may also function in this capacity regarding competency to manage funds or to stand trial in criminal cases. Sometimes referrals are made by insurance companies or government agencies for the general purpose of evaluating an individual's competency. The client may be pressing for compensation associated with a disability, and neuropsychological assessment is used to help form an opinion concerning employability or capacity for independent living. Aside from income, the matter of payment for custodial care, nursing home placement, or purchase of prosthetic devices placed in the home may be an issue. Often neuropsychological tests can be helpful regarding these matters, and probably benefit significantly by using measures of effort.

In summary, there are numerous consumer groups that make referrals for neuropsychological assessment and the field has gone far beyond its traditional role of evaluating neurological patients in hospitals. There is a common core of interest in associating behavior with brain function, but the areas of application are extremely varied, ranging from healthy children with learning difficulties to seriously ill neurological, neurosurgical, and psychiatric patients. There is also extensive variation in choice of tests used and the nature of the assessment, illustrated clearly by the matter of *fixed* versus *flexible* battery approaches. Such matters as computerized assessment and *online* testing with functional neuroimaging appear to represent the future of the field.

REFERENCES

Allen, D. N., Caron, J. E., & Goldstein, G. (2006). Process index scores for the Halstead Category Test. In A. Poreh (Ed.), *The quantified process approach to neuropsychological assessment* (pp. 259–279). Lisse, The Netherlands: Swets & Zeitlinger.

Barth, J. T., Pliskin, N., Axelrod, B., Faust, D., Fisher, J., Harley, J. P., et al. (2003). Introduction to the NAN 2001 definition of a clinical neuropsychologist. NAN policy and planning committee. *Archives of Clinical Neuropsychology, 18,* 551–555.

Benton, A. L., Hamsher, K. des, Varney, N. R., & Spreen, O. (1983). *Contributions to neuropsychological assessment.* New York: Oxford University Press.

Ben-Yishay, Y., Diller, L., Gerstman, L., & Gordon, W. (1970). Relationship between initial competence and ability to profit from cues in brain-damaged individuals. *Journal of Abnormal Psychology, 78,* 248–259.

Christensen, A. L. (1975). *Luria's neuropsychological investigation.* New York: Spectrum.

Delis, D. C., Kramer, J. H., Kaplan, E., & Ober, B. A. (2000). *California Verbal Learning Test* (2nd ed.). San Antonio, TX: Psychological Corporation.

Duff, K., Humphreys Clark, J. D., O'Bryant, S. E., Mold, J. W., Schiffer, R. B., Sutker, P. D., et al. (2008). Utility of the RBANS in detecting cognitive impairment associated with Alzheimer's disease: Sensitivity, specificity, and positive and negative predictive powers. *Archives of Clinical Neuropsychology, 23,* 603–612.

Folstein, M. F., Folstein, S. E., & McHugh, P. R. (1975). Mini-Mental State: A practical method for grading the cognitive state of patients for the clinician. *Journal of Psychiatric Research, 12,* 189–198.

Geschwind, N. (1984).Cerebral dominance in biological perspective. *Neuropsychologia, 22,* 675–683.

Goldberg, E. (2001). *The executive brain.* New York: Oxford University Press

Golden, C. J., Purisch, A. D., & Hammeke, T. A. (1985). *Luria-Nebraska Neuropsychological Battery: Forms I and II.* Los Angeles: Western Psychological Services.

Goldstein, G. (1994). Neurobehavioral heterogeneity in schizophrenia. *Archives of Clinical Neuropsychology, 9,* 265–276.

Goldstein, G., & Incagnoli, T. (Eds.). (1997). *Contemporary approaches to neuropsychological assessment.* New York: Plenum Press.

Goldstein, K. (1939). *The organism.* New York: American Book Company.

Goldstein, K., & Scheerer, M. (1941). Abstract and concrete behavior: An experimental study with special tests. *Psychological Monographs, 53,* (2, Whole Number 239).

Goodglass, H. (1986). The flexible battery in neuropsychological assessment. In T. Incagnoli, G. Goldstein, & C. J. Golden (Eds.), *Clinical application of neuropsychological test batteries* (pp. 121–134). New York: Plenum Press.

Goodglass, H., & Kaplan, E. (1983). *The assessment of aphasia and related disorders* (2nd ed.), Philadelphia: Lea & Febiger.

Green, M. F., Satz, P., Ganzell, S., & Vaclav, J. F. (1992). Wisconsin Card Sorting Test performance in schizophrenia: Remediation of a stubborn deficit. *American Journal of Psychiatry, 149,* 62–67.

Halstead, W. C. (1947). *Brain and intelligence.* Chicago: University of Chicago Press.

Hannay, H. J. (1998). Proceedings of the Houston Conference on specialty education and training in clinical neuropsychology. *Archives of Clinical Neuropsychology, 13,* 157–249.

Heaton, R. K., Chelune, G. J., Talley, J. L., Kay, G. G., & Curtiss, G. (1993). *Wisconsin Card Sorting Test Manual.* Odessa, FL: Psychological Assessment Resources.

Heaton, R. K., Miller, W., Taylor M. J., & Grant, I. (2004). *Revised comprehensive norms for an expanded Halstead-Reitan Battery.* Lutz, FL: Psychological Assessment Resources.

Heilman, K. M., & Valenstein, E. (2003). *Clinical neuropsychology* (4th ed.). New York: Oxford University Press.

Incagnoli, T., Goldstein G., & Golden, C. J. (1986). *Clinical application of neuropsychological test batteries.* New York: Plenum Press.

Kaminski, T. W., Groff, R. M., & Glutting, J. J. (2008). Examining the stability of Automated Neuropsychological Assessment Metric (ANAM) baseline test scores. *Journal of Clinical and Experimental Neuropsychology, 28,* 1–9.

Katz, L. J., Goldstein, G., & Beers, S. R. (2001). *Learning disabilities in older adolescents and adults.* New York: Kluwer Academic.

Kertesz, A. (1979). *Aphasia and related disorders: Taxonomy, localization, and recovery.* New York: Grune & Stratton.

Larrabee, G. J. (2007). *Assessment of malingered neuropsychological deficits.* New York: Oxford University Press.

Lezak, M. D., Howieson, D. B., & Loring, D. W. (2004). *Neuropsychological assessment* (4th ed.). New York: Oxford University Press.

Lopez, O. L., Becker, J. T., Jagust, W. J., Fitzpatrick, A., Carlson, M. C., DeKosky, S. T., et al. (2006). Neuropsychological characteristics of mild cognitive impairment subgroups. *Journal of Neurology, Neurosurgery, and Psychiatry, 77,* 159–165.

Luria, A. R. (1973). *The working brain.* New York: Basic Books.

Mason, R. A., Williams, D. L., Kana, R. K., Minshew N. J., & Just, M. (2008). Theory of mind disruption and recruitment of the right hemisphere during narrative comprehension in autism. *Neuropsychologia, 46,* 269–280.

Mattis, S. (1988). *Dementia Rating Scale: Professional manual.* Odessa, FL: Psychological Assessment Resources.

Nell, V. (2004). Translation and test administration techniques to meet the assessment needs of ethnic minorities, migrants, and refugees. In G. Goldstein & S. R. Beers (Eds.), *Comprehensive handbook of psychological assessment: Volume 1: Intellectual and neuropsychological assessment* (pp. 333–338). Hoboken, NJ: Wiley.

Prat, C. S., Keller, T. A., & Just, M. A. (2007). Individual differences in sentence comprehension: A functional magnetic resonance imaging investigation of syntactic and lexical processing demands. *Journal of Cognitive Neuroscience, 19,* 1950–1963.

Randolph, C. (1998). *Repeatable battery for the assessment of neuropsychological status manual.* Toronto, Ontario: Psychological Corp.

Reitan, R. M. (1955). Investigation of the validity of Halstead's measures of biological intelligence. *Archives of Neurology and Psychiatry, 73,* 28–35.

Reitan R. M., & Wolfson, D. (1993). *The Halstead-Reitan Neuropsychological Test Battery: Theory and clinical interpretation* (2nd ed.). Tucson, AZ: Neuropsychology Press.

Reitan, R. M., & Wolfson, D. (1997). *Malingering and the detection of invalid test results.* Tucson, AZ: Neuropsychology Press.

Rourke, B. (1985). *Neuropsychology of learning disabilities: Essentials of subtype analysis.* New York: Guilford Press.

Russell, E. W., Neuringer, C., & Goldstein G. (1970). *Assessment of brain damage.* New York: Wiley-Interscience.

Russell, E. W., & Starkey, R. I., (1993). *Halstead-Russell neuropsychological evaluation system: Manual and computer program.* Los Angeles: Western Psychological Services.

Schneider, B. C., & Lichtenberg, P. A. (2008). Executive ability and physical performance in urban Black older adults. *Archives of Clinical Neuropsychology, 23,* 593–601.

Slick, D. J., Hopp, G., Strauss, E., & Spellacy, F. J. (1996). Victoria Symptom Validity Test: Efficiency for determining feigned memory impairment and relationship to neuropsychological tests and MMPI-2 validity scales. *Journal of Clinical and Experimental Neuropsychology, 18,* 911–922.

Sohlberg, M. M., & Mateer, C. A. (2001). Improving attention and managing attentional problems. Adapting rehabilitation techniques to adults with ADD. *Annals of the New York Academy of Science, 931,* 359–375.

Tarnowski, K. J. (1988). Cognitive assessment and intervention: Captain's Log. *Research in Developmental Disabilities, 9,* 101–104.

Wechsler, D. (1987). *The Wechsler Memory Scale—Revised manual.* San Antonio, TX: Psychological Corporation.

Wechsler, D. (2008). *Wechsler Adult Intelligence Scale—Fourth edition (WAIS IV).* San Antonio, TX: Pearson.

Yassuda, M. S., et al. (2009). Neuropsychological profile of Brazilian older adults with heterogeneous educational backgrounds. *Archives of Clinical Neuropsychology, 24,* 71–79.

2

What Does Neuropsychology Mean to Patients and Their Families?

THOMAS A. HAMMEKE AND ROBERT F. NEWBY

Most of the general public knows little about the discipline of neuropsychology, what a neuropsychologist is, or what services a neuropsychologist can provide. They are unfamiliar with the training and expertise of the discipline. Little do they know how much a neuropsychologist has to offer to the understanding and treatment of themselves and their families. Families may not know that a neuropsychologist, by virtue of his or her education, training, and area of interest, is exceptionally well positioned to integrate information from a myriad of sources to bring a road map of understanding and strategy to bear on a personal crisis.

This chapter reviews some of the services neuropsychologists can provide to patients and their families. Three real cases, in which the names have been changed, will be used to assist in illustration. First, it is important to understand that the discipline of clinical neuropsychology operates in arenas that bridge basic and clinical neuroscience, as well as academic and social care systems of service delivery. Moreover, within the realm of clinical sciences, neuropsychology focuses on the boundary zones between clinical neurology, neurosurgery, rehabilitation medicine, and psychiatry, as well as clinical, developmental, and health psychology. A neuropsychologist is required to know and understand a good deal about each of these other disciplines and the disorders cared for by each in order to function properly within these boundary zones. It is the knowledge and understanding that comes from functioning within the boundary zones of these overlapping disciplines that enables neuropsychologists to provide a valuable service to the general public.

A good example of working within this boundary zone is the common expectation for neuropsychologists to assist other health care professionals to determine what aspects of a patient's presentation can best be understood as being behavior that is normal for that individual's age and education, versus what is related to psychological factors in that individual's life, versus what behaviors are best understood as being representative of brain dysfunction. This has historically been framed as the referral question for determining what pathology is *organic*, meaning due to brain dysfunction, and what is *functional*, meaning due to psychogenic factors.

Second, it is important to understand that psychologists in general and clinical neuropsychologists in particular have extensive education and training in techniques of measuring an individual's cognitive, emotional, and social behaviors. Neuropsychologists are experts in measuring cognitive capacities in normal and abnormal states of brain functioning. It is this foundation of knowledge and skills in measuring neurocognitive functions that enables neuropsychologists to be uniquely well positioned to differentially diagnose neurobehavioral conditions and assist in clinical decision making and rehabilitation planning derived from such diagnostic formulations. A differential diagnosis refers to a clinician's list of possible explanations for a presenting illness or disorder.

An illustration of differential neurobehavioral diagnosis can be found in Table 2.1. The table identifies 10 major categories of neurobehavioral syndromes and illustrates how the first five of these categories can be discerned from careful study of how well an individual performs on various tests of memory functions. Each neurobehavioral category has a discernable collection of behaviors associated with it and is linked to a profile of normal and abnormal brain functioning. For example, the category of dementia describes a collection of impairments in both new learning and recent memory that occurs with an impairment in some other category of cognitive function (e.g., body of factual knowledge about the world) that is listed under the broader category of *remote* memory and is seen in the context of preserved focus in the stream

Table 2.1

MAJOR NEUROBEHAVIORAL SYNDROMES

	MEMORY FUNCTIONS*		
	IMMEDIATE	RECENT	REMOTE
1. **Dementia**[1]	±	—	—
2. **Confusional States**[2]	—	—	+
3. **Dementia with Confusion**[3]	—	—	—
4. **Primary Amnesia**[4]	+	—	+
5. **Attentional Disorder (Aprosexia)**[5]	—	+	+
6. Aphasias[6]			
7. Nonaphasic Focal Deficit Syndromes of Dominant Hemisphere[7]			
8. Focal Deficit Syndromes of Nondominant Hemisphere[8]			
9. Frontal Lobe Syndromes[9]			
10. (Developmental Syndromes)[10]			

* For clinical purposes, declarative memory can be broadly grouped into these three categories: immediate (or span memory), recent (or episodic memory), and remote (autobiographical and semantic memory; Strub & Black, 2000).

1. A medical/neurological condition of decline in multiple cognitive functions, including memory, that is not due to an alteration in consciousness. The decline is sufficient in severity to cause impairment in activities of daily living (*DSM*, 1994; Kaufer & Cummings, 1997; Strub & Black, 2000).
2. These are conditions with altered states of consciousness associated with marked impairment in the ability to track events in the environment. Two general varieties are recognized—hyperkinetic state (delirium) and a hypokinetic state (stupor)—which are usually due to toxic or metabolic encephalopathies (Kaufer & Cummings, 1997; Mesulam, 2000; Strub & Black, 2000).
3. A useful condition to recognize since the combination is quite common and the confusional state is usually treatable (Kaufer & Cummings, 1997; Strub & Black, 2000).
4. A neurologic condition with marked impairment in the ability to form new memories seen in the context of normal consciousness and intellectual capacities (*DSM*, 1994; Strub & Black, 2000).
5. A condition of fluctuating attention that can be due to medical/neurologic mechanisms but most commonly is associated with psychiatric states of anxiety and depression (Strub & Black, 2000).
6. A collection of syndromes with impairments in one or more primary language functions due to dominant cerebral hemisphere dysfunction (Alexander, 1997).
7. Other focal brain syndromes of the dominant hemisphere that do not involve primary language functions (e.g., Gerstmann's syndrome, alexia without agraphia; Strub & Black, 2000).
8. For example, unilateral neglect syndrome (Mesulam, 2000).
9. A collection of behavioral manifestations that may include impairments in executive functions, initiation, and inhibition (Kimberg, 1997).
10. Whereas the other neurobehavioral categories typically are due to acquired neurologic conditions, this category might relate to developmental syndromes that may otherwise overlap to some extent in presentation to other categories (e.g., attention-deficit/hyperactivity disorder and developmental dyslexia; *DSM*, 1994).

Adapted from des Hamsher (1983).

of consciousness (identified here as preserved immediate memory). Additionally, confusional states, be they hyperkinetic (delirium) or hypokinetic (stupor) in character, share common features of profound impairments in the ability to sustain attentional focus, leading to impairments in immediate and recent memory, but have a preserved body of knowledge and capacity to discern concepts (to the extent that attentional capacities will permit them to be tested).

Each of the major neurobehavioral categories in Table 2.1 implies dysfunction in a set of neural circuits related to the profile of neurocognitive deficits that is characteristic of the category. Each category has subcategories (not listed in the table) that have unique profiles of neurocognitive deficits. In turn, the profile of neurocognitive deficits often has implications for the pathophysiological mechanisms that underlie the syndrome (e.g., neurodegenerative, vascular, metabolic, neoplastic, etc.) and its associated course, natural outcome, and responsiveness to treatment.

It is important to point out that through careful evaluation of the domains of neurocognitive function, a neuropsychologist is in a good position to determine the proper neurobehavioral diagnosis, which sets the stage for proper evaluation of the etiological condition causing the behaviors, planning of rehabilitation, and disposition. This, in turn, enables the neuropsychologist to be in an excellent position to assist everyone affected by the condition by providing education to the patient and his caregivers concerning the patient's condition, including its characteristics and its effects on the family. To illustrate these points, three cases are presented.

Case Example 1: A Pediatric Patient With Abnormal Skill Development

Maggie was referred for her first neuropsychological evaluation at 11 years of age. The evaluation was to assist in the process of designing and informing an appropriate intervention and to supplement pre-existing developmental, educational, and medical information about her that was available from other sources. Since early childhood, she had fine and gross motor coordination problems that were treated in occupational therapy through her public school district from ages 3 to 6 years. Early language was delayed (e.g., she spoke single words at 3 years), so she also received speech/language therapy during this period. She has always fatigued easily, both when engaged in physical activities and during sustained mental activities such as schoolwork. She had learning struggles, most notably in the areas of reading and written language, although she also needed extra review in math. She had received extra tutoring from the reading specialist at school during the previous 2 years, and Spanish and physical education were eliminated from her program during fifth grade to lighten her course load and provide time for the extra help.

Although the above scenario might have been readily evaluated by a child clinical psychologist, and, in fact, was amply assessed by a team of special educators during Maggie's preschool years, medical factors that were discovered later made it necessary to go the further step of conducting a specialized neuropsychological evaluation. Since early infancy, Maggie had shown large head circumference. Additionally, at age 10 years, after several months of increasing frequency and intensity of preexisting headaches, a brain MRI scan showed signs of elevated pressure inside the skull due to blockage of the flow of cerebral spinal fluid (i.e., hydrocephalus due to aqueductal stenosis), which was presumed to be chronic. A several-year history of tremor (more in the lower than upper extremities) was evaluated by a neurologist at age 10 years; this doctor also found general coordination delays, with greater difficulty hopping on the right foot than the left foot, as well as asymmetric gait. Neurosurgery was done to improve fluid flow (i.e., a third ventriculostomy), and thereby to reduce the hydrocephalus. After the surgery, her headaches returned to baseline frequency, but she developed persistent obsessive-compulsive disorder (OCD). Careful review of her history revealed a longstanding pattern of problems with planning and organization in both academic work and everyday life, which was compounded by her anxious cross-checking and intrusive repetitive thinking after her surgery. It was unclear what role her hydrocephalus and neurosurgical treatment might have had in the emergence of her obsessive-compulsive symptoms, and a family history of these characteristics was also important to consider.

Although most cognitive abilities and all core academic skills were normal, her executive dysfunction justified special education support and accommodations within the regular education program. These educational modifications included daily consultation with a special education teacher to balance organization needs with her anxious overattention to detail, as well as extra time in a separate quiet room to finish tests, when needed.

Maggie had two follow-up neuropsychological evaluations at ages 13 and 17 years. Fortunately, her medical situation remained stable during this time, and she progressed through school with generally average performance. Referrals for outpatient psychotherapy, several weeks in a specialized day treatment program, and carefully managed psychotropic medications improved, but did not eliminate her OCD symptoms. The second and third evaluations were similar to the first, supporting continued part-time special education support. Behaviors over time included reduced mental processing speed (which can probably be attributed to a combination of mental efficiency changes, as a result of chronic hydrocephalus, as well as a more deliberate approach to tasks) and continuing fine motor coordination deficits (more on the right than left, which led to a recommendation for return to occupational therapy at middle school age to optimize bimanual keyboarding for school). At all three evaluations, the neuropsychologist explained results and recommendations to parents in detail. The first evaluation was supplemented by an in-person consultation with teachers at school, whereas the feedback session for the third evaluation included Maggie, herself, out of respect for her own growth toward adulthood. In the last meeting, care was taken to emphasize her average skills and strengths, as well as the relatively weaker areas that needed extra instruction, therapies, and accommodations.

In summary, at three different points in Maggie's development, the neuropsychologist put into perspective a combination of neurocognitive and psychiatric factors, recommended psychosocial and educational interventions, and provided documentation for disability accommodations.

Case Example 2: A Middle-Aged Man With Sudden-Onset Brain Damage

John was a 35-year-old married man and father of two young children. He worked as salesman for a machine parts manufacturer. He had a gregarious disposition and knew his products well, making him quite successful in his work. His territory covered four states and required that he be on the road much of his workweek. While on one of his work trips, he was involved in a motor vehicle accident. He had just pulled into an intersection when his car was *T-boned* on the passenger side by a delivery truck that had run a red light. The force of the impact caused the passenger side of the vehicle to collapse. John struck his head on the support beam of the passenger door that had been pushed to the center of his car. He was rendered unconscious, and had a punctured lung and fractures of his skull, hip, and legs. He was taken by air ambulance to a regional trauma center. A computed-tomography scan of his head showed a depressed skull fracture in the right parietal region, with bleeding in the underlying brain tissue. In addition, there were small areas of bleeding scattered throughout both cerebral hemispheres. John was admitted to a surgical intensive care unit.

Neuropsychological consultation occurred at three junctures in John's medical care and rehabilitation. The first of these occurred while John was still in the intensive care unit. A neuropsychologist was called on to assist in determining his decisional capacity, competency to manage his affairs, and need for a guardian. Assessment of attentional, memory, and reasoning capacities are typically important to making a determination of competency. In John's case, the determination of incompetence did not require much in the way of clinical expertise as he remained in a coma for several days and showed signs of a confusional state when he first began to respond to communication. Specifically, as he recovered from his coma, he could not track conversation well, nor retain information provided to him for more than a few seconds. The neuropsychological expertise needed at this time was not so much in the assessment of incompetence, but in the prediction of his clinical course. Since most states and jurisdictions do not permit guardianship petitions in cases that have brief periods of incompetence, clinical judgment is needed to determine the permanence of the condition, or, at the minimum, to estimate the duration of the condition for temporary guardianship designation.

In John's case, the prolonged coma and neuroimaging findings predicted a protracted recovery course, thereby meeting his state's requirement for granting guardianship. The neuropsychologist prepared paperwork that described to the court the nature of John's cognitive impairment and limitations in reasoning capacities in order to facilitate the granting of guardianship. John's wife was designated as temporary guardian, which enabled subsequent medical and rehabilitation treatments to proceed efficiently.

The second neuropsychological consultation occurred when John's neurological and medical condition stabilized and recovery of cognitive functions had proceeded to a degree that would permit him to engage in a rehabilitation program. This occurred approximately two weeks after his injury. The purpose for a neuropsychological assessment at that point in his recovery was to better delineate the extent and character of cognitive strengths and deficits for the planning of rehabilitation and to establish a baseline against which recovery could be measured. Neuropsychological testing showed significant deficits in memory, information processing speed, problem solving, and initiation that likely related to diffuse brain (axonal) injury caused by the accident. The testing also found that John was not attending to things happening on his left side. The character of this problem was consistent with a unilateral neglect syndrome (a common focal brain syndrome that occurs with sudden injury to the brain hemisphere opposite the hemisphere with language functions) that likely was due to the contusion John sustained in his right parietal lobe. The presence of the syndrome indicated that rehabilitation staff would need to make special provisions in their treatment protocols, both to help John overcome this deficiency and enable him to make use of routine rehabilitation techniques. In addition to informing rehabilitation staff of the neglect syndrome and general profile of cognitive deficits, the neuropsychologist helped John's wife understand the nature of his functional strengths and weaknesses so that she could optimize her communications with her husband. This education was also useful to her in managing her own emotional adjustment to the circumstances. John made slow but steady progress in his recovery through a 2-week inpatient rehabilitation program and was transitioned to an outpatient program with daily speech, occupational, and physical therapies.

After 5 months of outpatient rehabilitation, John had made sufficient progress in his rehabilitation therapies, which caused two questions to be raised: (a) Had his recovery been sufficient to permit a return to work and (b) Did he still need a guardian? Neuropsychological consultation was requested to address these issues. Evaluation indicated that he had made substantial progress with good recovery of general auditory attention, language, and memory skills. The speed at which he processed information had improved, but was still about 25% below what was estimated as his baseline. He now used his memory and language skills to compensate for the unilateral neglect condition. This permitted him to attend to information presented to him on his left side, but often he missed details of information when there was competing information of relevance coming simultaneously from his right side. This persistent weakness in visual attention made it unsafe for him to drive a car; thus, returning to his previous job was not possible. However, because John had retained an excellent fund of knowledge about his company's products, the company was willing to work with rehabilitation staff to design a warehouse inventory and packaging job for John that minimized the impact of his neglect and processing speed deficits on his performance. John's general recovery and insight into his performance weaknesses had proceeded to a degree that the continued appointment of a guardian was no longer necessary.

In this case, neuropsychological consultation was used at multiple junctures in the continuum of care provided to a victim of brain trauma.

At each juncture, an evaluation of the patient's circumstances and neurocognitive status permitted the neuropsychologist to address questions that were pertinent to the treatment and dispositional planning.

Case Example 3: A Senior With Insidious Behavior Changes

Lena became concerned about her husband's behavior toward her. Although Dan was generally a patient and mild-mannered man, in recent years he gradually had become more impatient, curt, and occasionally belligerent toward her. He complained to her that she talked too much and made too much noise when cooking and cleaning house. He began to swear at her when meals were not on time and when he could not find what he wanted around the house, a behavior that was uncharacteristic of him earlier in their marriage. He no longer seemed to care about shaving on weekends or about what clothes he wore when around her. Lena felt that Dan had lost interest in her and was looking for another companion. Their sex life had essentially ceased. When Dan accused her of adultery, Lena's suspicion of infidelity on his part grew even more. Still, Lena was unsure of Dan's true motives and feelings, and wanted a better understanding. Lena told her primary care physician about Dan's behavior and her suspicions. Her doctor suggested that Lena arrange for Dan to see a neuropsychologist. Dan was 58 years old and an only child. His parents were deceased. His mother had died of ovarian cancer in her 40s and his father lost his life in a car accident in his mid-50s. Dan and Lena had met at college, married shortly after they graduated, and subsequently had two daughters who had since grown up and left home. Dan, a civil engineer, was a conscientious and dedicated employee, but had increasingly become less interested in his job. He occasionally turned in work that had not been proofed for errors and sometimes left work early without informing others about where he was going or what he was doing. When confronted with this by his supervisor, Dan became defensive and said, "too much was being made out of his personal affairs." Dan's supervisor expressed his concern to Lena at an office Christmas party.

Dan begrudgingly attended the appointment with the neuropsychologist, doing so only to appease Lena and prove to her that nothing was "wrong with him." He denied any changes in his behavior or mental capabilities. He expressed his opinion that any friction in his marriage was no more than what is typical of most marriages. Dan was quick to respond to questions during the interview and to test items, and often made mistakes because of this impulsivity. Although he caught himself on many of these mistakes and quickly offered alternate responses, he often was unaware of the errors that he had made. Neuropsychological tests showed an abnormal cognitive ability profile with general fund of knowledge; memory, speech, and language comprehension; and distance and angle judgments; and although motor and sensory perceptual functions were found to be well-preserved, weak performances occurred on tests of deductive reasoning skills. Specifically, he performed poorly on tasks that required him to deduce solutions to problems using feedback on his behavior. He was prone to make the same mistakes even when he was told that his strategy was incorrect. He also struggled when he had to rapidly shift between different response sets or deal with abstract information. Dan's performance on continuous performance tests provided additional evidence of response impulsivity that was apparent in his general behavior and in his difficulty to sustain his focus on tasks for more than a few minutes at a time.

Dan's cognitive problems suggest a dysexecutive syndrome with impairments in sustained concentration, response inhibition, the ability to shift his mind set from one task to another, and verbal abstraction. Additionally, his wife's report of temperament changes further suggests limited frustration tolerance and diminished awareness of these changes. These cognitive and behavioral problems are commonly seen with cerebral dysfunction in the frontal lobes. Additionally, the insidious onset of the problems, lack of other health problems, and the patient's age raise the question of a neurodegenerative disease involving the frontal lobes (e.g., one of the frontotemporal dementias) or a slow growing space-occupying brain lesion affecting primarily the frontal lobes (frontal meningioma).

The neuropsychologist communicated these impressions to Dan and Lena and stressed the importance of completing an evaluation by a neurologist specializing in neurobehavioral disorders and a neuroimaging study. The neuropsychologist also assured Lena that Dan's irritable and temperamental demeanor was not volitional on his part, but rather symptomatic of an underlying brain problem. Strategies of coping were discussed such as distracting her husband's attention away from unpleasant events and building more routine and structure into daily activities in order to optimize adjustment to his circumstances. Completion of the neurological workup would ultimately conclude that Dan had one of the frontotemporal dementing syndromes. Progressive behavioral and cognitive changes during subsequent years would ultimately cause him to lose his job. Documentation of functional deficits in the neuropsychological evaluation assisted in acquisition of disability status.

This case illustrates that the neuropsychologist's knowledge of neurobehavioral syndromes and common clinical presentations enabled the recognition of a serious neurological problem and the need for further neurodiagnostic workup. Additionally, education of the patient's wife enabled her to understand enough about her husband's problems that she was able to better tolerate and problem-solve when her husband's behavior was antagonistic.

COMMON QUESTIONS

How Does a Neuropsychological Examination Differ From Other Forms of Psychological Examination?

In addition to gathering information on presenting complaints and history, evaluations by psychologists may include an evaluation of general mental status, intellectual and other cognitive capacities, educational skills, emotional status, and personality traits. Usually one or more of these domains are evaluated with emphasis determined by the setting or the purpose of the evaluation. For example, in mental health settings where the focus is commonly general psychological well-being or psychodiagnosis, an evaluation that emphasizes assessment of current emotional (affective) status and personality traits typically occurs. These evaluations are referred to as *psychological evaluations*. When the purpose of the evaluation is learning about general vocational abilities or academic needs, a *psychoeducational evaluation* is commonly done, which emphasizes testing of intelligence and academic skills (e.g., reading, spelling, or arithmetic skills). *Neuropsychological evaluations* typically involve an assessment of a much broader range of cognitive abilities, such as intelligence, memory, language skills, visuospatial skills, attention and concentration, information processing speed, and executive functions (e.g., deductive reasoning, mental flexibility). Assessment of academic skills, sensory-perceptual and motor functions, and emotional status or personality may also be included. Typically in a neuropsychological evaluation, a more comprehensive picture of an individual's cognitive capacities is desired, thus, necessitating the inclusion of a broader range of tests and often several hours of testing time. Still, the focus of a neuropsychological examination can be focused on a narrow set of cognitive capacities that are pertinent to the referral question, for example, when determining the early success of surgery for hydrocephalus (excessive pressure in the skull due to blockage in the flow of cerebrospinal fluid), a brief assessment of attention, processing speed, memory and fine motor dexterity might suffice.

How Do I Know That I Need a Neuropsychologist?

There is no simple answer to this question. If you have problems that you suspect are related to abnormal brain functions and desire an evaluation to address this question, then, a neuropsychological evaluation seems most appropriate. Many forms of emotional problems are linked to medical conditions, and a neuropsychologist might again be in the best position to address this. When in doubt, discuss the need for a neuropsychologist with your primary care physician, neurologist, or psychiatrist, or call a neuropsychologist to help you sort out this question.

How Do I Find a Qualified Neuropsychologist?

As with any professional specialty, it is not the tools or techniques used that define the specialty, but rather what the individual knows about the tools and techniques of the trade and the constructs that are being assessed. Although all psychologists receive training in general intellectual, educational, mood and personality assessment, not all receive training in administering and interpreting the broad range of tests used in neuropsychological evaluations. Additionally, although many psychologists are exposed to tests commonly used by neuropsychologists during their training, their exposure to these tests and their training in the neurobehavioral conditions that are being assessed are often limited. Thus, to identify a qualified neuropsychologist, you will have to ask about the education and training of the individual. Current training for qualified neuropsychologists typically includes formal coursework in neuropsychological assessment and brain–behavior relationships, and completion of a 2-year postdoctoral residency in clinical neuropsychology. Thus, supervised training in the practice of neuropsychology is considered critical. Individuals who are board certified in clinical neuropsychology typically have the required level of education and training.

How Do I Make the Most Out of My Neuropsychological Examination?

It is useful for you to have a list of questions for the neuropsychologist to answer. Ask for a feedback session with the neuropsychologist that provides a summary of the evaluation results, explains any jargon that is unfamiliar to you, and reviews the recommendations and implications of the results for you. Request a copy of the evaluation report and review this before or during the feedback session so that questions raised in the report can be answered. Request a copy of the raw test scores and save these for possible comparison with future evaluations.

REFERENCES

Alexander, M. P. (1997). Aphasia: Clinical and anatomic aspects. In T. E. Feinberg & M. J. Farah (Eds.), *Behavioral neurology and neuropsychology* (pp. 133–150). New York: McGraw-Hill.

des Hamsher, K. (1983, Month). Paper presented at Midwest Neuropsychology Group Annual Meeting, Minneapolis, MN.

American Psychiatric Association. (1994). *Diagnostic and statistical manual of mental disorders* (4th ed.) Washington, DC: American Psychiatric Press.

Kaufer, D. I., & Cummings, J. L. (1997). Dementia and delirium: An overview. In T. E. Feinberg & M. J. Farah (Eds.), *Behavioral neurology and neuropsychology* (pp. 499–520). New York: McGraw-Hill.

Kimberg, D. Y., D'Esposito, M., & Farah, M. J. (1997). Frontal lobes: Cognitive neuro-psychological aspects. In T. E. Feinberg & M. J. Farah (Eds.), *Behavioral neurology and neuropsychology* (pp. 409–418). New York: McGraw-Hill.

Mesulam, M.-M. (2000). Attentional networks, confusional states and neglect syndromes. In M.-M. Mesulam (Ed.), *Principles of behavioral and cognitive neurology* (2nd ed., pp. 174–256). New York: Oxford University Press.

Strub, R. L., & Black, F. W. (2000). *The mental status examination in neurology.* Philadelphia: F. A. Davis Company.

Neuropsychological Testing for Children and Adolescents

3

An Introduction to Pediatric Neuropsychology

NADIA WEBB

Learning involves the nurturing of nature.

—Joseph Le Doux

Developmental maturation across childhood is an evolution from near total dependency to the complex balance of autonomy and interdependence in adolescence. At each point on that continuum, children remain, in some measure, dependent on the adults around them to serve as interpreters and advocates. When a child has sustained a neurocognitive insult, these twin roles become more urgent. Pediatric neuropsychological assessment data provides one vehicle for understanding and interpreting the child's behavior and capabilities in his or her changed state and provides a rationale for more effective collaborative interventions. For most adults, this degree of dependency is a novel and, usually, an unwelcome state. It is also a rare occurrence, except at the endpoints of a disease process or after a severe injury.

An adult brain is a relatively stable structure, whereas a child's brain is highly dynamic, particularly in infancy and early childhood. Adult neuropsychology tends to focus on known neurobiological substrates in the brain and the functional consequences of the damage.

51

Brain regions are typically viewed as modules that perform a particular task (e.g., Broca's area is associated with expressive language, Heschl's gyrus analyzes sound stimulus from the receptors in the inner ear before relaying it forward for interpretation.) These modules are part of a loops-and-feedback system that helps refine a function. However, the link with damage to a specific neuroanatomical region is less distinct in a child than it is in an adult (Bernstein & Waber, 2007).

NEUROCOGNITIVE DAMAGE AND DEVELOPMENT

The pathophysiology of disease or injury in a child occurs within the context of development, which is typically a natural unfolding of functional abilities that are behavioral expressions of neural development. The pattern of emerging and fading reflexes and abilities is a relatively fixed sequence that occurs within predictable timetables in a healthy child. The disruption of this sequence can disrupt critical periods, leading to failure to develop a basic skill to its full capacity. For example, a history of chronic, early ear infections can disrupt language acquisition (Rvachew, Slawinski, Williams, & Green, 1999).

Qualitative differences in thought processes require qualitative differences in the neural substrates; development is no different. Neural development typically includes gross structural differences, cytoarchitecture, myelinogensis, and subcellular neuronal differences (Spreen, Risser, & Edgell, 2005). All of these processes are in state of flux during childhood. In the case of injury, there may also be alterations in metabolic cascades secondary to the injury, which may be long term (Kochanek et al., 2000). Lastly, the identical injury sustained at a different age produces different outcomes. The rare but catastrophic consequence of a second concussion in close proximity to the first is a phenomenon limited to children because of their altered hemodynamics (LeBlanc, 2000). Infants with significant traumatic brain injury are less likely to lose consciousness than adults (Quayle et al., 1997).

A corollary of this is that children may not show the effects of damage until they are at the age when a developmental skill should emerge and does not. The damage to the neurocircuitry becomes apparent as a child matures. Toddlers have tantrums because of minor frustrations, which is more or less to be expected given their developmental level. A 12-year-old who throws himself on the floor because a parent offered the wrong kind of cereal is developmentally aberrant. Self-regulation and comportment that should be emerging is not. The study of the nature of injury, disease process, and the effect on neurocircuitry provides one dimension of assessment. The nature and scope of damaged brain tissue disrupts specific functions; however, it does not define them.

The brain exists in a state of bidirectional flow, continually influenced by and influencing the environment. During childhood, this sculpting process is more intensive and provides the foundation for development of later social, academic, and occupational competence. For example, the derailment of social development often begins in early infancy for the autistic child. Knowing the sequence and timing of the early social development of babbling, social smiling, increased interest in faces, molding against the caretaker's body, and *mirroring* by matching the mood of the caregiver's gesture or vocal quality. The infant who arches away from being held and is unresponsive to social reciprocity may be damaged at such a fundamental level that he or she may be incapable of independent living without early and aggressive intervention (Lord et al., 2006; Tadevosyan-Leyfer et al., 2003).

The practice of pediatric neuropsychology is rooted in the appreciation of the evolving nature of child development; practically speaking, in pediatric neuropsychology there is no such thing as a static injury (Silver, 2000). The loss of foundation skills, such as accurately perceiving speech sound relationships, disrupts later acquisition of reading or foreign languages. The injury at age 2 can predict life at age 22. In some cases, the preschooler who cannot wait to eat a marshmallow becomes the college student who has poorer self-regulation skills in avoiding the temptations of adolescence. In fact, Mischel's *marshmallow experiment* with toddlers was more predictive of college success than subsequent scholastic aptitude test (SAT) scores (Mischel, Shoda, & Rodriguez, 1989). In the midst of the immediate needs of an injured child and the clamor for help with academic accommodations and interventions, we often lose sight of the end goal, which is to foster a competent, humane adult. Learning the academic material of third grade may be pressing and immediate, but school is a domain in which children practice specific neurocognitive processes. A focus on long division can obscure the skills that we are really trying to teach such as prioritizing and sequencing information, memorization, recognition of absurdities, sustained attention, and visual scanning from the board to the worksheet, and comprehension of instructions, and so on. Knowing the state capitals can be a surface diversion from the fundamentals of the underlying processes of acquiring a broad range of self-regulation and problem-solving skills (Bernstein, 2000). The process of learning how to learn or how to reason is rarely taught explicitly, although it can and has been taught successfully. Ironically, one of the best sources of evidence for this is from Richard Herrnstein, author of the *Bell Curve* (Herrnstein & Murray, 1994), and proponent of the heritability model of IQ. After teaching seventh graders the scientific process of hypothesis testing, evaluating logic, propositions, constructing and challenging argumentation, probability and the like during 60 45-minute class periods, these seventh graders showed a .77 standard deviation improvement in decision making and a .50 standard deviation in inventive or divergent problem solving (Nesbitt, 2009). To give a sense of the magnitude of this change, it is roughly proportionate to leaping from a C+/B− performance to a B+/A− after 3 months of training. For children with neurocognitive injuries, formal training in memory techniques and problem solving is an entire subspecialty of cognitive rehabilitation that forms an important part of their recovery and/or readjustment over time.

Academic performance is not a measure of functioning per se; it is *one* domain in which to intervene. This is not meant to minimize the complexity of the task. The relationship between neuropsychology and pedagogy is its own area of expertise; educational psychologists are specialists in addressing student attributes and instructional processes. This distinction has become even more precise because of insurance reimbursement regulations; assessments that identify learning disabilities or academic underachievement are considered the province, and financial responsibility of the school system. In consequence, insurance companies do not reimburse for these services because they are not considered *medically necessary*.

The full expression of an emergent talent or deficit is a product of both internal and external factors. Mild, even subclinical impairments may express with sufficient challenge; moderate to severe deficits will be apparent when the child is confronted with simple tasks (Dennis, 2000). To further add to the complexity, abilities and disabilities can also be specific to cultural evolution. Talents must be congruent with their cultures to be appreciated. The same is also true of deficits (e.g., dyslexia could not have existed as a disorder before the invention of the printing press made text available to an ever-increasing audience).

Pediatric neuropsychology also extends into early adult years because of medical advances. Many children with previously lethal disorders of childhood now survive into adulthood, but the experts, with the background knowledge of the disease, remain the pediatric specialists. In addition, patients with childhood injuries, diseases, or developmental delays may be less psychologically mature than their chronological age, whereas effective behavioral and neurocognitive interventions are usually oriented to the patients' psychological age.

HISTORICAL CONTEXT OF THE SPECIALTY

Pediatric neuropsychology is the newest branch of neuropsychology. It began evolving as a recognizable specialty within psychology during the early 1990s for reasons that can be divided into the political, philosophical, and the practical. The idea of the generalist or lifespan neuropsychologist became increasing untenable at the extreme ends of the life span. Some members of the profession doubted whether such an evaluation were even possible, although it became clear that it was not only possible but, also, often critical in identifying and intervening with toddlers who have developmental delays, autism, or communication disorders.

Pediatric neuropsychology is a specialty that typically addresses the needs of children from infancy through adolescence and young adulthood. Brain development continues beyond childhood into adolescence or the early twenties. The challenge of practicing neuropsychology from the birth to 22 years of age is dauntingly broad. Although there are generalists who identify themselves as *lifespan* neuropsychologists, claiming expertise from cradle to grave, most pediatric neuropsychologists tend to subspecialize further. For example, some but not all pediatric neuropsychologists are qualified by their training and education to assess infants and toddlers. Whereas other pediatric neuropsychologists may have directed their training and clinical experience to the study of the neurocognitive consequences of a particular disorder (e.g., William's syndrome, velocardiofacial syndrome, or cancers of childhood such as acute lymphocytic leukemia [ALL] or posterior fossa tumors of the brain). Although most competent pediatric neuropsychologists can perform a thoughtful, workmanlike evaluation of a school-age child, parents and caregivers would do well to inquire about the neuropsychologist's training and the disorders or age ranges in which he or she specializes.

Pediatric neuropsychology tends to approach clinical assessment from a theoretical rather than an instrument-driven approach. This seems to be the case for two reasons. First, the assessment of children required more ingenuity because the formal instruments were not yet as readily available. Test instruments are regarded as tools for answering clinical questions, rather than determining the clinical questions. The NEPSY, one of the first standardized neuropsychological *batteries* for children 3 to 12 years of age, was not released in the United States until 1998.

Second, even in the early 1990s, several major texts in the field did not address the issue of pediatric neuropsychology as such, although they noted the specialty's relevance as a separate skill set. Muriel Lezak (1995), in the third edition of *Neuropsychological Assessment*, notes:

> The assessment of children and the consideration of brain disorders presenting prior to maturity have their own conceptual framework, methods, and data, *which are outside the scope of this book* [emphasis added]. (p. 7)

As the specialty of pediatric neuropsychology has grown, so, too, has the number of specific instruments that pediatric neuropsychologists use to assess children and adolescents. A review of the *Compendium of Neuropsychological Tests* (Spreen & Strauss, 1991) and the *Neuropsychological Evaluation of the Child* (Baron, 2004) indicated that 61 out of 177 instruments were designed exclusively for children. In addition, there are at least 14 to 20 tests originally designed for adults that have downward extensions appropriate for young children. Thus, the available array of published neuropsychological test instruments might number as many as 75 to 80 different tests (not including batteries with multiple subtests). However, the downward extension of adult instruments is often inconsistent with the needs of pediatric patients. The same measures often detect a quite different aspect of neurocognitive functioning in adults versus children. For example, confrontation naming is sensitive to emerging Alzheimer's disease-type dementia in an adult population. However, among children, the ability to name the ordinary through obscure objects is highly or significantly correlated with academic knowledge (Halperin, Healey, Zeitchik, Ludman, & Weinstein, 1989; Kaszniak, 1988). In children, the same test of confrontational naming (e.g., The Boston Naming Test) may not, in fact, be a particularly useful measure of word retrieval and language skills. The same task sheds light on different types of functioning depending on the age of the patient and how that functioning can be influenced by age-related illness and development at the extremes of the life cycle.

THE NEUROPSYCHOLOGICAL ASSESSMENT PROCESS

A pediatric neuropsychological assessment is hypothesis testing based in a developmentally driven theoretical framework. The manner in which children actively engage their environment is an active, learning process in which they attempt to understand and master their environment (Piaget, 1999). Children cannot stop *behaving* and provide data about their abilities and disabilities within the given task and context constraints (Koziol, 2007). Children continually exhibit behavior that reveals how the brain processes information and solves problems. At its simplest, neuropsychological assessment of a child is a systematic observation of a child's performance on a task that pushes a developing function to its limits, and often to its failure.

The test milieu, in which the neuropsychologist individually administers tests to a child, is by design as free as possible from most of the distractions typically present in real-life settings at home or in the classroom: There are no ringing phones, no teachers talking, or other children in the room, no parents, no siblings, et cetera. The intention of setting up the test environment in this way is to capture a reasonably reliable and valid indication of the child's current level of cognitive and emotional functioning. Although the real world is rarely this ideal, having consistent environments during testing allows for children to be compared to others in their age group because they were evaluated under the same conditions. The neuropsychological test battery and one-to-one test milieu offer a consistent structure in which to observe and document problem solving, attention, judgment, memory, visual perception and construction, motor dexterity and speed, and psychological state as developmental, functional benchmarks against which to gauge a child's performance. Performance on these structured tasks allows for reasonable predictions about how a child will perform in daily life when the performance data is integrated with contextual information. For example, injury to the orbitofrontal cortex (the frontal cortex near the eyes or orbits) is associated with exceptionally poor anticipation of danger. This child may need to be supervised as carefully as a toddler regardless of chronological age (Bechara, Damásio, Damásio, & Anderson, 1994; Price, Joschko, & Kerns, 2003). Psychometric tests physically comprised of pencil-and-paper problems, blocks, puzzles, flipbooks, and computer tasks provide the reliable structured opportunities to observe and compare the child's performance against known groups, such as age peers.

Evaluating Children With Brain Injuries

Pragmatically, the evaluation is designed to interpret the child in his or her new postinjury state to the family, treating physicians, and allied health professionals. A pediatric neuropsychological evaluation clarifies the nature of the core deficits, weaknesses, and strengths and serves as a foundation for intervention and support. Structurally, it may corroborate neuroimaging data, point to disturbed circuitry and neurotransmitter systems, and clarify diagnosis. Functionally, it may predict future developmental evolution and challenges, suggest interventions and accommodations, and track a child's developmental trajectory and the effectiveness of the interventions over time. Because of the complexity of the child's development, and injury or disease process, the assessment is often a case study of one (Bernstein, 2000), as the injury happens to a unique child, with a prior personality style, a particular family and community, and a particular set of aptitudes and weaknesses, and a particular set of aspirations. The degree to which the injury disrupts a child's life is a combination of the severity and extensiveness of the deficit, how fundamental the skill is across tasks, and the ability of a child to learn compensatory strategies.

An Integrated Neuropsychological Assessment

The quality that makes an integrated pediatric neuropsychological evaluation just that is dependent on the skill and knowledge base of the clinician. It is the clinical inference process, density of the pediatric and neuroscience knowledge base, and developmental perspective that produces comprehensive evaluation. Quality is not defined by the assessment instruments used, or poor performance by the child on specific neurocognitive measures. There are many legitimate methods and instruments available for the examination of pediatric neuropsychology patients, but at the most basic, a pediatric neuropsychologist would:

- Obtain a thorough history of the patient, the presenting problems, and reason for referral;
- Obtain all relevant medical, school, and developmental records and integrate them with the history;
- Design an appropriate battery to answer the referral question(s);
- Administer, score, and interpret the data correctly;
- Integrate the assessment data with the history and records;
- Derive an appropriate diagnosis accounting for all symptoms (and other factors, if relevant), including data that appears discordant or unexpected with the history or other data;
- Determine appropriate treatment recommendations;
- Integrate the findings within a theoretical framework about the child's behavior and performance;
- Use the behavior and performance to create a plausible hypothesis linking the pathophysiology of the disease process, the neural structures and circuitry involved, and the expression of those processes in the child's behavior;
- Predict the situations in which the child's particular pattern of strengths and weaknesses will be more and less adaptive, and help guide the family toward settings that will maximize the child's likelihood of independence, competence, and future success.

The assessment process requires pragmatism, a depth of knowledge about developmental and medical conditions beginning with pre- and perinatal history, a grasp of neuroanatomy and neurocircuitry, the ability to translate the findings into meaningful terms for those involved in the child's care, as well as facility with of the test materials, including the ability to critically evaluate the test, its construction, and the perhaps less obvious functional attributes that the test measures. Test selection is especially crucial when testing children because tasks need to be appealing and comprehensible to very different groups. Healthy functioning in a child of 3, 6, 12, or 18 years of age is quite distinct. The reasoning skills, attention span, fund of information, and dexterity are not comparable, unless development has gone awry. In those circumstances, the chronological norms may become a departure point or rough guideline. A 12-year-old child with moderate mental retardation may be functioning at a 3-year-old level, learning to recognize some of the letters in her name or to make a tower four blocks high. Chronological and functional age can oscillate closer and farther from one another, depending on the task and the integrity of the associated brain region and neurocircuitry. A 9-year-old with a right frontal lobe seizure focus may show a good command of *language*, but may speak in a monotone and show poor appreciation for tone of voice in others. This child fails to appreciate or use the inflection and cadence of language because of the location of the brain lesion. This same child may draw a picture of a bicycle that contains most of the correct *parts*, but fail to integrate them into a meaningful, recognizable whole.

The Qualitative Approach to Test Score Interpretation

On psychometric tests, the tasks are frequently designed to push a neurocognitive system to the point of failure, because the nature of the mistakes is illuminating. The process approach to test interpretation advocated by Edith Kaplan (Milberg, Hebben, & Kaplan, 1996) considers qualitative information as the heart of the assessment, but neuropsychologists appreciate that there are many paths to an *impaired* performance. For example, a task of *visual construction and recall* that asks a child to copy a complex design and then draw it from memory after a 5-minute and then a 30-minute delay may elicit a performance that is compromised because of problems the child is having with memory. The child's performance may also be compromised by a loss of visual information in one segment of the visual field, a visual neglect in which the child fails to fully attend to information on the left visual field. A low score on such a test measure may be an expression of poor planning and organization; a disorganized approach to copying the design means that the systematic, meaningful underlying principles or gestalt is lost because the child approaches and remembers the design in a piecemeal fashion. These findings may be developmentally normal or abnormal, depending on the child's age and or injury sustained. For example, a piecemeal approach is usually pathological if it persists beyond 12 years of age. Lastly, the problem may simply be one of motor execution. A child with poor dexterity or impaired motor planning may be unable to execute a copy of the design that he or she perceives correctly.

There has been increasing access to the psychometric assessment instruments, often with little regard to training or the credentials needed to use them properly. Although this might seem like an option that might broaden the availability of neuropsychological assessments, a marginal assessment is often worse than none. Having a collection of data without the theoretical understanding of tests and measures, the neuropathology, and the test construction, will lead to flawed conclusions and misdirect clinical interventions. If use of these measures is a sideline to a professional's core discipline, it will be impossible to maintain competence in the neuropsychology literature. The test manual alone will be insufficient. Manuals are released with the test at publication, often outlining the initial understanding of the test's utility. The subsequent published research may outline a very different portrait. Without an appreciation for remaining current in that literature, the interpretation of the child's performance on a given test will be obsolete. Tests also change and are reissued or new ones are created for any number of reasons. Using outdated test materials can be a transgression, because of outdated norms and test materials that are no longer culturally relevant (e.g., how many readers of this chapter are familiar with the game "drop the handkerchief," which was appropriately dropped from the MMPI [Minnesota Multiphasic Personality Inventory] personality test during revision.)

On the other hand, pediatric neuropsychologists Cecil Reynolds and Robert McCaffrey have persuasively offered a counterargument along the lines of "newer doesn't mean better." Test publishers benefit from the frequent release of new versions, but the science may not. This is particularly salient to pediatrics since pediatric norms for well-researched tests often have gaps in the pre-K and midteen years and for demographic subgroups (such as children who speak English as a second language or children with attention-deficit/hyperactivity disorder). This problem is not solved by the creation of a new test but by continued research on existing measures after they have been published. Each time a test is "updated" ongoing research is disrupted. A new version of a test instrument renders the research on the former version worthless, but research on the "new" version faces the same abbreviated life span. Just as we begin to understand how to appropriately modify test scoring and interpretation for unique populations, such as children with visual impairments or English as a second language, the test is replaced. Reinventing and re-researching our measures every 5 to 8 years is not intrinsically valuable, but is intrinsically disruptive to research and clinical understanding.

RESPONSIBLE TRAINING
IN PEDIATRIC NEUROPSYCHOLOGY

Neuropsychology, as a specialty branch of psychology, offers higher reimbursement rates that reflect the additional years of training and skill maintenance involved. However, pediatric neuropsychology remains a self-designated specialty, with little protection for the public. Only one state, Louisiana, licenses psychologists specifically as neuropsychologists of any stripe (Lamberty, Courtney, & Heilbronner, 2003).

Standards for training in pediatric neuropsychology are emerging, but the basic consensus is that training should be conducted in an *organized* setting and that this is a requirement for future practice and eventual board certification. Workshop training and conference attendance is *not* considered sufficient for establishing the foundation skills; rather, these informal activities are more appropriate for skill maintenance and refinement. As mentioned, pediatric neurologists are usually trained as doctoral level psychologists, with additional specialty training in basic neuroscience, development, and pediatric and clinical neuropsychology. A subsequent internship builds on that existing foundation and the postdoctoral residency provides the educational and experiential training necessary to allow the practice of pediatric neuropsychology at the independent level.

At this point, there is only one certification process within professional psychology that insures that individuals presenting themselves to the public as "pediatric neuropsychologists" have been examined and found competent in that area by review of clinical pediatric work samples by fellow pediatric neuropsychologists and by written examination assessing foundational pediatric knowledge. Specialty pediatric boarding remains the highest standard of proof of competence, although there are outstanding neuropsychologists who have never chosen to undergo boarding or are content with generalist boarding (Webb, Bos, Courney, & Dodzik, 2008).

SUMMARY

At its core, the interpretation of pediatric neuropsychological data involves pattern analysis, which is a uniquely human strength (Chellappa, Wilson, & Sirohey, 1995). The tests provide an accumulation of data points. The assessment is a process of weighing different information of varying granularity and importance, which is integrated with information about the child's development, context, and the medical history. The neuropsychological evaluation is also a quasi-psychotherapeutic process, since interpreting the child's behavior alters how others understand and respond to that child on a daily basis, at home, at school, and in the community. In terms of brain injury and its repercussions, the degree of physical damage, insult, or injury can precipitate both qualitative alterations, such as developmentally discordant performance or pathological errors not observed in neurologically intact children. The damage is also expressed in quantitative form. For this and other practical reasons, virtually all neuropsychologists include numeric scores in their reports, usually standard scores and/or percentiles (Donders, 2001).

Given that children remain more dependent on their environment, interventions require broader *systems level* intercession. The expression "it takes a village to raise a child" is particularly true for a child with a neurocognitive disability. Pragmatically this means enhancing the ability of those caring for the child by working collaboratively with school systems, the family, educational tutors, different types of physicians, from psychiatrists to neurologists, and other allied health professionals, such as occupational therapists, physical therapists, applied behavioral analysts, and speech language pathologists (Baron, 2004). The neuropsychological evaluation can provide a clear picture of a child's strengths and weaknesses, the neurocircuitry in the brain that may be compromised, and can track how effectively a child is responding to the various therapies or medication changes through standardized, quantifiable measures.

The body of knowledge and the skills involved in conducted a neuropsychological evaluation are sizeable. The training process includes doctoral-level training in psychology (with specialized coursework) and a formal apprenticeship at the pre- and the postdoctoral level. Maintaining the skills is an ongoing challenge given that our knowledge of the brain and its functions continues to evolve rapidly as the neuroimaging technology has permitted (e.g., functional MRI and diffusion tensor imaging). Unsurprisingly, neuropsychologists are conducting much of this research. As neuroimaging technology continues to evolve, we learn more about the interactions of development on brain functioning. Just as we can observe how a child's reasoning matures, we can now observe that the pattern of activation in regions of the brain is distinct and alters as children grow up (Casey, Tottenham, Liston, & Durston, 2005). Pediatric neuropsychologists, by virtue of their training, are uniquely suited to understand these intricacies, perform integrated neuropsychological assessments, and make meaningful recommendations that translate into interventions that can be helpful to children and families.

REFERENCES

Baron, I. S. (2004). *Neuropsychological evaluation of the child.* New York: Oxford University Press.

Bechara, A. Damásio, A. R., Damásio H., & Anderson S. W. (1994). Insensitivity to future consequences following damage to human prefrontal cortex. *Cognition, 50,* 7–15.

Bernstein, J. (2000). Developmental neuropsychological assessment. In K. O. Yeates, M. D. Ris, & H. G. Taylor (Eds.), *Pediatric neuropsychology: Research, theory, and practice* (pp. 405–438). New York: Guilford Press.

Bernstein, J., & Waber, D. P. (2007). Executive capacities from a developmental perspective. In L. Meltzer (Ed.), *Executive function in education: From theory to practice* (pp. 39–54). New York: Guilford Press.

Casey, B. J., Tottenham, N., Liston, C., & Durston, S. (2005). Imaging the developing brain: What have we learned about cognitive development? *Trends in Cognitive Sciences, 9*(3), 104–110.

Chellappa, R., Wilson, C. L., & Sirohey, S. (1995). Human and machine recognition of faces: A survey. *Proceedings of the IEEE, 83*(5), 705 –741.

Dennis, M. (2000). *Childhood medical disorders and cognitive impairment: Biological risk, time, development, and reserve.* In K. O. Yeates, M. D. Ris, & H. G. Taylor (Eds.), *Pediatric neuropsychology: Research, theory, and practice* (pp. 3–24). New York: Guilford Press.

Donders, J. (2001). A survey of report writing by neuropsychologists, II: Test data, report format, and document length. *Clinical Neurospsychology, 2,* 150–161.

Halperin, J. M., Healey J. M., Zeitchik, E., Ludman, W. L., & Weinstein, L. (1989). Developmental aspects of linguistic and mnestic abilities in normal children. *Journal of Clinical and Experimental Neuropsychology, 4,* 518–528.

Herrnstein, R. J., & Murray, C. (1994). *Bell curve: Intelligence and class structure in American life.* New York: Free Press.

Kaszniak, A. (1988). Cognition in Alzheimer's disease: Theoretic models and clinical implications. *Neurobiology of Aging, 9,* 92–94.

Kochanek, P. M., Clark, R. S. B., Ruppel, R. A., Adelson, P. D., Bell, M. J., Whalen, M. J., et al. (2000). Biochemical, cellular, and molecular mechanisms in the evolution of secondary damage after severe traumatic brain injury in infants and children: Lessons learned from the bedside. *Pediatric Critical Care Medicine, 1*(1), 4–19.

Lamberty, G. J., Courtney, J. C., & Heilbronner, R. L. (2003.) *The practice of clinical neuropsychology*. Philadelphia: Taylor & Francis.

LeBlanc, C. M. A. (2000). The management of minor closed head injury in children. *Pediatrics, 106*(6), 1524–1525.

Lezak, M. (1995). *Neuropsychological assessment* (3rd ed.). New York: Oxford University Press.

Lord, C., Risi, S., DiLavore, P. S., Shulman, C., Thurm, A., & Pickles, A. (2006). Autism from 2 to 9 years of age. *Archives of General Psychiatry, 63*(6), 694–701.

Milberg, W. P., Hebben, N., & Kaplan, E. (1996). The Boston process approach to neuropsychological assessment. In I. Grant & K. M. Adams (Eds.), *Neuropsychological assessment of neuropsychiatric disorders* (pp. 65–86). New York: Oxford University Press.

Mischel, W., Shoda, Y., & Rodriguez, M. L. (1989). Delay of gratification in children. *Science, 244*, 933–938.

Nesbitt, R. E. (2009). *Intelligence and how to get it: Why schools and culture count*. New York: Norton.

Piaget, J. (1999). *The construction of reality in the child*. New York: Routledge.

Price, K. J., Joschko, M., & Kerns, K. (2003). The ecological validity of pediatric neuropsychological tests of attention. *Clinical Neuropsychology, 17*(2), 170–181.

Quayle, K. S., Jaffe, D. M., Kuppermann, N., Kaufman, B. A., Lee, B. C. P., Park, T. S., et al. (1997). Diagnostic testing for acute head injury in children: When are head computed tomography and skull radiographs indicated? *Pediatrics, 99*(5), e11.

Rvachew, S., Slawinski, E. B., Williams, M. & Green, E. B. (1999). The impact of early onset otitis media on babbling and early language development. *Journal of the Acoustical Society of America, 105*(1), 467–475.

Silver, C. H. (2000). Ecological validity of neuropsychological assessment in childhood traumatic brain injury. *Journal of Head Trauma Rehabilitation, 15*(4), 973–988.

Spreen, O. S, Risser, A. H., & Edgell, D. (2005). *Developmental neuropsychology*. New York: Oxford University Press.

Spreen, O. S., & Strauss, E. (1991). *A compendium of neuropsychological tests: Administration, norms, and commentary*. New York: Oxford University Press.

Tadevosyan-Leyfer, O., Dowd, M., Mankoski, R., Winklosky, B., Putnam, S., McGrath, L., et al. (2003). A principal components analysis of the autism diagnostic interview-revised. *Journal of the American Academy of Child and Adolescent Psychiatry, 42*(7), 864–872.

Webb, N. E., Bos, J., Courney, J. C., & Dodzik, P. (2008, October.) *ABPdN Workshop: Historical perspectives, application process, and examination statistics*. National Academy of Neuropsychology, New York.

4

An Integrated Neuropsychological–Psychodynamic Approach to the Evaluation and Treatment of Preschool Children

LOIS M. BLACK

This chapter presents an overview of an integrated neuropsychological-psychodynamic approach to evaluation and treatment of preschool children.[1] It is an approach that emphasizes multiple factors—neuropsychological and psychodynamic—that may be at play and affect a child's emotional well-being. It emphasizes the impact that neurogenic differences can have on the child, without losing sight of the defensive, representational, relational, and fantasy-based dynamics that come into play in both the child and the family.

An integrated approach to evaluation and treatment is influenced by the known concomitance of neurodevelopmental disorders with emotional and behavioral difficulties, by findings on frontal-subcortical pathways implicated in a number of neuropsychiatric disorders, which make plausible both the heterogeneity and distinctness of different disorders, as well as the prevalence of comorbidities (Alexander, Crutcher, & DeLong, 1990; Bradshaw, 2001; Casey, Tottenham, & Fossella, 2002; Lichter & Cummings, 2001), and on clinical insights into the interweaving of neuropsychological dysfunction with psychological conflict (Black, 1995, 1997). Neurodevelopmental disorders and emotional and behavioral difficulties often go hand in hand. For example, about 50% of children with developmental language disorders

(DLD) in the preschool years have been shown to be at risk for emotional and behavioral disturbances as compared to a 14–26% risk in the general population (Baker & Cantwell, 1982; Beitchman, Cohen, Konstantaereas, & Tannock, 1996; Beitchman, Nair, Clegg, Ferguson, & Patel, 1986; Black, 1989; Black & van Santen, 2006; Cantwell & Baker, 1991; Cantwell, Baker, & Mattison, 1979; Egger & Angold, 2006; Prizant, 1999). As a wide, heterogeneous group, children with autism spectrum disorders (ASD) have been shown to have a number of comorbid neuropsychiatric disorders, including attention-deficit/hyperactivity disorder (ADHD), obsessive-compulsive disorder (OCD), depression, and anxiety (Corbett & Constantine, 2006; Kim, Szatmari, Bryson, Streiner, & Wilson, 2000; Leyfer et al., 2006; Simonoff et al., 2008). Even when there is a known brain basis to psychiatric disorders, neurologically based behaviors can easily become enmeshed with and exacerbated by psychological conflict. More often than not, young children, especially those with milder, atypical, or more subtle variants of disorders, are often first brought to mental health professionals because of emotional and behavioral issues and the family's or school's perplexities in dealing with them.

This chapter will present three cases of young, preschool-age children to illustrate an integrated neuropsychological-psychodynamic approach. What these cases are intended to show is how the dynamic interaction between a child, who has a neurodevelopmental disorder, and others around the child can often be amplified in negative synergistic ways, as well as on occasion more positive ways, as a result of neuropsychological dysfunction in the child—and how critical it is to uncover what may be an unrecognized disability in the child who presents with emotional or behavioral issues. A clear thematic in what will be presented is this: The more neuropsychological dysfunction goes unrecognized, the more it can masquerade as an emotional problem, be inextricably intertwined with psychological conflict, or be heightened or ameliorated by enmeshment in the fantasies and fears of the parents and the particular child–parent interactive system. This thematic includes the following factors:

First, neurogenic disabilities are *subjectively experienced* by any child who has them and taken up into his/her sense of self. Disabilities are given meaning and *explanation* by the child, elaborated upon in fantasies, and played out in behavior. This takes place alongside and in response to interpretations and reactions to such behaviors, conscious and unconscious, that have been made by family and others.

Second, there may be enmeshment of the behaviors in such an interpretive framework so that underlying roots of the difficulties are hidden. The interpretive framework (the meaning given by both child and others) can become itself a perpetuating factor in the child's emotional and behavioral problems. Unrecognized disabilities become overlaid with many issues.

Third, the task becomes one of *unbuilding* to find the disability in the child and its exacerbation or implication in psychological conflict, also within a family system. This is done while simultaneously finding the child's key strengths and opening channels for compensation and esteem enhancement.

Fourth, and a key point, is that to finally detect the underlying disability can result in circumscribing the weaknesses, damming the spill onto personality structure and family dynamics, and providing avenues of therapeutic intervention, remediation and growth.

The chapter will proceed as follows: First, three cases will be presented. These cases vary in detail. The first two are relatively short, the third somewhat longer. After this, the evaluation part of an integrated approach will be presented and some ways, formal and informal, to detect the kind of neuropsychological dysfunction found in these young children. Finally, intervention for one of the children will be briefly described.

Case Examples: The Children—Ken

I first became aware of the need to understand more about neuropsychological weaknesses, and how they affect the development of personality and defenses, when at the Mahler Nursery.[2] An observational nursery for normal infant–caregiver pairs, there was nevertheless a little boy there who was slower than the others, and which showed itself as time went on.

Ken began attending the nursery when he was about 10 months of age and was followed until he was almost 3 years old. Ken's problems, which included visual–spatial difficulties, motor coordination and motor planning problems, and slow auditory processing, had an immediate impact on the child–parent relationship, on his mother's mood state, and on his own emerging defenses and affect. Ken didn't walk until he was about 16 months old, at the upper end of the normal range. When he did learn, he stumbled frequently and stepped on toys directly in his path, as if they weren't there. He showed a particular difficulty in his left visual field when doing puzzles, seeming not to be very attentive to things in that area (implicating right posterior brain involvement). He had a high pain threshold and would rarely cry, even when he cut his lip. He also was very slow in responding to what was said to him: If someone asked Ken to get a crayon, he seemed not to budge. If you looked back at him, however, minutes later, there he was picking up the crayon, but the person who had asked for it was already gone. Most of the time people didn't notice that Ken was responding. They didn't know that he was simply slow to process what was said to him. So, Ken was described as obstinate and stubborn by others, and also by his mother, and in fact he also was frequently constipated and hard to cajole into moving from one activity or place to another.

Ken never seemed to go through a "love affair with the world," the period of newfound elation and the winning of healthy narcissism that is part of Mahler's practicing subphase (Mahler, Pine, & Bergman, 1975),—a subphase that is usually entered into when the child learns to walk, to climb, and to avidly explore his surrounds. When the other children were already climbing agilely on the jungle gym and experiencing joy associated with their mastery, Ken was still stumbling around the room or sitting rather fearfully to one side. The usual reservoir of internal self-esteem that comes with practicing and ameliorates the sometimes increased negativism of what Mahler calls the rapprochement phase was not there and Ken began to show increased, unmodulated negative states around 18 months. He seemed to enter both practicing and rapprochement at the same time, and began to take a certain joy in negativism. Not infrequently he would let out a long siren-like cry, sometimes when other children tried to take something from him, sometimes for apparently no reason, but always to the embarrassment of his mother. The participants in the nursery who chose to be *observed* with their children in a 2-year long normal, observational nursery were a pretty competitive bunch. Ken's differences were readily noted and reacted to by the others. Ken and his mother pretty much became *outcasts* in this normal nursery and kept to themselves. Ken's mother became overtly depressed.

What was interesting about this pair was that as Ken's mother became depressed, she also slowed down and the match between her and Ken improved. She used language more frequently to mediate their interactions and Ken's confrontation with the world, while slowing down her input and deflating her expectations. When left to themselves, she became very supportive of

Ken. She painstakingly elaborated for him in a very slow, sequential, methodical way how he could, for example, put one foot after the other on the jungle gym, and so helped him overcome his fears and eventually succeed. Ken's own primary coping strategy was to revert back to a preverbal, preambulatory, kinesthetic type of swaying and rocking when feeling frustrated; a throwback, perhaps, to a happier time that also served to connect him to his father, who was a musician and who sang and danced with him.

When Ken's expressive language set in, around age 27–30 months, there was a transformation in Ken and his development took off. His mother's earlier painstaking verbal mediations with him became an internalized model and we began to see him use his own dialogue and verbal questionings as a way of comforting and reassuring himself about things. He even showed a precocious sense of decentering in questioning his peers about whether they could hear other people talking the way he did — perhaps a verbal exploration of the intersubjective space he was unable to physically explore with ease earlier on. With Ken language became, par excellence, a way for him to compensate for his earlier losses and served to tie him into the social world.

With Ken, then, neuropsychological dysfunction and variation had an immediate impact on the development of personality structure and coping style. Through language Ken seemed to find a happy, natural compensation of his motor and visual–spatial difficulties, accomplished within the matrix of an evolving good parent–child fit. But in other cases, the route taken has to be more actively charted through assessment and intervention.

The next two children did receive comprehensive neuropsychological evaluations. I will first describe the children and later review the findings.

Frank

Frank is a little boy of 3 years whom I first saw in his classroom while consulting at the preschool he attended. The director and his teacher had expressed concerns about his behavior and, together with Frank's mom, wanted me to observe him first in class.

Although seemingly bright, talkative, and imaginative in his play, Frank repeatedly refused to join in on group activities, insisted on being off on his own rather than share or play with other children, and moved around the room like a small bulldozer, knocking into toys and others. Whenever Frank got out of a chair, "watch out, don't get in my way," seemed to be the message. Some days he came to class acting like this little bully powerhouse; other days he was sullen and somewhat withdrawn. He seemed to ignore requests made of him, with insistent demands having to be repeated time and again. If you asked Frank to get something in his cubby, he would end up in someone else's. His fondness for saying "no" appeared as stubborn contrariness, and he easily threw tantrums if his teacher insisted he do things with the rest of the class. Especially during transitions onto the playground, Frank would become particularly problematic and begin to pinch, push, and knock into others. He also would grab toys from other children and hit and bite. One time while painting with a little girl, in what seemed to be an unusual act of sharing, he suddenly and impulsively threw a container of paint in her face.

Frank's mom would come to the school dressed in tight clothes and overly made up. Frank would often be seen running down the hall and all over the place. Most of the time his mother didn't notice his whereabouts; if she did, while trying to retrieve her son, she might be heard embarrassingly stating what a problem child Frank was and blurting out that Frank also bit his cousin, and that he had no sense of remorse. His mom no longer worked and couldn't tell, when asked, how she spent her time. She appeared ill at ease, deflated, and downcast.

From the clinical interview with Frank's parents, I learned that Frank's dad came from a family of ambitious, dominant men who "liked their women at home." He worked long hours and was away from the family much of the time. He thought many aspects of Frank's behavior were the norm for little boys and an expression of Frank's independence. The more negative out-of-hand features he seemed to hold Frank's mom accountable for. He thought she was weak on discipline and didn't know how to control Frank. Frank's mom said she never wanted to have any more children. She confessed that she just didn't know how to handle Frank. She wanted to hit and bite him back to teach him not to do it by showing him how it felt.

So what's going on with Frank? Does Frank have a problem related to his mom's mood and helplessness, his parents' marital difficulties? Are his mom's difficulties with regulating and socializing him contributing to Frank's problems in self-control? Is he trying to rev up a depressed mom; or, finally get the mom to sweep him up in her arms, and, if not confess her love, at least confess other strong feelings? Is he identifying too much with his dad in being overly manipulative and controlling? Are his mom's attributions of "bad boy" and her feeling powerless about it, fueling Frank's misbehavior? All this may very well be at play. But what else is going on with Frank? Is there an unrecognized disability here that is masquerading as a behavioral problem or fueling emotional and behavioral difficulties that are also rooted in family stresses and tensions in the couple and mother–child relationships?

What the neuropsychological evaluation revealed was that Frank had an attention-deficit disorder and a mild expressive language problem with organizational issues affecting language formulation. He also had motor planning difficulties.

Later in this chapter I will present ways of recognizing elements of his observed behaviors in the neuropsychological profile. For now, it would be helpful to keep in mind this example of Frank and his parents as one in which there is a mutual exacerbation of neuropsychological dysfunction and psychological conflict that is kept in play, in part, by the ignorance of all concerned to the underlying disability and by the interpretations and misinterpretations made about his behavior.

If Frank presents as a child with aggressive behavior problems, the next child, Sara, was thought of as shy, passive, anxious, and somewhat bizarre.

Sara

Sara was 2¹/2 years old when her parents requested an evaluation. Sara's mother described her as extremely irritable, anxious, and unhappy—24 hours a day. Sara threw temper tantrums daily, while her mother's efforts to console and control her proved fruitless. Sara was vulnerable to ear infections, allergies, and was often sick. She was described as having a better relationship with her father and with strangers than with her own mother, and to act very different in public than she did at home. Sara's mother thought of her as having up/down mood swings: cheerful, active, engaging with others; clingy, dependent, and miserable at home. Other concerns were that she was "unusually repetitive" in play and focus. Once concerned about something, such as her father going to work, for example, she would repeat insistently, imploringly, and seemingly unendingly, "Daddy work? Daddy work? Daddy work?" Also, on occasion, she would interrupt an activity and carry on a conversation by herself as if she were talking to someone; sometimes while doing so she would become very anxious and start to cry. Her parents said she played with dolls and was attached to a stuffed bunny.

At the preschool Sara attended, she was thought of as shy, passive, and in her own world. She never had tantrums at school, but neither was she outgoing and engaging. She would, however, tune out and daydream a lot. Although she was said to show a desire to play with other children, she had a hard time with turn-taking and extended interactions. She appeared overly involved in her own play, so that if someone said something to her, it was at times like talking to a brick wall. Although symbolic, her play lacked elaborate or extended play schemas. She particularly disliked playing on any playground equipment and did not participate in singing songs at circle time.

Sara could be very verbal, even loquacious, and had an extensive vocabulary, especially for a $2^1/2$-year-old. She could repeat many things that had been said to her and remember them for quite some time—complicated expressions such as, "Mommy is a wife, Daddy is a husband" or after a vacation, with her mother's prompting, ask her teacher "Had a good time skiing in Colorado?" Often, however, Sara would insert expressions into verbal exchanges at inappropriate times. She could appear internally preoccupied while talking to herself in extended "monologues," using language almost like a transitional object to play with by herself. She showed at times a limited attention span, and her teacher was very concerned about her peculiar and withdrawn behaviors.

So, what is going on with Sara? Given such a description, neuropsychological weaknesses are not completely obvious, although many features of her behavior will be seen as very much related to her particular neuropsychological profile. In fact, the first diagnosis that suggests itself as a possibility is an anxiety or mood disorder. In school she appears excessively constricted, withdrawn, shy, and nonparticipating, possibly due to anxiety. Her mother is overtly concerned about her anxious reactions and describes repetitive worries that may be an early form of obsessive-like preoccupations. Her mother also raises questions about mood regulation and poor development of ego functions that could be related to excessive anxiety. In addition, especially because of Sara's tantrums, as well as because of the extreme disparity noted by her mother in her behaviors at home versus with others, one could also begin to question whether stresses at home and in parental care and management techniques may be essentially contributing to Sara's problems.

Before giving the results of Sara's evaluation, it would be helpful to describe Sara's parents briefly. Both appear to be sensitive and educated, but have a loaded family history. Sara's father had an aunt with schizophrenia and a grandmother who had manic-depressive illness. Sara's mother came from what she described as a chaotic, dysfunctional family. She had five younger brothers, all of whom had learning disabilities; one suffered from a sleep seizure disorder, one had a substance-abuse problem, another was reported to have abused a stepchild.

Sara's mother is the only one in her family who completed college and "made something of herself." She taught music at an Ivy League college. She is a highly verbal woman who, in fact, talks excessively.

Like Sara, her mother has a history of heightened susceptibility to allergies and physical illness; she is blind in one eye due to optic neuritis. She feels that her illnesses are related to stress. She became blind after her wedding and after having had an argument with her mother. (Her mother, too, was quite sickly, and when Sara's mother was a 14-month-old baby she was even given up by her mother to a relative because of this sickliness.) Sara's mother complains that her mother was never able to meet her needs but constantly required her to cater to *her*, to listen to *her* problems, and to take charge of her five younger brothers for *her*.

Although Sara's mother felt she had never been listened to or encouraged, and that everything she has since obtained for herself was in contradistinction to her family, she says she is not angry. She doesn't want to be angry. She feels, instead, sorry for her mother and speaks to her often on the phone. Her mother continues to be unsupportive and even resentful of her new values. If Sara's mother comments on her brothers' behaviors or on any of the family's "irrational" doings, she is told that she is selfish and judgmental and should be ashamed to talk about her own family like that.

Sara's mother has had a history of repeated bouts of depression since adolescence. She also describes a postpartum depression after Sara was born that lasted until Sara was almost 14 months old. She describes Sara as "straining away from her." "In the beginning," she said, "she stared at me constantly, but I would always fall asleep and she would avoid eye contact after that." She openly interpreted Sara's behavior as angry and rejecting of her from the beginning.

Both parents were asked about their "theories" of what was the matter with Sara. Both saw in her the threatened resurgence of bad genes. They feared that she might develop schizophrenia or manic-depressive illness, like the father's side of the family. And, indeed, in their initial descriptions of Sara, she seemed on the way. The mother was also frightened by Sara's possible resemblance to the mother's dysfunctional brothers. Was Sara brain-damaged? What was the matter with her? The mother, in particular, appeared alienated from her daughter.

Sara's mother's fantasy about having a child was of a baby who would amuse herself in a playpen while she played music. Her fantasy, in other words, was of a baby *who would let her be.* Instead Sara became the clinging, needy, dependent child—just as Sara's mother had experienced her own mother to be. The anger toward her mother, which Sara's mother denied, seemed to be displaced onto Sara. Sara's mother wanted to distance herself and turn away from Sara, who was a reminder to her of all the dysfunctional aspects of her family (and possibly of herself) that she was so ardently striving to disidentify from. So she focused on the mismatch between herself and her daughter, and on Sara's preference for others.

The question here for a comprehensive integrated assessment approach is how much do the mother's issues and fears affect parent–child interactions and contribute to Sara's emotional symptoms? Do they dominate the picture—is there a relationship disorder here, or is there a disability in the child, which is the primary source of difficulty; that is, is a possible underlying disability in the child the critical underpinning for both the child's emotional and behavioral symptoms as well as an important complicating factor in the quality of the parent–child relationship? Combining an understanding of the individual family member's psychological difficulties and defensive dynamics with neuropsychological assessment of the child may be the best way of answering these questions.

Turning to Sara's neuropsychological evaluation: On meeting Sara, she appeared—contrary to expectations—to be highly curious and to take pleasure in interactions with others. Play with mom was characterized as less focused than play with dad; but, then again, mom was either talking incessantly to Sara or, as was yet more often the case to me, could hardly focus on Sara. Sara showed good nonverbal skills, especially memory skills, and good cognitive, mechanical skills for figuring out how all the new things in my office worked. She also showed a creative bent in her symbolic play, which she enjoyed all the more when interactive and when affect was intensified. For example, after a peek-a-boo game that she initiated, she later gleefully initiated another such game with a tent-like test booklet that she called a "tunnel." After I laughed and admired her action, she then put an empty box on her head and smiled broadly, calling it a "hat."

The results of the evaluation showed that Sara was a child of above average intelligence who had a developmental language disorder (DLD), of the semantic pragmatic type (Rapin & Allen, 1983, 1987); also called *pragmatic language impairment* (Bishop & Norbury, 2002).[3] Characteristic of Sara, and this type of DLD, is a large discrepancy between receptive and expressive language abilities, with expressive language much better than receptive. On a formal language measure, Sara had a receptive language score at the 12th percentile, in the low average range, and an expressive language score at the 61st percentile, solidly average.

Also characteristic of this kind of DLD, and part of Sara's profile, is excellent rote verbal memory, or the ability to repeat long strings of words without necessarily processing their content. These features of good expressive language, large vocabulary, good rote verbal memory give others the *misleading* impression that the child can understand a lot more than s/he can. Receptive language processing is in reality an unreliable channel, making such a child easily nonresponsive to verbal commands. In this type of language disorder, moreover, pragmatics—that is, the ability to maintain a verbal topic or nonverbal interaction, or be appropriately responsive—is also characteristically weak. The inept pragmatics that are typically a part of this DLD picture usually have at their source both receptive language difficulties and serious organizational and attentional problems, so that the child easily gets sidetracked and goes off on tangents. This was the case with Sara.

During the assessment, Sara's organizational and attentional difficulties showed up also in her being self-directed and in the difficult time she had shifting her attention. She could be, on the one hand, overly absorbed or perseveratively stuck in something, or, on the other hand, highly distractible and disorganized with loss of attentional focus. Her activity level and mood appeared to change depending on the amount and kinds of materials used. The more multisensory, verbal, or numerous the materials were, the more she reacted with increased activity, unfocused regard, and a tendency to tune out. In observed interactions with her mother, this behavior was more typical than not, but then again, Sara's mother was constantly verbal with her.

By history Sara had sensory-processing problems with hypersensitivities especially to sounds, and fussiness (Miller, 2005). Not only was she hypersensitive to her mom's music playing, but also to sirens outside and to the lullabies of her overhead mobile. Consistent with such hyperreactivity is her continuing pattern to disorganize and withdraw with too much stimulation. A child with hypersensitivities can be easily overstimulated and find modulation of negative states and tension difficult. Such a child may also "learn" to be less reactive to others, or even avoidant of others as a form of coping.

Sara also showed motor planning and praxis weaknesses, that is, difficulties imitating and executing complex, sequenced movements, and responding to verbal requests to move in a certain way. This could account for her difficulties on the playground and in participating in circle-time singing.

Finally, Sara showed affect sensitivity problems, that is, difficulty reading facial affect cues.[4] Given the importance of affect sensitivity to early reciprocal social interactions between parent and child, it is not surprising that Sara's mom found her to be unresponsive and difficult to regulate. Affect processing is known to be important for the development of affect tolerance and affect modulation (Fogel, 1982; Krystal, 1974; Schore, 1996); for example, mothers are known to modulate and transform their babies' negative affect, as well as increase optimal levels of positive arousal, through their own exaggerated facial and vocal displays (Malatesta & Haviland, 1982; Stern, 1984, 1985). For this to work, however, the child must be able to pick up the affective signals communicated to him or her vocally, gesturally, facially, and cross-modally. If not, increased negative affect and tension can result, with poor coping and poor modulation, not to speak of avenues of healthy self-esteem and narcissism, of feeling admired by mother, and responding in turn going awry. Being able to read another's affective expression is also important for *disambiguating the world* and understanding when a situation is really frightening and so for alleviating confusion and anxieties. The social referencing study by Sorce, Emde, Campos, and Klinnert (1985) demonstrates how a typical 12-month-old baby placed on a *visual cliff,* in an inherently uncertain situation, will check back and read mom's affective expression to decide what to do. A child who has difficulties reading affect may thus appear more self-directed and less sure of itself and trusting of others to guide it through uncertainty. Such a child may also appear more confused, anxious, and disorganized when making transitions into ambiguous or unfamiliar situations.

Given this neuropsychological profile many of Sara's emotional difficulties could be better understood. An important item to note though, that Sara's mom didn't know, was that Sara had a hard time receptively processing verbal input and that, more generally, she had a difficult time regulating different kinds of sensory input and so was easily overstimulated. Although Sara's mother was aware, for example, of Sara's sound sensitivities and, of course, her early fussiness, she didn't understand Sara's hypersensitivity to too much stimulation. Thus, in an effort to be a better mother than her own, and feeling guilty about her depressive withdrawal, she tried to provide Sara with the cognitive stimulation she never got: So, besides talking to her a lot, she surrounded Sara with infant-stimulation paraphernalia, dumping lots of black-and-white striped objects and toys in her crib. The effects on Sara were to literally catapult her into disorganization and heightened periods of negative tension. This state of being so easily overwhelmed can adversely affect the development of signal anxiety, which in turn can make the child yet more prone to disorganizing diffuse anxiety states.

What Sara's mother also didn't know is how difficult it is for hyperreactive children like Sara, who also have weaknesses reading affect, to be regulated by their parents or to self-calm; typically these children have a tendency to avert their gaze and resist being held. These are typical early forms of coping with too much stimulation, not rejection. But the impact on the mother, who if she has depressive tendencies to begin with, can be precisely to elicit feeling rejected and projecting onto the child a motivational structure of dislike. This then worsens the poor quality of mutual regulation that is already difficult to achieve.

This case illustrates how neuropsychological dysfunction can become interpreted and enmeshed in the fantasies and fears of the parents and play havoc in the parent–child interactive system from very early on. It highlights the impact of neuropsychological factors on the parent–child interaction. Here vulnerabilities and challenges in the child set in motion or escalate psychological conflict in the parent and rebound back again to affect the child's cognitive growth and personality development. The neuropsychologically vulnerable child puts a hard developmental task onto any parent; for a parent with her own baggage, it's that much more difficult. The results were a compounding and exacerbation of those behaviors that had a neurogenic basis, such as perseveration, distractibility, and disorganization, and a twinning of them to heightened anxieties, and poor coping and social skills.

NEUROPSYCHOLOGICAL–PSYCHODYNAMIC EVALUATION

It may be helpful to briefly present the assessment format for this combined emphasis on neuropsychological evaluation with clinical understanding of psychodynamics.

Assessment Format

Before the initial session, the parents are asked to complete a comprehensive developmental, medical, and social history questionnaire. This information, along with any previous evaluations, is useful for orienting the clinical interview with the parents (without the child present) to areas of their concern and for raising initial hypotheses about what is going on psychodynamically with the child, couple, and family. Some clinically revealing questions asked, for example, include questions about parental fantasies and hopes about the child before the child was born; about parental "theories" about what is wrong with the child and why this is so; about what the parents' worst fears for the child are; about how each of them sees the child as like or unlike the other parent. These types of questions begin to elicit some of the deeper fantasies and fears as well as possible projections and defenses that may be orienting, even if not consciously, for each of the parent's interactions with the child. They start to bring into focus, as well, what the child may be experiencing and responding to in the family. In the case of Sara, because of her parents' complicated family backgrounds and personal histories, the parents were seen, both individually and together, a number of times without Sara present.

Assessment of the child begins with observation of the family during free play, where each of the parents is encouraged to interact and play with the child as usual. An observational visit to the school where the child attends is also useful, to get a picture of the school's view of the child and to see the child in another situation, in interaction with other children, as well as other adults. If necessary, a home visit is also made. This is followed by a series of more formal neuropsychological evaluation sessions, each about 1–2 hours long, for young children, where neuropsychological evaluation proper is carried out with one or both of the parents present, along with continuing clinical observations of interactions between child and family.

Neuropsychological Assessment: Brief Overview

Table 4.1 shows a list of functions typically assessed in a neuropsychological evaluation. This list stems from areas known to be affected in neurodevelopmental disabilities and neurological conditions of various kinds. They are skill areas that relate to different systems in the brain, with a neuropsychological evaluation seeking to find out whether consistent, known clusters or patterns of functioning within these different areas are conjointly affected. This list gives examples of functions assessed; it is not exhaustive. It is also updated and amended with ongoing neurobehavioral and neuroimaging research into various disorders.

Table 4.1

NEUROPSYCHOLOGICAL FUNCTIONS

Attention, Organization, and Executive Functions
   Initiating, shifting, inhibiting, sustaining attention
   Organized systematic functioning (e.g., visual search, planning, problem solving)
   Cognitive flexibility/shifting
   Working memory/mental tracking
   Response inhibition/impulsivity
   Generativity

Language-related functions:
   Auditory processing (e.g., phoneme discrimination, analysis, blending, memory)
   Phonological production & speech
   Auditory cognitive functions
   Receptive language focus
   Expressive language focus

Memory functions:
   Verbal memory
   Visual memory
   Memory and learning

Visual-related functions:
   Visual-perceptual functions
   Visual-spatial functions
   Visual-cognitive functions

Social cognitive functions:
   Affect sensitivity (e.g., facial, gestural, vocal)
   Facial recognition
   Social cause and effect

Sensory perceptual functions:
   Finger agnosia and stereognosis

Motor functions:
   Fine and gross motor coordination
   Graphomotor functions
   Motor praxis
   Motor tone

Neuropsychological assessment is necessarily comprehensive in the breadth of functions assessed as well as inherently developmental, incorporating an understanding of brain development as well as developmental expectations across all functions. It is transdisciplinary, with a necessary understanding, for example, of language disorders, movement disorders, neurological syndromes. Its procedures include both formal and informal methods that are intended to tap into targeted skill areas, whether or not a normed test is available. An important advantage, however, to using formal normed tests is the ability to generate a more precise picture of *intraindividual* differences in the child, which can be crucial for disclosing patterns of relative inefficiencies and a characteristic neuropsychological profile known to be reflective of a disability, such as a specific neuropsychological subtype of language disorder.

Also critical to a neuropsychological evaluation is analysis of the component skills necessary to perform any given task. Most formal tests do not tap into one skill, but rather demand use of multiple functions; in everyday life, activities are inherently complex. Thus, it is vital to ask not merely *what* a child scores or does but, more important, *how* he achieved that score or performance. It is the *how* that reveals which component skills are making him fall down, or what avenues of compensation he may naturally bring to bear or can be taught to use.[5] It is through reiterated testing of hypotheses about which skill areas are affected that intervention strategies can be discovered and hidden strengths found.

Here we can focus on only one or two of these skill areas. Because of their general importance in neurogenic conditions as well as their relevance for both Frank and Sara, it may be useful to look at attention, organization, and executive functions.

Attention, Organization, and Executive Functions

Executive functions are concerned with the regulation and control of behavior and thinking at all levels, automatic and reflective, conscious and unconscious—from regulation of motor movements to being able to step back and critically evaluate what you are doing.

Called *executive* and, in fact, comparable to *upper management* of a large organization, these functions correspond in the brain to the frontal cortex, that part of the brain that is most characteristic of man, and that takes the lead, is on *top of* other functions. It is also called the *brain's brain* and is *supramodal*. The frontal lobe is connected to many other parts of the brain through complicated fiber networks, so if other areas of the brain are affected, in many cases the frontal lobe will be, too. This accounts in part for why attention and executive function difficulties are so often copresent with many forms of disabilities.

Some children show a significant clustering of problems here. Frank's major difficulties are found here. That's why he's considered to have an attention deficit disorder—because problems here also relate to problems in attention, impulsivity, distractibility, and hyperactivity. In fact, ADHD has been associated most often with the frontal lobe, and through interconnecting fiber networks to subcortical areas, especially the striatum and cerebellum (Casey & Durston, 2006; Casey et al., 2007; Nigg & Casey, 2005; Swanson & Castellanos, 2002). Sara also had attentional and organizational weaknesses, so let's review what is involved here.

Table 4.2 gives some clues for detecting problems in attention and organized, systematic executive functioning. One can use them when administering formal measures, or informally to guide your focus when observing a young child in everyday life. Organized, systematic functioning can affect different and multiple levels of functioning, spanning, for example, motor functions, visual functions, as well as higher order processes such as play, problem solving, thinking, and reasoning.

Motor Movements. For example, observe how smooth and coordinated the child's movements are; look at the dynamic flow and modulation of movement. A child with problems here can show impulsive, jerky movements, and poor planning and sequencing of movements. With Frank, this was a major factor in his behavior in the classroom: Think about how Frank got up out of a chair and moved around. Frank showed poor motor planning and impulsive movements. Children with ADHD often are impulsive. Most of the time, people look at impulsivity in actions and style, such as blurting out thoughts, generally doing or saying things without first thinking. But, many children show impulsivity in their movements too—Frank did—because the same networks in the brain are involved. It's a sure sign when present together with impulsive style.

Impulsivity can also take the form of *disinhibition*, things done without thinking or self-control, like Frank's impulsive flinging of paint.

Table 4.2

CLUES FOR ATTENTION, ORGANIZATION, EXECUTIVE FUNCTION PROBLEMS

Motor: Jerky, nonfluid movements; poor motor planning; poor modulation of movements

Visual: Disorganized, random visual search

Mental tracking/integration of input: Poor ability to keep track of multiple commands, thoughts, input from different modalities

Attention (ISIS): Problems in ability to initiate, shift, inhibit, or sustain attention

Play: Problems in organized, sequenced, elaborate play schemas

Problem solving: Lack of goal-oriented behavior; poor awareness of cause and effect, past and future

Cognitive style: Impulsive, easily sidetracked style; compulsive, rigid, controlling style

Disinhibited behavior is often seen in people with frontal lobe dysfunction. How prevalent such behavior becomes, and the contexts in which it occurs may have, however, a lot to do with how the child experiences himself in doing it, and experiences and reacts to the feedback given him about it.

Visual Search.   One can also observe the degree to which the child's visual search and scanning of materials is organized and smooth. Can the child find things easily? Can the child select the relevant, essential details easily? Again, think about Frank. When Frank was asked to get something from his cubby he would end up at someone else's. If you had watched Frank look for his cubby and observed his eye movements, you would have seen disorganized, random darting eye movements here, as well. Both Frank and Sara had problems here when formally assessed. If you asked either Frank or Sara to find a *hidden figure*, they couldn't do it. Figure 4.1 shows an example from an old measure, the ITPA Visual Closure test, a timed task normed for children ages 2–10. Neither Frank nor Sara could find the hidden dogs here, not because of visual-perceptual or visual integration problems, but because of disor-

Figure 4.1 The ITPA Visual Closure Test.

ganized, random eye search movements. With Frank, this corresponds to the lack of fluidity in his overall motor movements.

Figure 4.2 shows an example from the Matching Familiar Figures Test, again an old measure used for children 5 years and older. Children with ADHD have a great deal of difficulty here because they will not guide their search for the exactly matching figure in a methodical,

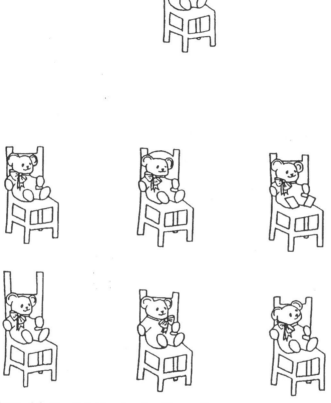

Figure 4.2 The Matching Familiar Figures Test.

organized double check-back way, but will impulsively use just one feature and then another, and blurt out their choices quickly.

Informally, in everyday life, you can watch the way a young child looks at pictures in a book, or, for example, if things are lined up in rows, how systematic their scanning and search for something is.

Mental Tracking.   Consider the child's ability to keep track simultaneously of two different trains of thought or commands as well as input from different modalities. This is known as mental tracking and makes use of working memory as well as the ability to flexibly shift attention and integrate information (e.g., in chess when you have to keep track of various moves as options in order to then choose the best one).

Consider Sara, who really couldn't function if too much input from different modalities was given to her at the same time. Sara didn't show merely hypersensitivity to noises but, across both auditory and visual input, and especially in the integration of input simultaneously from both modalities. For example, on the Bayley (2005), if given a number of objects to discriminate by name (e.g., a plate, cup, and box), she could identify the first item asked for (a plate); then, instead of responding to repeated directives to identify the other objects, she proceeded to play a feeding game with them. Thus, distracted by the toys, she appeared self-directed, with her own agenda, and was unable to attend simultaneously to any verbal input, although the particular verbal commands here were those she could comprehend and respond to if delivered without as many visual manipulatives.

Mental tracking or working memory can also involve keeping a sequence of verbal commands in mind, and remembering to remember. For example, think of Frank having to remember, "when you get your backpack, don't forget to put away the truck and the tractor." Working memory and mental tracking are important for remembering what to do in order to comply with commands.

Attention.   You may inquire about other specific features of attention such as the ability to initiate, shift, inhibit, and sustain attention (ISIS: a mnemonic coined long ago by Martha Denckla, a pediatric neurologist). So, ask: How difficult is it for the child to start a new activity or conversation, to *initiate* a conversation? How difficult is it for you to elicit the child's attention, to ease the child into a command or activity when the child has been absorbed in another task; that is, to *shift* or *switch* his or her attention? What are the child's reactions to transitions, to new activities? Consider whether Frank was intentionally not responding to his teacher or whether he was having a difficult time shifting his attention from what he was doing. Think about Sara's perseverative tendencies and inability to shift out of an activity, a thought, or a mood state. On formal assessment, and on tasks that had no great dynamic or emotional import, Sara showed real difficulties in shifting attention: On the Bayley, for example, she could not shift to draw a vertical line after drawing a horizontal one, but just repeated the same horizontal strokes. Or, on another task, the McCarthy Draw-A-Design (McCarthy, 1972), she could draw the first design asked for, a much harder-to-draw circle, but then could not shift to draw the simpler horizontal one, which of course she was able to do. Sara's obsessive and perseveratively insistent quality, seen in her repeated questionings, preoccupations, and repetitive behavior at home, may be an offshoot of these problems as they impact on personality style.

Also ask if the child is able to inhibit distractions, whether external (such as noises, sights) or internal (such as daydreams, bodily sensations). Ask whether the child can sustain attention, which doesn't mean being glued to the TV, but, rather, being able to follow through with variation and flexibility in focused attention.

Play. Observe the child's play and how spontaneously the child categorizes, structures and organizes it. Is there an elaborated *sequence* of activities using objects or themes that "belong together," or, does a random quality affect the child's play too? Does the child respond to structure? For example, if you set up a grouping of objects and model what to do with them, is the child's level of play improved upon? In other words, if you act like the child's frontal lobe, does it help the child? This can be important in sorting out whether a child is low functioning cognitively versus simply disorganized. Think here about Sara who was found to be very bright and whose play could be symbolic, but it was nevertheless described as lacking in elaborate play schemas, especially when she was left on her own, as she often was. Such a child needs the structured support from others to organize her play until she can internalize it and appropriate it for herself.

Problem Solving. What about the child's thinking and problem solving, at a higher level? For example, how capable is the child in predicting an outcome, using a goal, an intended result, to guide its own behavior, or to experiment and explore how new objects function?

Formal testing can be used, for example, the WPPSI-Mazes R (Wechsler, 1989); but informally you can see it in any problem-solving task, in the methodical double-checking, stop and think approach, rather than trial and error procedures, for example when a young child is asked to put shapes in a form board or to get an object that is out of reach.

In everyday life, you can ask if the child understands the causes and consequences of behavior, punishments and rewards, and is able to use these to guide his actions. Joaquin Furster (1989) in discussing the prefrontal cortex, refers to "the temporal organization of behavior," as the ability to use past and future to plan, regulate, and execute actions—or to reflect on one's experiences. As development proceeds (given a representational function to the prefrontal cortex), this is the basis for the accumulation of knowledge as "structured event complexes" (Grafman, 2006), as well as for coherent narratives about the self, and for "time binding," "mind binding," and "emotion binding" (Dennis, 2006).

So, ask if the child can so reason according to cause and effect, past and future? For example, was Sara able to automatically tell herself that when Daddy left for work in the morning, he would come back later? Was there a clear temporal organization implicit in her experience that would allow her to use past experiences to give herself the needed reassurance? Was Frank able to automatically remind himself, "When (in the past) I knocked into Bob, the teacher got mad"? Was he able to use this kind of conditional thinking to orient his behavior? Children with organizational and attentional problems cannot, do not, automatically regulate their behavior in accord with such *causal* principles.

Cognitive Style. What about the child's overall cognitive style: How flexible and naturally methodical is the child? Or, is the child disorganized here too? Children with organizational weaknesses, like Sara, are also known to fluctuate in style between an approach that is disorganized, impulsive, or easily sidetracked to one at the opposite extreme of being rigid, compulsive, perseverative. Children with frontal lobe dysfunction can show both these extremes.

It seems that the very problems that underlie the attentional difficulties may also codetermine defensive style and personality. The child who is highly distractible and unable to plan and guide actions in accord with rules or anticipated consequences shows an easy propensity to be impulsive in dealing with emotionally laden issues and to use, for example, defenses such as avoidance, denial, and blaming others. A child sensitive to experienced disorganization and loss of attentional focus as beyond her control, in an ego-dystonic way, may well opt for overcontrol and an obsessive style. Children who have difficulty shifting attention and show a perseverative focus will also show a rigid inflexibility cognitively that has all the appearances at times of an obsessive preoccupation with things.

Discrepancies and Their Subjective Experience. Beyond a more exacting look at the many other areas of possible neuropsychological compromise, an important clue for detecting the presence of a neuropsychological dysfunction, as well as for understanding its impact on emotional functioning, is the presence of discrepancies in skills.

For example, children with motor planning and praxis issues can show a great discrepancy between what they know and what they can do and between what they want to do and how they can use their body to do it. Children with language disorders can experience an enormous discrepancy between poor verbal abilities and excellent nonverbal reasoning abilities. It's important to ask: *"How does it feel to a child to experience this discrepancy?"*

Within the area of language disabilities, a child with expressive problems may not have receptive problems. Such a child may experience the frustrating and anger-provoking discrepancy between what he understands and what he feels himself capable of saying. In contrast, a child like Sara, who has better expressive, than receptive skills, constantly faces expectations that are higher than she can verbally meet. People talk to and expect her to respond because the impression from her own expressive language is that she has no language problem. Such a child may come to experience a defeating sense of inadequacy about verbal requests, and so withdraw.

If other people in the child's environment don't recognize these discrepancies or know how to account for them, what about the child? What is the child to make of it? The point is that the child can't help but to subjectively experience it, give meaning to it, and incorporate it into his or her sense of self. So, it's not unusual to find fluctuating self-esteem, images of self as good and competent sometimes, and as dreadfully incompetent at other times. How is the child to know, when no one else knows, when to predict he can do something and when he cannot. Esteem issues and heightened defenses become typical with such children.

Finding the weakness and circumscribing it becomes the goal—to dam the spill onto personality structure. To simultaneously find the child's strengths is a way of not only compensating for weaknesses and alleviating their impact on everyday life, but also for buoying up the child's psychological resilience and consistent sense of knowing *what he can do.*

So, when do you think that the aggressive, oppositional, or anxious behavior you may be seeing or hearing about from parents masks a neuropsychological difficulty or, at least, is fueled by some underlying problems?

With *aggressive behavior*, think of Frank. Was it the case that Frank was impulsive because of *intent* or did he have a constellation of problems that clearly went together and supported the inference of impulsivity due to poor frontal lobe function? Was it the case that Frank wanted to knock into children, step on their toys and hands, and charge out of his seat? Or, was it that his motor movements, his motor planning and sequencing were off?

Consider, too, how that lack of control over his motor movements was in itself experienced personally by Frank, experienced, perhaps, as a "sensed loss of control," and how would a child react to and give meaning to such an experience—especially when others around him were interpreting it as "bad boy" behavior, and intentional. Frank could easily have turned passive into active; instead of passively experiencing himself as the victim of his body, he could have *counterphobically* begun to actively plan aggressive motor acts so that his feared loss of control could be felt as mastered.

With *oppositional behavior*, think about Frank and Sara's seeming oppositionalism. With Frank, there was his lack of response to his teacher's requests and his refusal to join in on group activities. Was this, perhaps, at least at root, part of his attentional difficulties, part of his being *stuck* in an ongoing activity with difficulty shifting to a new one. Or, with Sara, how much of her inability to tune into a command had to do with her difficulties in keeping track of input from various modalities simultaneously, or to her receptive language problems? It is not unusual for children with receptive problems to "tune out," especially in classrooms where there are heavy auditory verbal demands, which is, most of the time, the case. This is why they can be so often misidentified as oppositional (which they then can also become). Or, recall Ken, who showed such slow speed of processing that others interpreted it as willfulness and negativism.

How about the child presenting with *withdrawn, anxious, or bizarre behavior*? Think of Sara. Was anxiety responsible for Sara's withdrawn behavior on the playground and during singing? Or was her behavior in part due to motor planning issues? Was she withdrawn and noninteractive, at least in part, because of her receptive language problems—

because of her sensed inadequacy of being able to reliably pick up on the meaning of what was being said to her? Was her isolation from others fueled also by her organizational difficulties that so clearly infected her play and responsivity? Sara would go off on tangents and easily "lose set" or focus, as well as the established connection to another. This caused her pragmatics to be perceived as poor and her interactions to appear lacking in extended, reciprocal turn-taking volleys.

Many of Sara's emotional preoccupations and "anxious worries" seemed to be engendered, if not aggravated, by a cognitive inability to readily shift focus or mood. This being stuck—overwhelmed by negative affect and tension, and tendency to diffuse anxiety states—also had a long history in her sensory processing problems and weak affect processing, as these were overlooked or misinterpreted by others.

Most important, some of Sara's *bizarre* behaviors seemed very much a part of the particular neuropsychological profile that she showed—that of a semantic pragmatic DLD—where expressive skills are better than receptive, where there is excellent rote verbal memory, but weak semantic processing of content, and organizational problems. Such children, as was the case with Sara, may develop scripts that they often say over and over again and insert at inappropriate times into conversations (because they do not fully understand the entire content of what they're saying), or use in seeming monologues with themselves. This, above all, gives others the sense that they are *bizarre*. But if, instead of interpreting this as evidence of social problems and unrelatedness, one listens closely to such *scripts*, one often hears messages from mother and other remembered significant interactions. In other words, sometimes they are not evidence of social unconnectedness but, on the contrary, *are* used as transitional phenomena to mediate connectedness to others.[6]

At the same time, however, because all of these difficulties are taken up and subjectively experienced by the child and played out for others where they can be interpreted and misinterpreted, there may well be a coterie of psychological defenses (both adaptive and maladaptive), as well as family problems and stresses feeding into, maintaining, or exacerbating the difficulties.

Also, be aware that it can work the other way around too. Some neuropsychological-looking symptoms may, on the other hand, have emotional underpinnings: ADHD-like symptoms can also be a defensive strategy against depression, especially in boys. Impulsive, disorganized behavior can also be produced by anxieties and reactions to stress.

INTERVENTION

Feedback to Parents and Recommendations

What about feedback to the parents? Although parents actively seek out an evaluation because of the need to obtain greater clarity about their child, they can, nevertheless, be ambivalent, even fearful, of the results. Given the amount of new information also to absorb, resistances can be heightened. Typically, feedback about a neuropsychological evaluation is given in one too brief of a session, with parents leaving with a written document and not enough time to question or review it, much less integrate it into their vision of who their child is or what he needs. At the end of a comprehensive, integrated neuropsychological-psychodynamic evaluation, the challenge is even greater. In order to help parents process and use the information, feedback is best tailored to the particular family with clinical attention to what and how the information is communicated, and over what period of time.

In the case of Sara, the feedback information was taken up in a number of feedback sessions, and then in the course of therapy to allow the family time to appropriate and use it at a pace that they felt comfortable with. In this way, accurate diagnostic formulation and description could have the effect of demystifying difficulties and tempering parents' anxieties, which in Sara's case, had taken such a stranglehold on their understanding and interactions. The couple appeared, in fact, relieved to hear that there were identifiable reasons for so many of Sara's behaviors. Also, because the evaluation of Sara's strengths and problematic areas, as well as of the family's, was so detailed, specific recommendations addressing core issues could be made. The family was glad to be given a diagnostic formulation that was adjoined to a plan of action.[7]

Critical to the treatment plan was understanding the ways neuropsychological weaknesses had been involved and had interfaced with others' reactions, so as to affect parent–child interaction patterns, as well as Sara's coping style and personality development. The need presented itself, on the one hand, to work therapeutically on Sara's heightened anxieties, disorganization, and difficulties in mood and self-regulation, and at the same time to actively incorporate an understanding of the neuropsychological weaknesses underlying them and how to address them: Therapy with the child would be modified then to incorporate remedial-type strategies. On the other hand, what also had to be addressed were the parent–child interaction patterns and family issues— and how they were affecting the family, and, in turn, affecting Sara. It was, thus, decided that treatment should include twice–weekly psychotherapy sessions with Sara, together, with her mother. These joint sessions would attempt to address both aspects of the child–parent system that needed support to facilitate change: They would focus on strengthening Sara's coping and regulatory capacities while facilitating more adaptive engagement between mother and child.

Sara's parents' understanding of Sara's weaknesses and sensitivities, and of how to compensate for them, also at home, would be addressed in a more focused way in separate once a week parental guidance sessions. These meetings would also be used to further discuss the parents' feelings or, more generally, the impact that caring for Sara was having on them individually and as a couple.

It was also recommended that individual therapy sessions with Sara's mother may be of value to help her come to terms with her own complicated reactions to her past which, rekindled by her concerns and reactions to her daughter, were spilling over into her present relationships.

Although sometimes, a parent may benefit from her own private therapist, in this instance, issues related to the mother were bound to surface in the joint sessions with Sara, which could then be brought up again and productively used in the mother's own sessions.

In addition, it was recommended that Sara enter a structured half-day intervention program. Given the extent of her organizational, language, and motor planning difficulties, such a program could provide her with a small peer-group environment where predictable routine and structure could foster learning, cooperation, and a sense of well-being. It could also give onsite language and occupational therapy to directly address her language, sensory, and motor difficulties, and so obviate the organizational stress that would befall Sara's mother if she had to arrange and coordinate this herself. In a small school classroom, moreover, there would be many adult-enhanced opportunities for free play and more focused attempts to mediate interactive peer play for Sara.

A consultation with a pediatric allergist, for evaluation and control of her often occurring allergies, was suggested. It was also recommended that the family consult an audiologist trained in auditory integration training for possible treatment of Sara's hypersensitivities to sound.

Treatment Course

The family was helped in finding out how to obtain funding for an intervention program as well as in selecting the best program for Sara. An important consideration in program choice was the extent to which sensory input would be regulated, and how calm, nurturing, and tranquil an atmosphere would be available. Given Sara's hypersensitivities, a classroom was sought where toys and materials were stored neatly and presented in simple and uncluttered ways, distractions were kept to a minimum, sound and noise regulated, and transitions through busy areas avoided. Sought, was a program with a multidisciplinary approach—where the teacher would incorporate into the classroom curriculum some of the goals and strategies of the other professionals working with Sara, and where coordination with the outside therapist and the family would also be routinely embraced. Fortunately, such a program was found. The teacher was very sensitive to Sara's receptive language and organizational-attentional difficulties and was able to keep verbal comprehension demands reduced, help Sara with shifts in the everyday routine, and help her participate in activities (e.g., to motor plan during circle time singing or on the playground) through simple verbal rehearsal of what was expected along with nonpressured practice over time. An occupational therapist trained in sensory processing disorders advised on self-calming and focusing techniques that became part of Sara's everyday school routine.

Therapy sessions with Sara and her mother fostered mother–daughter engagement and connectedness in an approach such as that described by Stanley Greenspan and Serena Wieder (Greenspan, 1992; Greenspan & Wieder, 1998) where the child's lead is followed and elaborated upon, intentions are facilitated, attentional focus is enhanced, and symbolic play is extended and made more interactive. In order for this to work, Sara's mother needed to apply much of what she had been unaware of about Sara: This included reducing her language input to Sara; adding drama to the play, which would build on Sara's own focus while using more exaggerated affect, in face and voice; helping Sara engage in longer sequences of play through, for example, helping her to understand cause and effect and by modeling such sequences for her (e.g., if baby doesn't see daddy, then she will be sad, and then she will cry); reducing Sara's distractibility by presenting a minimum of toys and by punctuating Sara's abrupt attentional shifts with gently spoken statements like "If you want to stop playing with the bunnies, lets put them away first." This had the impact of reminding Sara of what she had just forgotten, and made any shift more willful and conscious. Sara's poor modulation of affect was addressed by helping her elaborate and recognize in more representational ways (in play and through language) those times when she would fall apart, feel anxious, and lose control. This was important for helping to develop signal anxiety—for helping Sara, and Sara's mother as well, *understand and anticipate* situations and feelings that could lead to intense experiences of disorganization. More effective calming and coping strategies could then also be played out in the therapy hour as well as at home.

The therapeutic process was particularly beneficial for Sara's mother because she came to see how she could gain Sara's positive responsivity to her. The joyful gleam in Sara's eye, seen during the evaluation as something she was so capable of, finally became directed to and joined by her mother. Sara's mother began to feel admired by her daughter, and more positive interactions began to characterize their relationship.

The approach of following the child's lead was of particular value for Sara because it helped raise her subjective sense of control, accomplishment, and mastery, and, in doing so, provided an important antidote to her tendency to anxiously withdraw, tune out, and be self-directed in her play. Sara's mother's attunement to Sara's sensitivities and weaknesses—in particular Sara's being overwhelmed by too much stimulation, her problems integrating input from different modalities at the same time, and her limited semantic comprehension and closing down when spoken to incessantly—began to lessen Sara's tendency to disorganize and subjectively feel out of control. For Sara, it thus also added to increasingly more positive experiences of the self as capable of feeling affectively well-modulated, especially while being with a significant other. This went a long way in helping Sara's regulatory difficulties.

The parental guidance sessions were instrumental for reviewing impressions of therapy sessions, for problem-solving about issues that were recurrent at home, for helping integrate the school's goals and strategies with those of the family and therapy. Issues that came up

included how to manage Sara's negative behaviors, her crying, tan-
truming, and perseverative tendencies, which were more prevalent at
home. Specific strategies were discussed, for example, to make the home
routine also more predictable and structured for Sara, especially the
parents' comings and goings; to arrange her bedroom and play areas
in a simple way free of clutter; for toys to be put away in an organized
way; for soft, calming places to be made available to retreat to. Firm
but kind limit setting was practiced to deal with tantrums, whining,
and negative behaviors. Although the auditory integration training that
was carried out, appeared to help some of Sara's hypersensitivities to
sounds, she continued to be sensitive to her mother's music, and other
sounds at home. One strategy that appeared to work was to get Sara
her own musical instruments to play, and allow her to control other
noisemaking things, such as a taped recording of her mother's music,
making it louder and softer, turning it on and off. Calming strategies
were also developed, always keeping in mind Sara's hypersensitivities.

Individual therapy sessions with Sara's mother became quite important to Sara's treatment. For example, an obstacle presented itself
early on: Sara's mother started to doubt that Sara had any problems
understanding language, and began anew to talk constantly in an overly
verbose way to her. This occurred at a point when Sara's mother felt
the therapy was not making adequate progress, and that Sara's behaviors
weren't changing fast enough. At this time, in individual sessions, her
mother started to describe herself as having been a verbally precocious
child who spoke in full sentences at age one. Thus, Sara's mother, who
had originally seen little similarity between herself and her daughter,
who didn't want to see any similarity, began to see Sara's expressive
language abilities—her locquacious vocabulary and her ability to repeat
long strings of words her mother said to her—as being the one area in
which she could identify with Sara. Her hopes for things normalizing
had been shaken by a period of what she perceived as little movement
in Sara's therapy. Denial of Sara's language issues in some way helped
her, during this period of uncertainty, to remain connected to Sara and
connected to the hope of things being normal for Sara, and for Sara
and herself. In sessions, she became more aware of this wish, also as
it reflected on hopes, repeatedly threatened, about her place in her
larger family. In individual sessions she was also able to explore the
anger she felt especially toward her mother, and the ambivalence she
felt toward her own success. Most important, individual sessions al-

lowed Sara's mother to obtain the needed attention and recognition that she felt she had never gotten. In turn, she was able to give that much more to Sara.

In sum, neuropsychological conditions are taken up actively and psychodynamically by children and affect the child's emotional well-being and behavior. Neuropsychological dysfunction plays a role in how self-image, personality, defenses, and relations to others develop. Integrated neuropsychological-psychodynamic assessments that pay heed to psychological dynamics and family systems considerations are a vital tool for differential diagnosis and for providing guidelines for appropriate intervention. The medium for intervention becomes, in part, exploration with the parent of who the child is, and what the fantasies and misreadings are that the parent, because of his or her own history, may bring to the exchange. Intervention with the child and the parent is guided directly by knowledge of the constitutional make-up of the child. Accurate diagnostic assessment can thus be critical in outlining a therapeutic course of action. Disclosing strengths or positive avenues of access to the child while, at the same time, keeping in mind the dysfunctional channels and their impact on both the child and others, can be used as an important instrument of intervention.

NOTES

1. Earlier versions of some of the material presented in this chapter have appeared in previous publications (Black, 1995, 1997).
2. During the years 1980–1982, The Mahler Observational Nursery was at the Graduate Faculty of the New School for Research; the nursery was directed by Robin Persky and codirected by Lois Black.
3. Some would subsume a profile such as Sara's under an autism spectrum disorder (ASD) and diagnose her with PDD-NOS (and essentially equate "semantic pragmatic disorder" with ASD). However, as originally thought of by Rapin and Allen (1983, 1987, 1998), semantic pragmatic disorder was one type of language disorder among others, found in both ASD and DLD, albeit at different prevalence rates (higher in ASD than DLD). Moreover, there is still ongoing debate about this and uncertainty as to where to draw the boundary on what may be a continuum between ASD and DLD (see Bishop,

2000, 2003; Bishop & Norbury, 2002; Whitehouse, Barry, & Bishop, 2007).

4. When looking at affect sensitivity in facial, vocal, and situational contexts, Black (1989) found that, among neuropsychological subtypes of DLD, a "C" type, which corresponds to Rapin & Allen's "semantic pragmatic disorder," had the most problems in recognizing affect in facial expressions; with "P" and "B" types, which correspond to "phonological syntactic disorders" (the most frequently occurring), having the most affect sensitivity problems across all modalities.

5. Barbara C. Wilson, PhD, a neuropsychologist, is known for this important message.

6. One can distinguish "scripts" that are more characteristic of ASD from those that Sara displayed: In ASD they more typically derive from videos, for example, rather than overheard conversations of others; are spoken more "in the air" rather than to someone with the intent to communicate; are more bizarre, and typically lack more in coherence and relevance to an interpersonal exchange.

7. For Sara, formal diagnosis according to *The Diagnostic and Statistical Manual of Mental Disorders* (APA, 2000), would refer to childhood disorder, NOS (to emphasize the emotional and behavioral aspects), mixed receptive-expressive language disorder, and attention deficit disorder. Formal diagnosis according to DMIC (2005), DC:0-3R (2005), and DC:0-3 (1994) would refer to a regulatory disorder or regulatory-sensory processing disorder: over-responsive, fearful, anxious pattern, and a language disorder.

REFERENCES

Alexander, G., Crutcher, M., & DeLong, M. (1990). Basal ganglia-thalamocortical circuits: Parallel substrates for motor, oculomotor, "prefrontal" and "limbic" functions. *Progress in Brain Research, 85,* 119–146.

American Psychiatric Association. (2000): *Diagnostic and statistical manual of mental disorders* (4th ed., text rev.). Washington, DC: American Psychiatric Press.

Baker, L., & Cantwell, D. (1982). Psychiatric disorder in children with different types of communication disorders. *Journal of Communication Disorders, 15,* 113–126.

Bayley, N. (2005). *Bayley scales of infant and toddler development* (3rd ed.) Upper Saddle River, NJ: Pearson Publishing.

Beitchman, J., Cohen, N. J., Konstantaereas, M. M., & Tannock, R. (1996). *Language, learning and behavior disorders*. New York: Cambridge University Press.

Beitchman, J., Nair, R., Clegg, M., Ferguson, B., & Patel, P. G. (1986). Prevalence of psychiatric disorders in children with speech and language disorders. *Journal of the American Academy of Child Psychiatry, 25,* 528–535.

Bishop, D. V. M. (2003). Autism and specific language impairment: Categorical distinction or continuum? In G. Bock & J. Goode (Eds.), *Autism: Neural basis and treatment possibilities* (pp. 213–234). Chichester, UK: Wiley (Novartis Foundation Symposium).

Bishop, D. V. M., Chan, J., Adams, C., Harley, J., & Weir, F. (2000a). Conversational responsiveness in specific language impairment: Evidence of disproportionate pragmatic difficulties in a subset of children. *Development and Psychopathology, 12* 177–199.

Bishop, D. V. M., Chan, J., Adams, C., Harley, J., & Weir, F. (2000b). Pragmatic language impairment: A correlate of SLI, a distinct subgroup, or part of the autistic continuum? In D. V. M. Bishop & L. B. Leonard (Eds.), *Speech and language impairments in children: Causes, characteristics, intervention and outcome* (pp. 99–113). Hove, UK: Psychology Press.

Bishop, D. V. M., & Norbury, C. F. (2002). Exploring the borderlands of autistic disorder and specific language impairment: A study using standardised diagnostic instruments. *Journal of Child Psychology and Psychiatry, 43*(7), 917–929.

Black, L. M. (1989). Subtypes of language disordered children at risk for social-emotional problems. *Dissertation Abstracts International, 50,* 3B. Ann Arbor Michigan: UMI, No.8910782.

Black, L. M. (1995). The interweaving of neuropsychological dysfunction and psychological conflict. *Zero to Three, National Center for Clinical Infant Programs, 15*(4), 26–35.

Black, L. M. (1997). Regulatory disorder. Type I: Hypersensitive. The fearful and cautious child. *Casebook for 0-3: Diagnostic classification of mental health and developmental disorders of infancy and early childhood* (pp. 195–232). Washington, DC: Zero to Three.

Black, L. M., & Stefanatos, G. (2000). *Neuropsychological assessment of developmental and learning disorders: Clinical practice guidelines.* Bethesda, MD: ICDL Press. Available at: www.icdl.com

Black, L. M., & van Santen, J. (2006, July). *Social-emotional problems and affect sensitivity in subtypes of developmental language disorder.* Paper presented at the INS/SVNP/ GNP Meeting in Zurich, Switzerland.

Bradshaw, J. L. (2001). *Developmental disorders of the frontostriatal system.* Philadelphia: Psychology Press.

Cantwell, D., & Baker, L. (1991). *Psychiatric and developmental disorders in children with communication disorder.* Washington, DC: American Psychiatric Press.

Cantwell, D., Baker, L., & Mattison, R. (1979). The prevalence of psychiatric disorder in children with speech and language disorder: An epidemiologic study. *Journal of the American Academy of Child Psychiatry, 18,* 450–461.

Casey, B. J., & Durston, S. (2006). From behavior to cognition to the brain and back: What have we learned from functional imaging studies of attention deficit hyperactivity disorder? *American Journal of Psychiatry, 163*(6), 957–960.

Casey, B. J., Epstein, J. N., Buhle, J., Liston, C., Davidson, M. C., Tonev, S. T., et al. (2007). Frontostriatal connectivity and its role in cognitive control in parent–child dyads with ADHD. *American Journal of Psychiatry 164*, 11, 1729–1736.

Casey, B. J., Tottenham, N., & Fossella, J. (2002). Clinical, imaging, lesions, and genetic approaches toward a model of cognitive control. *Developmental Psychobiology, 40,* 237–254.

Corbett, B., & Contstantine, L. (2006). Autism and attention deficit hyperactivity disorder: Assessing attention and response control with the integrated visual and auditory continuous performance test. *Child Neuropsychology, 12,* 335–348.

DC: 0-3. (1994). *Diagnostic classification of mental health and developmental disorders of infancy and early childhood (DC:0-3).* Washington, DC: Zero to Three Press.

DC: 0-3R. (2005). *Diagnostic classification of mental health and developmental disorders of infancy and early childhood* (rev. ed.; DC:0-3R). Washington, DC: Zero to Three Press.

Dennis, M. (2006). Prefrontal cortex: Typical and atypical development. In J. Risberg & L. Grafman (Eds.), *The frontal lobes* (pp. 128–162). New York: Cambridge University Press.

DMIC. (2005). *Diagnostic manual for infancy and early childhood (DMIC).* Bethesda, MD: Interdisciplinary Council on Developmental and Learning Disorders (ICDL-DMIC).

Egger, H., & Angold, A. (2006). Common emotional and behavioral disorders in preschool children: Presentation, nosology, and epidemiology. *Journal of Child Psychology and Psychiatry, 47*(3/4), 313–337.

Fogel, A. (1982). Affect dynamics in early infancy: Affective tolerance. In T. Field & A. Fogel (Eds.), *Emotion and early interaction* (pp. 25–56). Mahwah, NJ: Lawrence Erlbaum.

Furster, J. (1989). *The prefrontal cortex: Anatomy, physiology, and neuropsychology of the frontal lobe* (2nd ed.). New York: Raven Press.

Grafman, J. (2006). Human prefrontal cortex: Processes and representations. In J. Risberg & J. Grafman (Eds.), *The frontal lobes* (pp. 69–91). New York: Cambridge University Press.

Greenspan, S. I. (1992). *Infancy and early childhood: The practice of clinical assessment and intervention with emotional and developmental challenges.* Madison, CT: International Universities Press.

Greenspan, S. I., & Wieder, S. (1998). *The child with special needs: Intellectual and emotional growth.* Reading, MA: Addison Wesley Longman.

Kim, J. A., Szatmari, P., Bryson, S. E., Streiner, D .L., & Wilson, F. J. (2000). The prevalence of anxiety and mood problems among children with Autism and Asperger's. *Autism, 4,* 117–132.

Krystal, H. (1974). Affect tolerance. *Annual of Psychoanalysis, 3,* 179–219.

Leyfer, O. T., Folstein, S. E., Bacalman, S., Davis, N. O., Dinh, E., Morgan, J., et al. (2006). Comorbid psychiatric disorders in children with autism: Interview development and rates of disorders. *Journal of Autism and Developmental Disorders, 36*(7), 849–861.

Lichter, D. G., & Cummings, J. L. (2001). *Frontal-subcortical circuits in psychiatric and neurological disorders.* New York: Guilford Press.

Mahler, M., Pine, F., & Bergman, A. (1975). *The psychological birth of the human infant.* New York: Basic Books.

Malatesta, C. Z., & Haviland, J. (1982). Learning display rules: The socialization of emotion expression in infancy. *Child Development, 53*(4), 991–1003.

McCarthy, D. (1972). *McCathy scales of childen's abilities.* Upper Saddle River, NJ: Pearson Publishing.

Miller, L. J. (2005). *Sensational kids: Hope and help for the child with sensory processing disorder* (SPD). New York: Putnam.

Nigg, J., & Casey, B. J. (2005). An integrative theory of attention-deficit/ hyperactivity disorder based on cognitive and affective neurosciences. *Development and Psychopathology, 17,* 785–806.

Prizant, B. (1999). Early intervention: Young children with communication and emotional and behavioral problems. In D. L. Rogers-Atkinson & P. L. Griffith (Eds.), *Communication disorders and children with psychiatric and behavioral disorders* (pp. 295–342). San Diego, CA: Singular Publishing Group.

Rapin, I., & Allen, D. (1983). Developmental language disorders: Nosologic considerations. In U. Kirk (Ed.), *Neuropsychology of language, reading, and spelling* (pp. 155–184). New York: Academic Press.

Rapin, I., & Allen, D. (1987). Developmental dysphasia and autism in preschool children: Characteristics and subtypes. In *Proceedings of the First International Symposium on Specific Speech and Language Disorders in Children* (pp. 20–35). London: Association for all Speech Impaired Children (AFASIC).

Rapin, I., & Allen, D. (1998). The semantic-pragmatic deficit disorder: Classification issues. *International Journal of Language and Communication Disorders, 33,* 82–87.

Schore, A. (1996). *Affect regulation and the origin of the self: The neurobiology of emotional development.* Hillsdale, NJ: Lawrence Erlbaum.

Simonoff, E., Pickles, A., Charman, T., Chandler, S., Loucas, S., & Baird, G. (2008). Psychiatric disorders in children with autism spectrum disorders: Prevalence, comorbidity, and associated factors in a population-derived sample. *Journal of American Academy of Child & Adolescent Psychiatry, 47*(8), 921–929.

Sorce, J. Emde, R., Campos, J., & Klinnert, M. (1985). Maternal emotional signaling: Its effect on the visual cliff behavior of 1-year-olds. *Developmental Psychology, 21*(1), 195–200.

Stern, D. (1974). Mother and infant at play: The dyadic interacton involving facial, vocal, and gaze behaviors. In M. Lewis & L. Rosenblum (Eds.), *The effect of the infant on its caregiver* (pp. 187–214). New York: Wiley.

Stern, D. (1984). Affect attunement. In J. Call, E. Galenson, & R. Tyson (Eds.), *Frontiers of infant psychiatry* (Vol. 2, pp. 3–14). New York: Basic Books.

Stern, D. (1985). *The interpersonal world of the infant.* New York: Basic Books.

Swanson, J. M., & Castellanos, F. X. (2002). Biological bases of ADHD: Neuroanatomy, genetics, and pathophysiology. In P. S. Jensen & J. R. Cooper (Eds.), *Attention-deficit hyperactivity disorder: State of the science, best practices* (pp. 7–20). Kingston, NJ: Civic Research Institute.

Wechsler, D. (1989). *Wechsler Preschool & Primary Scale of Intelligence—Revised.* San Antonio, TX: Psychological Corporation.

Whitehouse, J., Barry, J., & Bishop, D. V. M. (2007). The broader language phenotype of autism: A comparison with specific language impairment. *Journal of Child Psychology and Psychiatry, 48,* 822–830.

5 Neuropsychological Testing and Psychoanalysis in Adolescent and Young Adult Patients

MARTHA PIERCE AND AYAME TAKAHASHI

NEUROPSYCHOLOGICAL TESTING AND PSYCHOANALYSIS

The basis of psychoanalysis and psychoanalytic psychotherapy is that of the therapeutic relationship. One of the premises of psychoanalytically informed psychotherapies is that this relationship is the foundation that patients build on in order to deepen their understanding of themselves, which in turn develops insight and improves understanding of their functioning. Children or adolescents who are the object of parental and community concern are most likely feeling troubled and highly anxious about most aspects of their lives. An adult who has an undiagnosed learning disability or another neuropsychiatric condition is more likely to have struggled in many areas of his or her life, in addition to having had major academic challenges. An empathic clinician will work with his or her adult patients, and his or her young patients, along with their families to clearly define and supply understandable reasons for any form of intervention, with the intent to ease the undue burden and mystery caused by casual or colloquial use of diagnostic terminology that may or may not be an accurate depiction of the patient's behaviors. Such inexact reference or conceptualization of diagnostic categories or labels can inadvertently increase the patient's confusion and anxiety. It may not be an overstatement to say that clinicians who make reference to the individual's *bad brain* or poorly functioning frontal cortex are speaking more from their own need for expertise than from empathic or constructive concern for the patient.

The evaluation of learning disabilities and the emotional fallout from these difficulties have often become much less thoughtful and more constrained by time and financial circumstances in today's managed care environment. The academic institution, whose classrooms are quiet and contained, will generally *weed out* the individual whose educational performance is not commensurate with the other individuals within the classroom. These individuals will be referred to either the school psychologist or child study team whose job is to evaluate the child's academic needs. Informed parents may then seek alternative consultation from their pediatrician or a mental health professional. In many of these circles, the immediate psychopharmacological intervention has replaced the thorough neuropsychological evaluation and a carefully honed psychotherapeutic evaluation and intervention.

The following section will review the thinking about learning disabilities, attention-deficit/hyperactivity disorder (ADHD), and other neuropsychiatric disorders as they present themselves in psychoanalysis and psychodynamic psychotherapy. The purpose of this discussion is to remind us of how we can begin to think about emotional conditions and subsequent behavioral functioning.

Neuropsychology and Psychoanalysis

We cannot do justice to any discussion of neurobiology and psychotherapy without first mentioning the father of psychoanalysis and modern psychiatry, Sigmund Freud. Although psychoanalysis has been considered the ultimate psychological *talking cure,* Freud was a neurologist by training. He was very much a *biologist* of the mind, seeking to understand and integrate his clinical observations of cases where very physical symptoms occurred in individuals who did not have any discernable physical ailments. Take, for example, the case of Anna O. (Bertha Pappenheim), who presented with hysterical paralysis. In conjunction with Josef Breuer, Freud found that hypnotic suggestion temporarily would *cure* her symptoms. This eventually set the stage for Freud's theorizing of the unconscious mind. In the book *Studies on Hysteria*, Breuer writes about the neurophysiologic basis of hysteria and Freud writes of the psychological basis (Freud, 1895). In his day, Freud did not have access to the diagnostic tools available now, and he primarily relied on his clinical observations to fuel his theories. The analytic method of listening to his patient's verbalizations, *free association,* and dream analysis were his tools of peering into unconscious mental processes. These were not tools amenable to use in the scientific method, hence the study of the mind headed off on a different path from the scientific study of the brain (Kandel, 2005).

Over the last 30 years there has been an explosion in the understanding of the biological underpinnings of psychiatric disorders as well as an understanding of learning disabilities associated with reading, writing, speech, and all forms of communication that we as human beings engage in. As a result of the unfortunate schism that developed since Freud's time within the field of psychiatry between the theorists of the *mind,* the psychoanalysts, and the scholars of the brain, traditional psychoanalysis had a tendency to view neuropsychological testing somewhat suspiciously. At the time, learning disabilities were viewed more as defensive mechanisms used, consciously or unconsciously, to defend against deeper conflicts. In fact, psychoanalysis was thought to cure a whole host of what we now know are biologically determined learning problems (Giffin, 1968).

Recently there has been more of a *rapprochement* between the psychological and biological sciences. From fields outside of psychiatry, such as cognitive psychology and neuroscience, new findings have been giving credence to Freud's observations (Kandel, 2005). Studies in learning and memory, especially such discoveries on explicit and implicit memory, are much like Freud's observations on the conscious and unconscious mind. A new field is also emerging, called *neuropsychoanalysis*, which seeks to bring together these areas of scholarship in attempt to *reintegrate* the theories of the brain and mind (Solms, 1995).

Neuropsychoanalysis is generally defined as a discipline that integrates the empirically driven fields of neuroscience, psychology, and psychiatry with traditional Freudian psychoanalysis. Although Freudian psychoanalytic theory dominated treatment approaches for psychological disorders and diseases early in the twentieth century, neuroscience brought technology and objective, empirically derived theories to treat the same problems. Over time, however, many revisited Freudian theory as it became clear that Freud provided powerful and accurate insights that complimented modern neuroscience's technology and valued empiricism. Quoted in a *Newsweek* interview, the Nobel laureate Dr. Eric R. Kandel of Columbia University, stated psychoanalysis is "still the most coherent and intellectually satisfying view of the mind" (Kalb, 2006).

In his article, "Freud Returns," Mark Solms elaborates on neuroscience and psychoanalysis, and the integrative strength of the new discipline neuropsychoanalysis (Solms, 2004). Solms reviews the Freudian concept of unconscious motivation. He states that Freud suggested the mental processes that determine our daily thoughts, feelings, and volitions, occur unconsciously. This notion that unconscious processes drive apparently conscious actions was rejected by many of Freud's peers. However, cognitive neuroscientists can now distinguish between conscious (explicit) and unconscious (implicit) memories and thoughts. Patients with brain injuries often fail to consciously remember events, people, or general information that was encoded prior to the injury or insult to relevant brain regions; yet, the behavior of these patients is often influenced by the information encoded prior to the brain damage.

Further support for Freud's contention that information is processed unconsciously, yet, profoundly influences conscious behavior has been repeatedly demonstrated by fear conditioning studies. Emotionally charged information may bypass the cortex and the hippocampus, the structures important for encoding information and processing memories. Individuals may not be able to consciously identify emotionally charged information or events. Studies by Joe LeDoux, Elizabeth Phelps, Antonio Damásio, and others clearly support Freud's concept of unconscious information influencing motivation and behavior (Solms, 2004). A variety of technological innovations, such as the ability to scan patients brains while testing them, demonstrating size and location of brain lesions, tumors, injuries, and so on have allowed neuroscientists to empirically test Freud's ideas, often supporting the original theories.

Very much in this vein, the psychoanalytic view of the utility of psychological testing has been gradually changing. For example, someone with ADHD has difficulty with impulse control, organization and functions associated with the frontal lobe, and with what is traditionally considered to be *ego functions* in psychoanalysis (Bellak & Marsh, 1997). Instead of viewing the symptoms of ADHD as themselves being defensive, the refusal to get appropriate treatment or forgetting to take needed medications may be more fodder for the psychotherapeutic treatment.

ADHD has traditionally been seen as a disorder of childhood, and, erroneously, it was believed that in adulthood one mostly grew out of the symptoms. Children are more impulsive and hyperactive than adults. However, in the course of normal development, children develop an increasing ability to modulate their impulses. Children with ADHD also mature over time, but development may appear *patchy*, as some symptoms become much better, whereas others may only show minimal improvement over time. For example, the symptom of hyperactivity often does get much better over time (hence the belief that people with ADHD *grow out of* the diagnosis), however, some of the cognitive symptoms, such as inattention, difficulty with multistep commands, and poor organizational skills, may remain relatively immature relative to the individual's chronological age.

People also differ in their ability to compensate for these relative deficits, and this is an area which possibly could be more psychodynamically determined. The symptom of impulsivity in adults with ADHD may manifest as a tendency toward action before thinking, or can manifest as more verbal impulsivity. There may be less of a *filter* for unconscious content, which may spill out in embarrassing moments. The nature of these impulsive outbursts often is psychodynamically determined.

Growing up with the deficits associated with learning disabilities or ADHD can leave the individual prone to a multitude of problems in later life. There may be chronic self-esteem, or *narcissistic* issues, difficulties with intimate relationships, and difficulties in the work place (Garber, 1988). How someone views the disorder, can very much become part of their overall self image. Often there are adults seen in psychotherapy, who have never been diagnosed with either learning disabilities or ADHD, who have struggled with these issues their entire lives. These may be folks who are quite verbal, intelligent, and seem to chronically function below what would be expected given their seeming intelligence. In fact they may sometimes be *great patients* in a psychodynamically oriented treatment situation given that they are quite adept at free association and accessing unconscious material. Yet, at the same time there may be a curious lack of progress or *learning* from session to session, and lack of movement in the patient's personal and professional life. Interpretations of conflicts may be correct, however, may not lead to any increased fruitful understanding, as it is only a piece of the whole picture. It is in these situations that both a referral for psychiatric assessment and neuropsychological testing may be indicated. The testing may help to clarify and *tease out* areas of relative strengths and weakness, and detect more subtle learning issues that previously had been overlooked. This can in turn help the patient and the clinician to redefine how they looked at certain problems, and perhaps even seek additional avenues for treatment.

Occasionally there may be individuals who, as a result of idiosyncratic uses of language, poor reality testing, and a tendency toward primary process type thinking, may end up being misdiagnosed with a psychotic disorder (Marcus, 2002) and mistakenly deemed inappropriate for more expressive psychodynamically oriented therapy or psychoanalysis. Yet again, in day to day functioning, or during the course of a supportive treatment, one may discover surprising areas of strength and insight.

Dyslexia is one such learning disability, which may severely impair an individual's ability to learn, and to learn appropriate impulse control. Typically it is thought of as a *reading* disorder, as an inability to decode the symbolism of letters and sounds into words. Dyslexia also manifests, in addition to the difficulties with reading, in difficulties with spelling and writing. In essence, over the past 20 years, dyslexia has been found to be a language-based learning disability with difficulties in language processing (Migden, 1998). Language is what makes human beings unique in their ability to transcend instinct and impulse. Imagine how having this very core ability impaired would affect one's ability to develop those skills that help us in controlling our emotions and behavior.

It is not uncommon for individuals with dyslexia to be diagnosed with comorbid ADHD. When individuals have an impaired ability to both communicate and to be understood, both impulse control and frustration tolerance are likely to be impaired as well (Migden, 1998). All the *ego deficits* mentioned earlier about ADHD would then doubly apply to dyslexia. Treatment with stimulant or other medications for ADHD alone is rarely enough for the individual to achieve optimal functioning. Ideally, this is a diagnosis that should be made early on, so that the individual can get as much educational intervention as possible throughout his/her school years.

OBTAINING APPROPRIATE EVALUATIONS

Parents and outpatient mental health providers are faced with important questions: "What is it that my child really needs?" is commonly asked by parents who may feel helpless and "How do I supply this missing information concerning my child's needs, given my fixed income and lack of knowledge of the system?" The answer within groups of individuals who do not have adequate access to or information about various forms of advocacy is never readily obtained. Many parents continue to be told more about budget cuts and overcrowded classrooms rather than what interventions are available to address their child's academic needs. Even some middle-class suburban school districts shy away from acknowledging certain emotional factors that interfere with learning, and they are ready to establish strict parameters that do not include any form of out-of-district funding for education or mental health care.

Certain types of emotional illness do allow for classification and will support school district funding and action. Districts that cannot provide a suitable educational program for a student do provide a series of Individualized Educational Plan (IEP) meetings, which eventually outline a suitable educational program. These meetings are held within the confines of educational law and adhere to the structure of state guidelines. These guidelines vary from state to state. Parents may desire legal consultation with an individual specializing in educational law. School advocacy services may also be helpful throughout the process to the parent whose budgets do not include funds for legal counsel.

Common mental health conditions that may be cause for educational classification for emotional reasons, may initially present themselves in the confines of the therapeutic relationship. These psychological conditions, otherwise referred to as emotional disorders (ED), range from issues with attention, anxiety, mood, and behavioral dyscontrol to other manifestations of dysfunction that can be seen as a byproduct of the student's psychosocial environment. The real attunement on the part of the parent and the clinician is the willingness to approach the individual's inability to process abstract information and incapacity to organize abstract thoughts. This may indicate a variety of diagnostic considerations such as an undiagnosed attention deficit disorder, affective disorder (different varieties of depressive illness or other mood disorders), or an underlying psychotic process. The subtlety of symptoms that may somewhat emerge within the clinical therapy hour regarding autistic-like thinking, or the behavioral patterns demonstrated in Asperger's disorder, may best be supported with solid neuropsychological test data. In terms of emotional and personality functioning, the results of an integrated neuropsychological evaluation can also reveal suicidal ideation and other forms of self-destructive wishes or in-depth processes ferreted out with projective testing, which is a strong predictor of behavior. In an integrated neuropsychological report, the projective testing is typically supported with a variety of self-report inventories, which tend to help shed light on diagnostic characteristics. In addition, integrated neuropsychological batteries often include behavior rating scales that provide objective ratings on a patient's behaviors across settings at home and at school. All of this information is extremely helpful to the clinician who sees the child or adolescent in therapy.

Other conditions that may have been considered in the past, within certain psychoanalytic circles, as *resistance* to the psychotherapeutic process may also underscore specific learning styles, which are not conducive to some forms of understanding and integration of information. These highly classifiable learning disabilities such as a nonverbal learning disorder (NVLD) and expressive and receptive language difficulties can greatly impede the child or adolescent from attaining both their social and educational goals. Disorders that include a lack of capacity to accomplish basic academic tasks such as reading, writing, and mathematical exercises may surface in the course of psychotherapy, but are mostly visible in a classroom environment. They are classifiable under the heading of learning disorder (LD).

The general concern regarding the neuropsychological evaluation of these conditions is two-fold and pertains to the financial and psychological considerations within each individual circumstance. Financial constraints are inherent to the therapeutic process and essential to the patient and the family seeking help for their child or adolescent. It is an essential skill and important in the therapeutic process to discuss fiscal matters with the patient. To quote Freud (1913):

> The point that must be decided at the beginning of treatment is the one of money. Money is the medium for self-preservation and for obtaining power. Money matters are treated by civilized people in the same way as sexual matters with the same inconsistency, prudishness and hypocrisy. The analyst is therefore determined from the first not to fall in with this attitude, but in his dealings with his patients, treat money matters with

the same matter-of-course frankness to which he wishes to educate them in things related to sexual life. (p. 131)

Following Freud's lead in these matters, the informed mental health practitioner must find ways in which they are able to manage the importance of the clinical intervention with the essential diagnostic information obtainable only through the process of neuropsychological testing. Clinicians who favor their own clinical acumen in exchange for solid neuropsychological data are sorely misinformed and perhaps even negligent in their own way of viewing their patient's needs. The investment both in time and money in neuropsychological testing is invaluable. Many neuropsychologists direct families to their primary care physician whose referral to a neurologist can prompt insurance companies to at least partially fund the process of obtaining a full battery of neuropsychological tests. The evaluation, despite the financial burden it may place upon many families, must be recommended in addition to ongoing clinical work whenever there are questions about academic or social functioning, or when there is school district involvement.

Neuropsychological evaluation is also mandatory when there is pending litigation due to a school district's refusal to fund essential services to the student. Educational testing performed by a school psychologist will not usually be sufficient. Psychoeducational testing (which emphasizes intellectual functioning and academic achievement) is typically provided by the school district. However, for some students, psychoeducational testing may not be enough, because this type of testing lacks the nuances and descriptive integration between and among cognitive functioning, personality functioning, and the emotional factors that interfere with intellectual functioning and social development. As a result, psychoeducational batteries may not elicit a truly comprehensive picture of the scope of the various needs of the child or adolescent. This lack of information may further the academic and social deterioration within the school setting, by not availing the family of reasonable options provided by impartial out-of-district evaluators. Although never formally orchestrated or overtly stated, some school districts may also be quite reticent to support anything other than in-school special educational services to students. Plus, schools do not typically employ neuropsychologists as part of their paid in-house staff, which means that parents and caregivers must seek neuropsychological testing outside the school.

In the following three sections, we provide three composite case studies. The case studies are designed to illustrate the ways in which an integrated neuropsychological evaluation may yield a richer and more practical portrait of a child's or an adolescent's actual capacity to demonstrate their intellectual skill level and the ways in which their neuropsychological functioning has an impact on their emotional and academic future.

THE QUESTION OF NEUROPSYCHOLOGICAL TESTING IN CHILDREN AND ADOLESCENTS: A PSYCHODYNAMIC FRAMEWORK

The purpose of this section is to understand the psychosocial aspects of intellectual functioning and emotional development upon neuropsychological functioning. Each of these three composite cases describes a patient who was seen in psychoanalytic psychotherapy for between 1–4 years. These individuals have experienced different psychosocial stressors and are at varying levels of intellectual and psychological development by virtue of their chronological age and often complex life circumstances. The case studies portray patients who range from 7 to 16 years of age and will mostly demonstrate the variety and individual differences both in diagnostic composition and reasoning around referral for neuropsychological testing. Each case is a composite sketch and does not represent an actual patient or treatment case. The story of each patient is composed of pieces of real life situations combined to illustrate our clinical thinking and reasoning surrounding the actual process that would spawn a referral for neuropsychological evaluation.

In each case, neuropsychological testing was used to optimize the treatment. Much of what transpired was the inability of the patient to function academically at a reasonable level. It was also clear that the treatment team was unable to suggest or intervene in ways that would allow the patients to make the necessary changes needed to strengthen their academic performance.

Case Example: Alan R.

The first case is a summary of a young boy with dyslexia and ADHD who was in child psychoanalysis for almost 1 year. Concurrently he was also placed in a specialized school for children with learning disabilities and treated with medications. This case is illustrative of the advantages of early diagnosis with educational intervention combined with intensive psychotherapeutic treatment (Migden, 1998). The four-times-weekly treatment was especially helpful in that Alan's learning issues and resulting difficulties with emotional regulation made it difficult for him to hold on to gains made in less intense treatment.

Reason for Referral

Alan was a 7-year-old, adopted Vietnamese boy, who was referred to me for psychoanalysis by a colleague (Dr. C.) who had seen Alan in twice-weekly treatment for the year prior. Alan was referred to me for a couple of reasons, one reason being that his family was moving and Dr. C. felt that my being an Asian therapist might make Alan feel more comfortable and able to engage in treatment.

Alan was described as a very charming little boy with great capacity for fantasy play, yet who had multiple difficulties functioning both at home and at school. Although socially Alan had many friends, he had been rapidly falling behind in school this past year (second grade). He could not read or write, and had great difficulty following instructions. He became confused easily and had tremendous difficulties with transitioning from task to task. He received neuropsychological testing about 6 months prior to his starting treatment with me, which showed severe learning disabilities, including disorder of written expression, reading disorder (dyslexia), and attention deficit disorder, combined type. However, Alan was highly intelligent and verbal, and, in spite of his learning disabilities, he had a verbal IQ of 128. His full-scale IQ was 108, with significant scatter throughout the subtests. His strengths were in the verbal reasoning skills and expressive vocabulary, scoring in the superior range. However, in other subtests, he scored down into the 5th percentile. His particular areas of weakness were on tasks requiring sustained attention, visual motor integration, and working memory. He had also received an occupational therapy assessment that showed significant weaknesses in his fine motor and visual–motor sensory-processing skills.

In sessions with my colleague, Dr. C., Alan had tremendous difficulty ending sessions and would frequently have to be held during sessions to keep from getting too destructive. As treatment progressed with Alan, Dr. C. felt that twice-weekly sessions were not enough to contain the level of aggression often present. Dr. C. had also attempted a stimulant trial with Alan. However, more often than not, Alan would refuse to take the medication, causing huge power struggles at home.

Developmental History

Alan was adopted at 4–5 months of age from Vietnam. His birth mother was 17 years old and in good health. The pregnancy was normal and there was no reported drug or alcohol use. His birth weight was 6 pounds. He spent the first few months in a foster home, but developed pneumonia and was in the hospital for 2 months prior to his adoption. His adoptive parents have another child, an adopted girl from China, who was 7 years old at the time of Alan's adoption. The couple was initially planning to adopt another child from China, but found out that adopting from Vietnam might possibly happen faster. They were also hoping to adopt a little boy this time, and little boys are rarely up for adoption in China. As an infant, Alan was reportedly a happy, engaging baby, who was bottle-fed and apparently ate well. Motor milestones were achieved on time, but speech was somewhat delayed. He was trying to speak by 2 years of age in two-word sentences. Shortly after, however, his speech was mostly unintelligible, until about 3 1/2 years of age.

By the time I began seeing Alan in treatment, Alan's parents had been divorced for 4 years, and his father had remarried about 1 year earlier. Alan had tremendous difficulty transitioning from home to home and would get aggressive with his mother often upon returning from his father's home. Alan had frequently expressed to his mother that he didn't want to go to his father's; yet, when Alan was staying at his father's home, he would do very well. Upon returning home to mother, Alan would often fall apart; he would become highly emotional—having temper tantrums, and *meltdowns*, during which he would break his toys, bang his head on the floor, and would need to be held sometimes for up to 30 minutes before calming down. He was undoubtedly fearful of expressing to either parent the degree to which he actually enjoys being with the other, for fear of alienating their affections toward him. Given Alan's learning disabilities, he may have found the transition between homes and rules quite confusing and distressing, beyond that of other children of divorce who do not have learning issues.

Treatment Course

Alan initially had great difficulty with the idea of switching therapists. He is a very cherubic Asian boy who was quite articulate for his age, and told his mother prior to our first session that he was determined not to like me. At our first meeting, he sat playing his Gameboy outside of my office and initially refused to make eye contact. Finally, he reluctantly came into my office and after an initial period of talking very briefly, he started to explore my office.

He was active and easily distractible. Even at the end of the first session, he showed difficulty in ending our session. He grabbed a large lump of clay, tore it up into little pieces, and stuffed the pieces in a messy pile inside my business-card holder as his mother was trying to pull him out of the office. This symbolism becomes much clearer later in the treatment, but, often in psychodynamic terms, play with clay can represent play with feces, and was a possible representation of how he felt about separations. For about 6 weeks during the initial phase, Alan was seen two to three times weekly. During this period he not only had extreme difficulty ending the sessions, but he also had to borrow a toy to take with him between sessions. This demonstrated a fairly intense level of separation anxiety and difficulty with object permanence. The object from my office would enable him to *hold onto* a piece of me between sessions (a transitional object). Developmentally speaking, separation anxiety in general starts about 18 months of age and in most children is resolved by age 3. This is a good example of how learning disorders can interfere with the development of object constancy (Rothstein, 1998). He would also sometimes bring toys from home, and once he insisted on leaving his toy car with me, stating "let this be a sign of trust between us." Just about every session ended with him flinging toys about my office and then going for the lump of clay and tearing it up. He even started to stuff the clay into the toy toilet in the doll's house (a fairly clear representation of feces). Several times it was a piece of the clay that he wanted to take home with him.

During the sessions, however, he played very well, with many varied and rich themes. During the initial period, when he was seen two to three times per week, we mostly played Olympics. He set up a basketball and dart-throwing competition in which he would joyfully cheat and then laugh maniacally when I lost. At one point, irritated that I was continually losing and then being mocked, I complained about always having the disadvantage. To this he replied, "You're a grown-up!" I then stated, "And kids never have the advantage in real life, huh?" He then replied solemnly, "That's exactly right, kids never have the advantage."

When the session frequency was increased to 4 times weekly, the play changed. I was his partner and accomplice in hunting "aliens." He would often need to take the play outside my office to the waiting area where his mother and sometimes his older sister would be sitting. He would tell them to hold up their hands or he would shoot and then when they did, he shot them anyway, again laughing hysterically. At times he would tell them that they had bulletproof vests on, and then suddenly he would take the vests away and shoot them. In my office, there would be random shooting at the "aliens" and it would not be clear why they were our enemy. He would often incorporate his mother into the play, sometimes she would be an ally and sometimes the enemy and this could switch at any moment without clear reasons why. During these periods, I would often just reflect on how it is difficult to tell who our friends are and who are our enemies, to which Alan would say very little in reply. This confusion in the play I felt was symbolic of both how he felt about the divorce, as well as his perpetual state of confusion as a result of his learning issues. The ADHD caused him to miss key things going on in his environment, and, in addition, the dyslexia caused him to misinterpret things that were said to him. Given his verbal skills and overall brightness, Alan was well aware of many of his deficits, thus the way the world works always seemed to not quite make sense. One time when I was late to a session, I had initially tried to get him to express how he must have felt angry with me. However, he denied this, and talked instead about how he thought he was at the wrong office and had proceeded to go down the hall and knock on the doors of all the offices. When I reflected how confused he must have felt, he readily acknowledged this and seemed very relieved. Later in the session he took some clay and fashioned it into a letter "L," he then started chanting, "L is for lion, L is for lake, and L is for LATE!" He then shaped the "L" into a heart and asked me to keep it safe in my office somewhere. In my making an empathic comment about the confusion, he felt more understood, and felt safe in entrusting me with his heart.

Alan also liked to go on my computer and find short video games. The characters he chose in the games reflected how he was playing during the session. One game he played for a number of weeks involved raising fish in an aquarium and then shooting aliens that invaded the tank. If the fish were raised properly, they would "poop out" gifts of money. This was very much like his play at the end of the sessions with the clay, symbolic of both aggression and love by the leaving of the "feces." There were also a number of plain "shoot 'em up" games. The objective was to shoot the enemy of course, but at times Alan would get frustrated and then start randomly shooting even the "innocent" people in the game and then laugh. In spite of the sadistic play, he also showed a lot of kindness and a forgiving attitude. I once clumsily dropped a Lego ship he had built over a number of sessions, and after I apologized he remarked that it was okay, it could be rebuilt, and rebuilt even better than it already was. The aggression at the end of the sessions was more subdued once the session frequency was increased, and his need to borrow a toy from my office also decreased.

At the end of the first month of four-times-weekly sessions, he was still having a great deal of difficulty transitioning between his mother's household and his father's home. He was still often aggressive toward his mother and his mother was often beside herself with how to help him contain himself. Given that he would only take liquid medication, I chose to start him on Risperdal Elixer at 0.5 mg. He responded remarkably well to this low dose, and the tantrums and aggression at home stopped. The aggressive/sadistic play in the sessions continued, but had a more organized quality. He remarked a couple of weeks after that he felt like he was "getting my life back."

Alan was curious from the beginning about my ethnicity, however, was shy about asking himself. He told his mother to ask me at the beginning of one session, and he refused to participate in any attempts at exploration saying loudly "I just want to know, just tell me!" I told him I am Japanese. Interestingly, his mother told me a couple of weeks later that he had forgotten and was asking her again about what ethnicity I was. He seemed to want to identify with me. Once he commented on how my bangs were shorter, and the next day, he would come in with his bangs cut as well. He also made comments to his mother about how he was to be my "heir." "You know, like when they show in those (Kung Fu) movies of the master handing down his sword to his student." Within a couple of weeks of having attended four-times-a-week sessions, he insisted on having his mother present in the room during the sessions. There are a number of possibilities for why he seemed to need this. He may have had the fear that one person may not be able to contain him, given how volatile he was. There were times, in fact, that I was relieved to have his mother present given how unpredictable he was at the end of the session. There may also be a wish to have two mothers, with me as a stand-in for his Vietnamese birth mother. As his mother showed a remarkable ability to play and to understand the necessity of allowing him to direct the play, I decided to try and resolve this analytically, as opposed to telling his mother she should not be in the sessions.

During the sessions, he would have episodic periods of emotional dyscontrol. These often centered around an inability to do things in the way he envisioned them. His play around the aliens and killing aliens shifted after a while to Lego play on the floor. We would build ships together, and also build gardens and supply yards full of food. He would sometimes have difficulty building what he wanted, and sometimes would in frustration throw down the ship he had been building and destroy it. At times this was not enough and he would start wailing, throw himself on the floor, and start banging his head on the floor. He would sometimes ask his mother for the "cocoon," which meant being wrapped in his coat tightly, until he was able to calm himself down. Apparently this was something they did at home when he would get emotionally overwrought.

Over time, he developed new strategies for coping with his fine motor difficulties. He would often admire the ship I was building and then ask to switch ships, so he could "improve" on my design. Eventually he would incorporate his design into mine. Likewise in school, he was learning both to read and write and making a tremendous amount of progress. Occasionally he would bring his homework into the sessions, in part to have me "help" him, but also to see how much mastery over reading and writing he had gained over the months. His play on the computer as well as in the sessions became increasingly more organized. On the computer, he started to "follow the rules" of the games and would no longer randomly shoot at people in the "shooter" games. The play in the sessions developed overarching themes. He would often play with the spaceships we built out of Legos, and place them in the "Star Wars" universe. We would in turn battle the "separatists" or go out on science missions to find food. "Good" and "evil" became more clearly defined. Aggression at the end of the sessions continued, but in a much more contained way. Eventually we developed a ritual for the end of the session, where he would build a tall tower out of cardboard castle blocks, and then knock them over on top of me. Once this was done, he was able to leave quietly without delay. Eventually he was able to give up even this display of aggression (by about 6 months into treatment). However, he was not able to give up having his mother in at least part of the treatment session. I believe this was still partly an issue of containment of his aggression. He was noticeably more subdued during sessions when she was not present, and he felt that he was unable to play as freely. At times when a babysitter would bring him to the sessions, he would want the babysitter to come in with him as well. He broke his arm on the playground at school, and for the period of time he had his arm in a cast, he was able to tolerate being alone in the room with me for longer periods of time. This was interpreted and reflected to him although he did not have much response at the time.

Eventually, themes centering around his adoption and ambivalence about it began to emerge. At times, Alan would comment that if there was another war between Vietnam and the United States, he would have to choose Vietnam—"no offense!" he would say. Also around this time, more Oedipal themes also started to emerge. At age 8, or around the time children are in third grade, most children are solidly in what Freud termed the Latency stage. Early in this treatment, according to Freud's psychosexual stages, this child was developmentally *stuck* in the anal/sadistic stage. Issues of control versus dys-control, aggression, and sadism were the dominant themes. By 6 to 7 months into the treatment, he progressed to the Oedipal stage. Alan started talking to me more about his relationship with his mother. He intimated once that he would sometimes "spy" on her in her room, and sometimes he would even hear her crying. Once when his mother was present, he offered to put her picture up on a dating site on the internet, because he had decided that she needed to "get out" more. In fact, in one of the rare communications from Alan's adoptive father, the father expressed concern that Alan had become the "man" of the house and almost a substitute "husband" to his ex-wife. This may have been the other piece of why Alan found it so difficult to exclude his mother from the sessions, because of her needs, and his need to take care of her.

In a particularly poignant session toward the end of the treatment, there was a baby left on a battleground—Alan had taken one of the dolls in my office and left it on the floor in the middle of the room. Notably, the baby couldn't speak, was ill, and also very confused. There were no parents around. When I asked if we should send him to get adopted, he stated, "No, he doesn't want to be adopted; besides no one asked him." In Alan's statement, themes revolving around both the divorce and adoption merged together. Shortly after this session, his mother announced that they were moving again and would no longer be able to continue the treatment, since they would be too far away geographically (although, in actuality the physical distance was only about 20 miles). Alan would continue in his same school for the next year, but probably not the year after. Although his mother had been previously very positive about the treatment and the progress made, there was a sense of great disapproval toward the end, which she was not able to discuss with me. My sense is that as Alan was able to verbalize more of his thoughts and feelings about the divorce and adoption, he was moving toward greater separation and autonomy, which his mother was not yet emotionally ready to confront. Although the termination of this treatment was less than ideal, even in the short but intensive treatment period, Alan showed tremendous psychological and educational gains, which I hope continue to make progress.

Case Example: Bradley S.

The case of Bradley S., a 16-year-old public school student, presents the reader with the common dilemma found in many children and teens whose low mood, irritability, and aggressivity initially point to the diagnosis of some form of a depressive condition. His parents suspected that Bradley had a problem with substance abuse, which they feared might be a contributing factor to his poor performance in school. Bradley was very unwilling to acknowledge this, much less discuss any of these current concerns with his family, and also refused to see his school psychologist for treatment. How does the clinical evaluation proceed with the knowledge that Bradley's scores on the previous psychoeducational testing indicated possible learning disability? At the time I received a referral to treat Bradley in psychodynamic psychotherapy, he had never received a neuropsychological evaluation.

Reason for Referral

Bradley S. was a 16-year-old Caucasian male whose adoptive parents referred him for individual psychotherapy during his sophomore year in a public high school. Treatment was sought for him by his parents on the advice of his school psychologist. Bradley's school principal also suggested he be referred for this evaluation as a result of the serious disciplinary actions he received on two different occasions. My involvement with Bradley's school district was extensive. Many of my patients are deemed appropriate for special education services. This typically involves my attendance at CSE (Committee on Special Education) meetings and frequent consultation with Bradley's school psychologist.

As is customary at the very beginning of therapy with any child or adolescent, especially one who is under 18 and legally a minor, I met with Bradley's parents alone to take as complete a developmental and psychosocial history as possible. At this time I let them know about how important it would be for me to work with their son and maintain confidentiality. I also explained the evaluation process and emphasized how the therapeutic relationship was an essential part of their son's growth and development. They agreed to meet with me once a month and supply any essential information about their interactions with Bradley.

Developmental History

Bradley is the youngest son in a sibship of two children adopted by an Irish American family. Mr. and Mrs. S. were desperately wanting their own biological children when it was determined that Mr. S.'s sperm count was abnormally low. Several rounds of fertility treatment failed to produce any success and left them feeling devastated. Both parents had come from large families and all of their siblings had produced numerous children. It was at that time that Mr. and Mrs. S. made a decision about adoption. Bradley's older sister Molly was adopted by the S. family at birth. Bradley came into the S. family when he was already 2 years old. He spent his first 2 years in a foster home in the southern United States. Molly is 3 years older than Bradley and is an exceptionally bright academic student who obtained a full academic scholarship to an Ivy League university.

Bradley's early developmental history prior to the age of 2 was very sparse according to the records from the adoption agency and the foster family. It was known that he was the biological child of two high school students from Mississippi and that his mother was a relatively healthy young woman whose maternal grandmother was known colloquially to be somehow "not all there." This was not reported as being due to either her intellectual incapacities or psychotic illness. Bradley's father's history was not known other than the fact that there was no known medical or psychological difficulties reported in his biological father's family history. After the age of 2, Mrs. S. described Bradley as quite a docile child with little or no trouble meeting developmental milestones.

Bradley entered school at the age of 5 and seemed to have little difficulty following teacher's directions. It was noted in many of his report cards in first and second grade that he was a "daydreamer" and was often seen to be "in another world with difficulty finding his way back to the subject matter being taught." Mrs. S. reported that much emphasis and attention was given to Molly at that time due to the enthusiasm on the part of her teachers because of her intellectual giftedness. Bradley quietly did what was expected of him so the daydreaming was not brought to the attention of the family until his fourth-grade teacher made mention of her concerns after looking at his lower test scores on the required state test examinations. It was then that he was referred to the school psychologist for a psychoeducational evaluation.

Bradley's mother was very attentive during the course of the first meeting and supplied necessary medical records and educational documentation from Bradley's early school years, including results of psychoeducational testing performed 7 years ago by the public school district. The last time Bradley had received any formal, psychometric testing was in fourth grade, when he was 9 years old. Results of psychoeducational testing on intellectual functioning and academic achievement indicated some clear concerns about Bradley's ability to attend to tasks and organize himself. There was not much detail in the report, but his intellectual profile was as unevenly matched, with his verbal scores in the average to above-average range. The nonverbal tasks fell in the low-average range or below. No follow-up testing had ever been discussed or recommended by the school district, nor was there any form of special education services recommended to the family.

Treatment Course

More recently, Bradley's parents reported that for months in high school, Bradley had demonstrated an increase in moodiness, irritability, and shortness of temper, as evidenced by an increased number of heated arguments with his family and actual physical fighting after school with his schoolmates on the school grounds. Bradley was suspended from school for fighting on two occasions within a 6-month period.

Bradley was failing in his high school coursework and was unwilling or unable to keep up with assigned academic work. He also was limited in his willingness to discuss any of this with his adoptive family and remained quite angry with both his parents and his only female sibling, when it was suggested that he seek some sort of help to aid him in these struggles. At one point his parents shared how he threw his school books out of the second story window of his house, while screaming obscenities at them. He often accused them of only caring about his success and not really "loving" him. This brought about long and heated arguments, which usually ended only when Bradley stormed out of the house. On these occasions, he typically did not return until long after his family had gone to bed. His parents were not able to tell me where Bradley would go overnight. The only solace they had was that somehow, he would eventually come home.

His family was also concerned that Bradley often appeared to have slurred speech. Bradley did not seem to socialize with friends. His parents often observed Bradley with dilated pupils and reddened eyes at different times during the week and on the weekends. The family correctly suspected that Bradley might be experimenting with different forms of illegal substances and/or alcohol. As is the case with many parents, Bradley's parents had little way of knowing what to do about their concerns. Bradley's guidance counselor referred Bradley to the school psychologist on several occasions to address his poor school attendance and failing grades; yet, Bradley refused to go to the school psychologist for help.

Bradley was finally persuaded to see me twice a week for individual psychotherapy, but only after his parents offered him the following incentives. His parents told Bradley that if his behavior "improved," he would get a car once he was licensed to drive. For a teenager suspected of alcohol abuse, this was not an appropriate form of reward. Also, Bradley's parents did not define a time line or describe how or to what degree Bradley would have to improve his behavior, which only fed Bradley's confusion, unrealistic expectations, and misunderstanding of what his parents wanted in terms of reformed behaviors.

It would have probably been much more helpful if Bradley's parents had been very forthright in outlining realistic, focused guidelines in concrete terms that Bradley could relate to easily. For example, instead of vaguely telling Bradley that they wanted to see his behavior "improve," his parents could have stated specifics, such as "If you complete all your homework assignments for the next week, then on Saturday you will receive that music CD you wanted," or "If you are not suspended for the next month, you will be allowed to have your friends over to the house on a weekend evening."

Upon entering my office for the first session, Bradley stated that he was not really interested or willing to seek psychotherapy for any of the above mentioned difficulty. He reported that it was his parents who had insisted upon his attendance in therapy and that the only reason he was going to show up was the vague hope that someday his parents would allow him to get "a driver's license and a car."

Our first several meetings were palpably painful for both of us. Bradley sat sullenly slouched in his chair and had little to say. On one occasion during the first month of psychotherapy, Bradley asked if he could leave the session to smoke a cigarette outside of my office building. I thanked him for asking, but asked if I could chat with him while he was smoking. He muttered, "sure" with a puzzled tone, almost to say "what is up with you?" Outside of the office we spoke about the kind of cars that were parked in front of the office. He told me about how he wanted to buy a used car from his grandfather and fix it up so he could drive to school. This was the beginning of the conversation that revolved around his love of cars. He spoke little about his family and never mentioned friends, with the exception of the few individuals who smoked with him during lunch.

After 3 months of twice-weekly individual psychodynamic psychotherapy with no significant change in his academic or social functioning, Bradley was referred to a child psychiatrist. The psychiatrist's initial response was to address Bradley's substance abuse. Bradley was told he would not be a suitable candidate for any psychiatric medication trials unless he was able gradually to cut down on his use of marijuana and alcohol. It was at that time that Bradley's parents and I went to the school to also address how his failing grades and poor school attendance could be related to possible learning disabilities or neuropsychological deficits. The family had mentioned the idea of residential treatment because they felt that they were unable to do anything to influence Bradley's behavior for the better.

I conferred with Bradley's psychiatrist and let him know that referral to a neuropsychologist would aid in making the case for intervention based on actual data about Bradley's intellectual functioning, attention, memory, language, motor skills, academic achievement, and emotional functioning. Both the psychiatrist and I felt that Bradley's emotional difficulties were in part also interfering with his capacity to both attend school and take in information. I worked with Bradley for about a month prior to his first visit to the neuropsychologist. Bradley was not convinced that giving up marijuana and alcohol would aid him in attending to his schoolwork, but he agreed to stop using for 6 weeks in order to complete the testing. This was progress, and I almost wanted to believe that Bradley trusted me just a little bit. I also kept in the back of my mind how he felt I was the only one who could persuade his parents to let him get his driver's license.

Results of Bradley's neuropsychological evaluation revealed that Bradley's neurocognitive profile was consistent with a nonverbal learning disability (NVLD) and a co-occurring attention-deficit/ hyperactivity disorder—combined type. Based on his dysphoric and anxious mood, Bradley was self-medicating with drugs and alcohol to numb his feelings of failure both at school and with his peers. Bradley does not sort out information well nor is he able to capture the "big picture," all consistent with the nonverbal learning disorder. His weaker perceptual reasoning and visual spatial integration difficulties along with major problems with social cueing behaviors and poor interpersonal relationships mirrored the nonverbal learning disorder profile.

As Bradley's therapist, I made a clinical intervention by using the neuropsychological test data in the following way: I explained to Bradley's parents about the major learning difficulties that he was experiencing, based on information gained from the neuropsychological evaluation. His parents were much more sympathetic given that these learning issues were major factors that interfered with Bradley's capacity to learn in school and navigate reasonable social relationships. Bradley was also made aware of how his attempts to self-medicate and fit into a peer group had not served him well. He and the child psychiatrist were able to negotiate a medication regime that reduced Bradley's ADHD symptoms and targeted his clinical depression and anxiety, which in turn addressed issues around Bradley's self-esteem.

The first year of treatment was somewhat productive, although most of the time was spent in efforts to work toward sobriety and avoid any discipline problems in school. Bradley's parents had given an ultimatum to him, therefore the goal of obtaining his driver's permit had been the only reason he initially attempted to attend our twice weekly sessions. He also agreed that he would be allowed use of their car if he tested negatively to weekly drug screens. Bradley and I had sessions together for 2 years and had additional family sessions with both of his parents approximately once or twice a month to address familial concerns. Initially, I was wary of bringing his parents together with their son, but at his request we met with his parents to discuss extending his curfew after he had demonstrated 6 months without any form of school suspension.

Bradley's anger seemed to subside markedly, according to his parents. He had been started on Wellbutrin by his psychiatrist to address his attentional difficulties. Although Bradley occasionally admitted to drinking on the weekends, this was much less frequent than in previous years. He began to show interest in one of the young women in his homeroom and spent time with her and her friends on weekends and after school. He spoke about the verbal fights that occurred between them. Most of them centered around small misunderstandings with her group of friends. Bradley could not understand how his perception of her "flirting" with other young men was not usually accurate. I helped him with these concerns, but mostly listened to his confusion and overreactions, which at times resulted in my asking him to lower his voice in the office. At one point he told me that having a girlfriend helped him because she studied and wanted to go to college, whereas, at other times he wanted to break up with her after his jealous outbursts. His grades also seemed to improve slightly and he proudly showed me his report card and expressed interest in finding a way to be able to design cars. I encouraged him to speak to his guidance counselor about looking at different programs and discussing what kind of grades he would need to enter an engineering program. His mother phoned me the next week in disbelief after the guidance counselor phoned her with a different kind of report on Bradley.

I see myself as an emotional global positioning system (when I think of how this type of therapy helped Bradley). His parents became much more understanding of his learning challenges, and, at my urging, they hired a tutor to aid Bradley in organizing himself. They also were able to recognize how much of Bradley's anger was in response to their focus on his sister and lack of attention to his learning needs. Bradley was now outgrowing the label of "underachiever" and finding his parents much more willing to see his academic struggles as part of his learning style and not strictly "misbehavior."

I also found myself wondering how Bradley's unanswered questions about his adoption and his birth parents also raised havoc with his image of himself. During most of our later sessions he would bring up the topic of adoption and then become angry at me for asking him questions. He was very scared about being "attached" to me, while at the same time, he was developing a much better relationship with his parents. I knew that after he started looking at colleges at the end of his junior year, the thought of leaving his parents continued to stir up painful doubts about whether he would be able to actually live away from home. I recommended several college programs that specialized in services for students with learning challenges. I wrote a letter to request special accommodations for his learning needs. I also enclosed his neuropsychological testing with his permission, which nicely outlined practical suggestions for these accommodations. Bradley's girlfriend also was looking for these types of programs and at the time we ended our treatment relationship, both of them had settled on a school fairly close to home with dormitory provisions. Bradley was spending his summer working at a camp as a counselor for children with developmental disabilities, 2 hours away from his home. He promised to e-mail me and said he wanted to stay in touch. I received one e-mail after he had been at camp for 2 months and he promised to contact me before he left for college, but I never heard from him.

Last week, I received a phone call from his mother late one evening, after having been out of touch with Bradley for close to a year. Her lengthy message detailed how Bradley had phoned her and wanted to come back to see me during his summer break and that he would be phoning me to make an appointment. She also spoke about how he was majoring in psychology and wanted my ideas about internships for next summer.

Case Example: Heather B.

This vignette is a snapshot of the psychological complexity found in the lives of many teenagers following their discharge from a short-term stay at an inpatient psychiatric facility for depression and inability to function. Heather's refusal to attend school had been nearly impossible to manage prior to the hospitalization, despite heroic clinical efforts on Heather's behalf. Heather's discharge plan demonstrates the lack of careful aftercare planning, which overlooked an intervention and plan for her return to school. Hospital-based clinicians followed the short-stay mandate set by Heather's managed care company. The outpatient clinician was given the work of setting up external structures for Heather and her family. This initially seemed like an impossible task, given the chronicity and severity of her physical symptoms, parental divorce, mother's illness, and the dynamic between the family and the current school district.

Reason for Referral

Heather B. was a 13-year-old Caucasian female referred to my practice for psychotherapy following her brief hospitalization after refusing to attend school and her lack of willingness to participate in any form of outpatient treatment. The recommendation by her parents, school officials, and also the hospital staff following discharge from the psychiatric floor of a general hospital in her suburban town, was participation in psychotherapy at least 2 times per week. Initially, I felt Heather should have had a committee on special education (CSE) meeting set up prior to her discharge given the recalcitrant nature of her school refusal. I also clearly conveyed my thoughts concerning the discharge plan when speaking with her parents during my first visit with them. My expertise with situations such as these is extensive and allows me to make more realistic and less idealized plans for this type of situation. It was clear during the course of the interview that Heather's parents wanted her home, rather than in a therapeutic boarding school. I then proceeded to gather information that would aid the family with formulating the best possible intervention.

Heather is the middle child of a sibship of four. She is the oldest girl and has one older brother and two younger sisters. Heather's parents, Mr. and Mrs. B., are in the process of a divorce and have been embroiled in marital conflict since Heather was 4 years old. Heather's father is a successful real estate developer in the metropolitan Boston area and her mother is an audiologist practicing out of the family home. Heather's mother has suffered with a mild form of multiple sclerosis since Heather was 5 years old and has had bouts of illness, which somewhat incapacitate her functioning. Her private practice has been limited to 4 days per week and her hours begin around noon, mostly, she states, because of Heather's refusal to attend school. Mr. B. remains in the family home despite a legal separation agreement. This is because he is concerned about Heather's refusal to attend school unless he actively pries her from her bed and insists that she be ready, so he can transport her to school before he leaves for work. Heather mostly reports feeling quite dizzy and lightheaded following the intensive family intervention designed to escort her to her first class. She then pleads with her parents to allow her "one more hour of sleep" to assure herself that she does not "faint." When Heather was $4^1/2$ years old, she witnessed an episode in which her mother passed out in a movie theater prior to the time when her mother was diagnosed with multiple sclerosis. Heather's school attendance was fairly good until fifth grade. At that time Heather's oldest brother was picked up by the local police for defacing public property. Parental attention was shifted to her 15-year-old brother and her parents spent enormous amounts of time and money both in family therapy and in lawyers' offices trying to prevent him from future arrests. By the end of fifth grade, Heather had missed 23 days of school and her teacher had passed on concerns to her new sixth-grade teacher.

Prior to entering twice-a-week intensive psychodynamic psychotherapy, Heather had been seen by numerous mental health professionals in the Boston area all of which preceded the family's move to the New York area. The family had moved several times because of the career aspirations of both parents, and Heather had been in four different schools by the time she was 10 years old.

Developmental History

Heather was reported to be a healthy second child of what was noted by Mrs. B. to be a "reasonably decent marriage." Both parents had finished their graduate education and very much wanted a second child. Mr. B. reports that prior to Mrs. B.'s pregnancy with Heather, the couple had made the decision to abort a second pregnancy following Mrs. B.'s disclosure of an affair she had been having with Mr. B.'s best friend. Mr. B. had been away for 6 months on business in the Middle East and the couple had little contact because of the security and top secret nature of the project, which involved Mr. B.'s constant attention. It was during this time that Mrs. B. found out about her second pregnancy and upon Mr. B.'s return, the couple entered marital therapy to address the multiple factors that were impacting their lives. The 6-month marital treatment concluded shortly after the couple announced Mrs. B.'s third pregnancy with Heather. The B. family began to happily plan for Heather's arrival and seemed to celebrate their "newly found love" for each other.

Mrs. B. reports an uneventful and healthy pregnancy with Heather. She notes that Heather met all of her developmental milestones within normal limits with the exception of some nocturnal enuresis and encopresis that persisted until Heather was in the second grade. Heather's pediatrician sent the family to a behavioral therapist for 5 years, and with the help of a medication for the enuresis, the problem seemed to subside by the time Heather was in third grade.

Heather started in a local nursery school for a half day of school when she was 4 years old. She was noted to be quite shy and did not easily interact with the other children in the class. Teacher comments at the end of the year noted the teacher's observations and concerns about Heather's isolative behavior and notably her exceptional intellectual capacity. Following her year of full-day kindergarten, the family moved to another school district fairly far from the family home. She began her first-grade year and it was noted to be academically uneventful with the exception of teacher comments about the overly anxious behavior she displayed with her other classmates during recess and her shyness during class discussions. The B. family made plans to move halfway through Heather's second-grade year, this time due to her mother's desire to be close to her parents. Heather was taken from the school she was in for a year and a half and placed in a small private school near their new home. She finished out the second-grade year, but it was noted by her father that toward the end of the year she began to report small stomach upsets prior to and during school. The stomach upsets continued through Heather's third- and fourth-grade years, though school attendance was mostly good with the exception of a problem with chronic tardiness. Her mother explained that this was somewhat a problem due to her own illness, but also said that Heather had a "hard time with mornings."

By the time Heather reached my office, she was a quarter of the way through the first semester of seventh grade. I reviewed Heather's school records and had discussed with the family how the recommendation for outpatient psychotherapy had followed what was a very brief hospitalization. Upon her discharge from the psychiatric hospital, no plan had been put in place either for her reentry to school, nor was there any mention of the possibility of attending a therapeutic boarding school. It was at this point that I asked for any prior psychometric testing due to the fact that I was stymied as to what could be done next for this young woman.

Treatment Course

Heather entered twice-a-week intensive psychodynamic psychotherapy following her brief hospitalization after refusing to attend school. Prior to the hospitalization, Heather refused outpatient therapy and had taken to her bed. The myriad of medical examinations had left both family and the physicians stymied. Despite what sounded like realistic physical complaints, none of the diagnostic tests revealed any valid medical condition. If Heather did not have a headache, her stomach was always upset. The family was unable to work out a plan that enabled her to attend school for more than 2 days in a row.

After reviewing the initial psychiatric evaluation, I determined that Heather might benefit from an integrated neuropsychological evaluation to rule out any other medical or psychiatric conditions that may be causing her difficulties. The neuropsychological evaluation would serve the twofold purpose of both evaluating underlying learning problems and also outlining clearly the emotional impediments, which could then be presented to the school district in the form of recommendations if a higher level of care were to be needed. I knew that Heather's case might be a clear-cut case for residential placement. It was also a matter that might require legal involvement due to the current state-funding cutbacks. This was another reason to obtain full neuropsychological testing. Hard evidence such as test reports fare much better when combined with clinical data and academic records, as a means of presenting solid evidence on which to base school placement decisions. The results of the neuropsychological evaluation yielded fruitful results that were helpful in approaching Heather and informing the family of how easy it would be to see Heather as a "bright kid who was just being stubborn." Heather's superior use of language skills led both her parents and teachers to believe that she was "just faking" and could get out of bed whenever she wanted to and get to school. Other indicators from the neuropsychological evaluation demonstrated that although Heather appeared to be capable of talking about reasons she could not readily attend school, there were other indicators that demonstrated a more average ability level, which may or may not be a result of emotional interference. The testing also demonstrated Heather's major deficits, which may in part be based on severe anxiety and inefficient cognitive capacity when it came to processing visual and verbal social cues. The tasks that entail planning, visual organization, and temporal sequencing increase in difficulty for most students upon entrance to middle school. Heather was not able to meet the academic expectations that her family set for her, and, despite missing 23 school days at the end of fifth grade, everyone kept "hoping" she would turn things around and "get back on track."

The personality portion of the integrated neuropsychological evaluation also brought forth important points that confirmed my hypothesis about Heather's physical symptoms. Heather experiences her anxiety and dysphoria as physical symptoms. The personality testing also indicated that when Heather becomes stressed or emotionally overwhelmed, the internal distress is somaticized. The defenses of denial, avoidance, and repression are used to defend against negative mood states. Furthermore, Heather outwardly responds with annoyance and a nonchalant attitude in an effort to mask the anxiety in social situations. This gave me a key into reasons the family and the school were reticent to look for any other solution, other than to forcefully pry Heather out of her bed on weekday mornings.

Heather was certainly not an easy customer when it came to setting up a therapeutic relationship. I initially did not think she would ever make it to my office yet her parents were quite clear with her about the matter. The only way for her to stay out of the hospital would be to attend and participate in outpatient therapy twice a week. The mainstay of psychodynamic psychotherapy is the relationship. Heather was not about to enter into this without checking me out first. It was also important that despite my behavioral interventions with her parents, my work with Heather centered around getting to know her. Although I did feel her school attendance was the ultimate goal, the treatment plan for psychotherapy was focused on developing a relationship and finding out what Heather wanted for her life. Heather was clear with me about how "bad" she felt about not being able to attend school. I reviewed the results of the neuropsychological testing with her and her parents in order to frame Heather's symptom picture as aiding her in surviving an emotionally painful situation within her family. This was a hard pill for them to swallow. The idea that Heather was "really medically ill" became quite useful as a clear directive for her parents when other aspects of their lives, including a muddy divorce, were still confused, and/or in an upheaval. Heather began to talk about how her worry and fear "came from her stomach" and also how much of what she was feeling could not be shared with her family. The brunt of conversations also revolved around Heather's constant feelings of sadness and despair. She felt that none of this would ever get better. After a month of hearing about Heather's extreme anxiety and feelings of worthlessness, I began to think that perhaps the medication recommendation, prescribed when she was in the hospital, was not incorrect. Heather had refused to take it and her parents did not insist.

Referral to a child psychiatrist was made for a review of her medication. After the child psychiatrist received the results of Heather's neuropsychological testing, he clearly was convinced that the medication intervention given by the hospital was not only necessary, but essential to any form of academic success. Heather had initially refused a trial of an antidepressant that would target her severe anxiety symptoms. It was also more apparent that Heather's parents needed to set firm rules and expectations around school attendance and require that, unless she had a significant fever or debilitating pain, she needed to attend school, or the truant officer would be called. Heather was also told that therapeutic boarding school would be the next step for her academic career if she failed to attend 85% of the school days per academic year. I supported her through what was extreme anger toward her family, yet encouraged her to abide by their guidelines. She was deathly afraid of leaving home and the thought of boarding school terrified her. Heather also regularly became overwhelmed when discussing her parents' impending divorce. After several months of conversation she was able to stay in the office and not request to return home because her head or stomach hurt.

Heather's parents were referred to a divorce mediator and it was recommended that each parent seek individual psychotherapy in order to aid them in better helping their daughter. The course of individual psychoanalytic psychotherapy was started after 3 months of Heather's improved attendance at school. She was able to address how difficult life had been within her household and how painful the frequent moves had been in her life. After Heather's mood improved, she was also seen to better organize her school work and rely on her homework coach, who enabled her to actively improve her grades.

Most school refusal cases are not this clear cut. The myriad of complications usually far outweigh the solutions and many older children and adolescents do end up in therapeutic boarding school placements. Sometimes, the child is fortunate to be removed from the parents' circumstances, especially in the case of chronic substance abuse or severe emotional difficulties in one or both of the parents. Neuropsychological testing becomes an essential part of treatment even if the child or adolescent is able to return to school. Oftentimes the clinician requires a roadmap into the outward manifestation of internal conflicts. Results of the neuropsychological testing serve as this roadmap. It is well worth stating that if any of these teenagers knew how to solve their social and emotional dilemmas, they would. It is more likely that with the aid of a strong clinical team and good therapeutic relationship with a therapist, the adolescent and family can poke their heads above water and begin to swim and make sense out of an endless sea of unanswered questions.

CONCLUSION

Neuropsychological testing plays an important role in the clinical evaluation of many children and adolescents, including, if not especially, some of the most difficult and challenging cases. In order to fully understand and be empathic toward our patients' suffering, one has to take into account data and facts to inform and better aid the process of therapeutic intervention. The relationship formed by the psychoanalyst with her or his patients can only be enhanced by acknowledging the neurobiological workings of the brain that can in part be accessed by the scores generated by an integrated neuropsychological profile. In our case studies, these patients and families, each in their own way, attempted to find solutions to complex and often painful life circumstances. The neuropsychological evaluation aided in providing a more complete roadmap for the patient, clinician, and the families to find the way back to the core of the problem. Once identified, the intellectual and emotional deficits revealed in the test data could be used as signposts to guide not only academic, but important clinical interventions as well.

We live in a world in which the neuropsychological evaluation may not be readily available to those who need it most. Just as psychoanalysts find themselves in a world where the thorough nature of an analysis is afforded to the very socially fortunate, the neuropsychologist exists in that very same world. Practitioners in both worlds must creatively strive to modify and make available these interventions to more than just a chosen few.

We hope that health insurance reform will make these services more affordable and available to a wider sector of the population. Meanwhile, psychoanalytically oriented psychotherapists, neuropsychologists, and other mental health providers can maintain our voices to advocate for the care we provide, adjust our practices to be more inclusive, and continue to offer a more reflective and inward search to individuals entrusted to our care.

REFERENCES

Bellak, L., & Marsh, H. (1997). The use of ego function assessment for the study of ADHD in adults. *Psychiatric Annals, 27*(8), 563–571.

Freud, S. (1895). Studies on hysteria. *Standard edition* (vol. 2). London: Hogarth Press.

Freud, S. (1913). Totem and taboo. *Standard edition* (vol. 13). London: Hogarth Press.

Garber, B. (1988). The emotional implications of learning disabilities. *Annual of Psychoanalysis, 16,* 111–128.

Giffin, M. (1968). The role of child psychiatry in learning disabilities. *Progress in learning disabilities* (Vol. 1, pp. 62–82). New York: Grune and Stratton.

Kalb, C. (2006). Biology of the mind (interview with Eric Kandel). *Bulletin with Newsweek, 147*(13), 47.

Kandel, E. R. (2005). *Psychiatry, psychoanalysis and the new biology of mind.* Washington, DC: American Psychiatric Press.

Marcus, E. R. (2002). Organic mental syndromes. In E. Marcus (Ed.), *Psychosis and near psychosis, ego function, symbol structure, treatment* (2nd rev. ed., pp. 203–219). Madison, CT: International Universities Press.

Migden, S. (1998). Dyslexia and self control, an ego psychoanalytic perspective. *Psychoanalytic Study of the Child, 53,* 282–299.

Rothstein, A. (1998). Neuropsychological dysfunction and psychological conflict. *Psychoanalytic Quarterly, 67,* 218–238.

Solms, M. (1995). New findings on the neurological organization of dreaming: Implications for psychoanalysis. *Psychoanalytic Quarterly, 64,* 43–67.

Solms, M. (2004, May). Freud returns. *Scientific American,* pp. 82–89.

6 Neuropsychology and Child Psychiatry

LYNN GRUSH, ELLEN B. BRAATEN, AND BRIAN WILLOUGHBY

Pediatric neuropsychology and child psychiatry have much in common. Evolving from adult clinical disciplines, both bring a developmental perspective to the understanding of the relationship between brain activity and behavior. Over the past 20 years, both disciplines have seen the diagnosis and treatment of behavioral disorders shift from a reliance on theoretical models to a more evidence-based approach. Recent advances in related fields such as genetics and functional neuroimaging have further enriched both fields' work, as exemplified by current understanding of reading disorders.

Child psychiatrists and pediatric neuropsychologists are frequently called upon to collaborate. Good communication increases the effectiveness of the care that both provide. The psychiatrist's comprehensive knowledge of the patient and his or her family, often acquired over time, can assist the neuropsychologist to rapidly develop a nuanced picture of the child. A well-formulated referral question aids the neuropsychologist in developing hypotheses to be tested. The psychiatrist's and neuropsychologist's mutual understanding of normal development, developmental psychopathology, and comorbid conditions is thus united in the effort to reach an accurate diagnosis and provide effective treatment recommendations.

Effective clinical collaboration is to some extent predicated on the clinician's education. Child psychiatry trainees are not expected to learn how to perform psychological test batteries, but do need to understand the principles of neuropsychological testing. Similarly, neuropsychology trainees do not prescribe medications, but do need to understand the full range of treatment options available to the patients that they evaluate. Psychiatry trainees value explicit instruction in the evaluation and interpretation of testing reports, whereas neuropsychology trainees value instruction in psychopharmacology and psychotherapy. Training programs that encourage coteaching by child psychiatrists and neuropsychologists foster the development of collaborative and interpretive skills.

A child psychiatrist may be called on to translate neuropsychological findings for parents, educators, and other clinicians. The language and terminology used in assessments and educational meetings can sometimes create a barrier to understanding and communication. For many parents, a visit to a child psychiatrist is an entry point for obtaining a second opinion regarding their child's school performance. Parents may be concerned about the adequacy and validity of psychological testing performed in the school setting. A knowledgeable child psychiatrist can do much to allay or confirm an anxious parent's fears. Much time and expense can be spared if the child psychiatrist is able to evaluate the quality of testing. On the other hand, when faced with inadequate testing, the psychiatrist can advocate for further evaluation to clarify diagnosis.

In the sections that follow, we will describe the domains typically assessed as part of a neuropsychological evaluation. The most frequently used measures within each domain, along with guidance on how scores in each domain may help to inform diagnostic impressions will be included. The typical domains assessed in a neuropsychological evaluation are general intelligence, memory/learning, language function, attention, motor function, visual–motor function, higher-order planning, and academic achievement (Luciana, 2003). Overall, the neuropsychological evaluation appreciates the need for broad-based assessment instruments (Bengtson & Boll, 2001). The use of a broad spectrum of tests is the usual strategy that is employed (Fletcher & Taylor, 1997).

A thorough neuropsychological evaluation includes either a general clinical interview or a structured diagnostic interview such as the Schedule for Affective Disorders and Schizophrenia for School-Age Children (KSADS; Ambrosini, 2000). Family and developmental history should be reviewed. Whether the child is interviewed alone will vary with age; however, even young children can provide valuable information if the interviewer tailors the interview to the child's developmental level (Kamphaus & Frick, 1996). During the course of the evaluation, the evaluator will be making careful behavioral observations and gauging whether the test results are valid, based on the child's attentional and behavioral presentation.

INTELLECTUAL FUNCTIONING

The evaluation of intellectual functioning is a critical part of almost all neuropsychological evaluations. Intellectual functioning is a necessary component for identifying disorders such as mental retardation and learning disabilities, but it may also contribute to, or be affected by, a wide variety of behavioral and emotional problems. The most common measures of intellectual functioning include the following:

Wechsler Preschool and Primary Scale of Intelligence, Third Edition (*WPPSI-III*; Wechsler, 2002), a test battery that can be used with children ages 2.6 to 7.3 years.

Wechsler Intelligence Scale for Children, Fourth Edition (*WISC-IV*; Wechsler, 2003), a test battery for children ages 6–16 years.

Differential Abilities Scale, Second Edition (*DAS-II*, Elliot, 2006), a test battery used for children ages 2.6–17 years.

Kaufman Assessment Battery for Children (Kaufman & Kaufman, 2004), used for children ages 3–18 years.

Stanford Binet (Roid, 2003), used for children and adults ages 2 through 85+ years.

All of the above-mentioned tests are individually administered and yield an intelligence (IQ) score, for which the average score is 100 and the standard deviation is 15. Each test battery measures different global constructs such as *Verbal Abilities* (e.g., vocabulary, knowledge of general information), *Nonverbal Reasoning or Spatial Abilities* (e.g., solving matrices, puzzles, visual-spatial reasoning), *Working Memory* (e.g., ability to hold information in one's mind while performing a task or developing an idea), and *Processing Speed* (e.g., the ability to quickly complete rote tasks).

Assessment of intellectual functioning in very young children requires a specialized type of assessment instrument. Unlike the above mentioned intelligence tests that emphasize language and abstract reasoning abilities, these tests emphasize sensorimotor skills and social skills. These tests are useful in determining a young child's current level of functioning, but are not very predictive of future intellectual potential. The most popular instruments include the:

Bayley Scales of Infant Development (Bayley, 2005), which assesses children from 2–42 months of age.

Mullen Scales of Early Learning (Mullen, 1995), which assesses children from 0–68 months of age.

Scores reflected in the intellectual functioning section of the report may provide initial clues about the child's diagnosis. One of the first aspects to consider is whether there is variability between factor scores, such as a significant discrepancy between a child's verbal and nonverbal/perceptual abilities. If verbal abilities are significantly below nonverbal skills, it could be a possible indication of language concerns. Conversely, if nonverbal abilities are significantly below verbal abilities, it could be an indication of a nonverbal learning disability. In either of these cases, the information gained from other tests (such as those mentioned below) would help to prove or disprove the initial hypothesis.

ACADEMIC FUNCTIONING

The academic achievement section of a report details information regarding a child's ability in core academic areas, such as reading, writing, and mathematics (Katz & Slomka, 1990). The most common tests of academic functioning include the *Weschler Individual Achievement Test—Second Edition* (WIAT-II; Wechsler, 2001), *Wide Range Achievement Test—Fourth Edition* (WRAT-4; Wilkinson & Robertson, 2006), and *Woodcock Johnson Tests of Achievement—Third Edition* (WJ-III; Woodcock, McGrew, & Mather, 2001). Within the reading domain, common areas of assessment include single word reading, nonword decoding, reading speed (fluency), reading accuracy, and comprehension. Prereading skills, such as identifying letters and sounds, may be assessed in the very young child. Writing is typically assessed by having a child write sentences, paragraphs, or short essays. These writing samples are then judged for adequate grammar, spelling, punctuation, and story ideas. Young children may simply be required to write letters or letter-sound combinations. Areas that are typically assessed in mathematics include computation math (i.e., paper-and-pencil math problems), word problems, and math fluency (e.g., speed and accuracy of completing math problems).

A child's performance on academic domains is important in determining whether a child meets criteria for a specific learning disability. That is, if achievement in a particular area is significantly discrepant with a child's intellectual functioning, a learning disability may be present. In a reading disorder, performance on various measures of reading will be below aptitude-based expectations. The same is true for a mathematics disorder or a disorder of written expression. A learning disability can also be diagnosed if a child is performing below grade-based expectations in a specific academic area. In some cases, academic performance may also inform other diagnoses. For instance, if math problems are coupled with a verbal-performance split, as well as additional visual motor concerns and social pragmatic issues, a diagnosis of a nonverbal learning disability may be considered. In other cases, academic fluency issues (i.e., reduced speed and accuracy under timed conditions) may be a concern for children with depression or ADHD.

LANGUAGE FUNCTIONING

Language functioning is typically evaluated as part of a comprehensive neuropsychological evaluation. If significant concerns are observed in this domain, a more comprehensive speech and language evaluation will often be recommended. The areas of language that are most commonly assessed include receptive language (i.e., how much a child understands), expressive language (i.e., how well a child can communicate), and pragmatic language (i.e., social comprehension and use of language), as well as language at the single word level (e.g., identifying sounds within words). Receptive language is typically assessed by having the examiner read words or sentences aloud and then asking the child to carry out an action or identify a picture that best portrays the meaning of the word or sentence. Commonly used receptive language tests include the *Peabody Picture Vocabulary Test* (*PPVT-4*, Dunn & Dunn, 1997) and the receptive language subtests of the *Clinical Evaluation of Language Functioning* (*CELF-4*; Semel, Wiig, & Secord, 2003). Expressive language is typically assessed by having the child name pictures, define words, or explain how to perform an action. Expressive language tests may include the *Expressive Vocabulary Test* (*EVT2*; Williams, 1997), the *Expressive One-Word Picture Vocabulary Test, Revised* (*EOWPVT-R*; Brownell, 2000), the expressive language subtests of the CELF-4, and the Oral Expression subtests of the WIAT-II. The verbal subtests of the WISC-IV are also used to assess expressive language. Assessing pragmatic language can be challenging as there are few standardized measures, with the most common test being the *Test of Pragmatic Language* (*TOPL-2*; Phelps-Terasaki & Phelps-Gunn, 2007). If phonological processing is an area that needs to be more specifically assessed, which is a question often raised when considering reading disorders, common measures include the *Comprehensive Test of Phonological Processing* (*CTOPP*; Wagner, Torgesen, & Rashotte, 1999) *and Lindamood Auditory Conceptualization Test, Third Edition* (*LAC-3*; Lindamood & Lindamood, 2004). These tests require children to blend sounds, rhyme words, and identify sounds and syllables within words.

Diagnostically speaking, a child's performance on language subtests will indicate whether or not a child meets criteria for a language disorder. An expressive language disorder is indicated when expressive language skills are suboptimal but receptive skills are intact. A mixed receptive-expressive language disorder indicates that both receptive and expressive skills are impaired. When reading problems are coupled with difficulties at the single word level (i.e., suboptimal phonological skills), dyslexia may be diagnosed. There is not a specific diagnosis for pragmatic language difficulties, although pragmatic language problems are commonly found in children with NVLD and autism spectrum disorders.

MOTOR, VISUAL MOTOR, AND VISUAL CONSTRUCTION FUNCTIONING

Neuropsychological evaluations typically include at least a screening of a child's motor skills, as well as a screening of how well a child can integrate visual information with motor output (also referred to as visual–motor skills). During the course of the evaluation, both fine and gross motor skills are assessed. Gross motor skills are commonly assessed via behavioral observations, such as watching the child walk or sit, whereas fine motor skills can be evaluated in a more standardized way, such as manipulating small objects under timed conditions. Common tests include the *Grooved Pegboard* (Trites, 1977) and *Purdue Pegboard* (Tiffin, 1968). Neuropsychologists also commonly evaluate how well children integrate both visual and motor abilities, such as copying drawings or putting together pieces of a puzzle. The most common visual–motor tasks include the *Developmental Test of Visual Motor Integration* (*VMI;* Beery, Buktencia, & Beery, 2005), *Bender Visual Motor Gestalt Test* (Bender, 2003), *Hooper Visual Organization Test* (Hooper, 1958), and *Rey Osterrieth Complex Figure* (*ROCF;* Rey, 1941).

Performance in the motor or visual–motor domains may inform diagnostic impressions. Children with NVLD, for instance, typically have marked difficulty with both motor and visual construction skills. Additionally, children with a history of delayed motor milestones (e.g., sitting unsupported, crawling, walking) with current motor control difficulties may meet criteria for a developmental coordination disorder. Visual–motor weaknesses are commonly observed in children with attention-deficit/hyperactivity disorder (ADHD) and executive function weaknesses. For instance, children with ADHD may have difficulty organizing their approach to the drawing of the Rey figure, which can affect their overall performance on the task.

MEMORY FUNCTIONING

The assessment of memory skills may be approached in several different ways. Memory can be parsed into domains of verbal memory (memory for verbally based information), visual memory (memory for visually based information), and working memory (holding information in one's mind while performing a task or developing an idea). Within the verbal and visual memory domains, short-term memory (memory immediately following presentation of the information) and long-term memory (memory following a delay) are commonly assessed. One of the most commonly used assessments of visual and verbal memory (both short and long term) is the *Wide Range Assessment of Memory and Learning,*

Second Edition (WRAML2; Sheslow & Adams, 2003). Other tests of learning and memory include the *Children's Auditory Verbal Learning Test (CAVLT*; Talley, 1990) and *California Test of Verbal Learning (CVLT-C*; Delis, Kramer, Kaplan, & Ober, 2000). On these latter tests, the child is asked to recall a list of words that is presented repeatedly over five learning trials. Memory for the list is tested after each presentation; with interference, cued recall, and long delay conditions. Working memory tests are typically included as part of an intelligence test battery, such as the *WISC-IV* or *DAS-II*.

Performance on memory tests may provide insight into a child's learning style and may inform recommendations for school accommodations, such as supplementing verbally based material with visual aides. In fact, memory issues such as problems encoding or retrieving information, may be underlying a child's learning disorder. For instance, if a young child has poor auditory memory recall, he or she may not remember lessons or steps to complete addition and subtraction problems. Thus, their performance in math may falter. Significant memory issues may also indicate a broader neurologically based deficit, requiring follow-up from a neurologist.

EXECUTIVE FUNCTIONING

Executive functioning is a broad term that encompasses various abilities, including attention, planning, organization, transitioning from one activity to another, self-monitoring, and inhibition of impulses. There are a variety of tests specifically designed to broadly measure executive functioning skills, as well as measures targeting specific aspects of executive functioning. For instance, a commonly used standardized measure of attention is the *Conners' Continuous Performance Test (CPT-II*; Conners, 1994). On this test a child is presented with computerized visual cues and asked to respond as quickly and accurately as possible. A child's performance is then compared to both nonclinical and clinical ADHD samples to determine the "best match." Examiners may also use the ROCF (Rey, 1941), wherein children are asked to copy a complicated design. This test provides qualitative insight into the ways children organize information and how they approach complicated tasks. It is also common for parents and teachers to provide feedback to the examiner about attention and executive functioning skills via paper-and-pencil report. One common rating scale is the *Behavior Rating Inventory of Executive Functioning* (*BRIEF*; Gioia, Isquith, Guy, & Kenworthy, 2000), which consists of items assessing domains such as set-shifting, planning, organizing, and emotional control.

BEHAVIORAL AND EMOTIONAL FUNCTIONING

There are a wide variety of checklists and rating scales that can be used in the course of a pediatric neuropsychological evaluation. Some of the more commonly used instruments include the Child Behavior Checklist (Achenbach & Rescorla, 2001), the Personality Inventory for Children (Wirt, Lachar, Klinedinst, Seat, & Broen, 2001), and the Behavior Assessment System for Children (BASC-2; Reynolds & Kamphaus, 2004). Some rating scales have been developed for use in particular populations, such as the Conners Parent Rating Scale-Revised (Conners, Sitarenios, Parker, & Epstein, 1998), which is used in assessing the possibility of ADHD. These rating scales can help the evaluator judge the child's behavior against a normative sample and rating scales that are completed by different informants can help the evaluator get a better sense of the child's behavior in various settings. Studies have shown these instruments are valuable tools for clinicians and researchers (Frick & Kamphaus, 2001).

In addition to the above mentioned measures, projective tests can be used as a way to measure psychological functioning. Projective tests allow a child to project his or her thoughts, defenses, and impulses onto a neutral stimulus. For example, on the Rorschach test, the child is asked what he or she sees in each of ten inkblots. The most common scoring system evaluates the characteristics of the child's response, such as what portion of the blot was used (location), the factors (such as color, shading or form) that the child considered in making a response (determinant), and what he or she saw in the blot (content) (Exner & Weiner, 1995). Other tests, such as the *Thematic Apperception Test* (Murray, 1943), the *Children's Apperception Test* (Bellak & Abrams, 1997), and the *Roberts Apperception Test* (McArthur & Roberts, 1982) provide the child with pictures for which he or she is asked to make up a story. The examiner will look for consistent themes in these stories as a way to gauge the child's inner thoughts and defenses.

TEACHING NEUROPSYCHOLOGY WITHIN
A CHILD PSYCHIATRY TRAINING PROGRAM

A comprehensive understanding of psychological and neuropsychological testing is necessary for child psychiatrists, but often little time is available for its teaching. By virtue of regular clinical instruction and practice, a child psychiatrist quickly learns to perform a thorough and competent psychiatric evaluation of a child. Child psychiatry trainees are not typically given formal instruction in how to evaluate, interpret, and make recommendations based on neuropsychological test results. It thus becomes difficult for trainees to develop, retain, and increase expertise in this area.

At Massachusetts General Hospital, we are piloting a course for child psychiatry fellows on the interpretation and utilization of psychological testing. We take a pragmatic approach, attempting to distill the essentials and teach them in a clinically applicable way. Our course is embedded in the school psychiatry program, which provides fellows with a comprehensive didactic and clinical exposure to the field of school consultation.

Our goal is to demystify psychological and educational testing thereby increasing trainees' feelings of competency early on in their training. We specifically focus on the clinician's understanding and use of the neuropsychological data in ongoing clinical work. We make the assumption that most of the trainees have had little exposure to schools, other than their own educational experience, and minimal prior exposure to pediatric psychological and educational testing.

Trainees are given a copy of *Straight Talk About Psychological Testing for Kids* (Braaten & Felopulos, 2004). This book is written for parents and provides trainees a preview of what the well-informed parent may ask of them. It also provides them with a resource that they can recommend to parents who are looking for more information.

Throughout the course, we emphasize the role of the child psychiatrist as an advocate for his or her patients and highlight the dual responsibility this entails. This is to ensure that children with identified psychiatric disorders are adequately screened for and supported, if they have learning disabilities, and to ensure that the emotional and psychiatric needs of children with diagnosed learning disabilities are not overlooked.

We point out the task of the child psychiatrist to translate and integrate the findings of different disciplines. The language and terminology used in assessments and educational meetings can create barriers to understanding and communication. This can be especially confusing when disciplines have not reached a consensus. It is very helpful for the trainee to know that educators, speech and language therapists, and neuropsychologists do not necessarily agree amongst themselves or across disciplines on the definition of a particular disorder.

Our approach to teaching neuropsychological testing to child psychiatry residents is three-pronged. All sessions are cotaught by a licensed neuropsychologist and a board certified child psychiatrist. Coteaching allows us to model a multidisciplinary approach and a collegial atmosphere where no question is "too basic." As in other areas of medicine, gray areas exist and closely held theories may later be disproved. We ask questions and emphasize material that may be particularly challenging or useful to the child psychiatrist. We point out areas of disagreement as well as consensus.

Our course is composed of:

1. A didactic seminar in which we introduce an approach to the reading and interpreting of tests frequently used in neuropsychological evaluations.
2. An integrative seminar in which we meet in a small group and review topics of interest and/ or controversy.
3. A drop-in supervision during which residents present cases for review.

Didactic Seminar

The didactic seminar is our opportunity to introduce trainees to a sampling of tests used by pediatric neuropsychologists. We describe tests that are commonly used in our local school districts and point out issues of sensitivity and validity. When possible, we demonstrate the actual test materials so that fellows have the opportunity to see them. This makes it much easier for them to remember the tests and also gives fellows a sense of what the testing experience may be like for their patients.

We use a template to describe an approach to reading and interpreting neuropsychological tests. This is our road map for nonneuropsychologists to navigate testing reports. The template includes the follow steps:

1. Orienting to the report:
   a. Date of testing: Is it recent or remote?
   b. Age of child.
   c. Where was the testing performed and who completed the testing?
   d. Background information: Has an adequate history been obtained and considered in the planning of and interpreting of test results?
   e. Is there evidence of a consultative question and hypothesis generation or does the testing seem part of a standard package with little specificity for the clinical or educational concerns?
   f. Is there a narrative describing the child's performance during testing and does that match with your clinical knowledge of the child? If testing was difficult to perform, are the areas of difficulty described adequately?
   g. Are the tests that were used well validated? (Any normed tests, such as those described above would be considered well-validated measures).
   h. Are scores reported with enough details to allow adequate interpretation by a clinician who did not perform the testing?
   i. Is the rationale for the conclusions and impressions clearly elucidated and based on test results?
   j. Are the recommendations clear?
2. Organizing the report data:
   a. We recommend a systematic approach and suggest developing a spreadsheet of the data. We include individual test items as well as summary scores. This is very helpful when measures have been repeated and need to be compared.
   b. A consistent approach aids developing familiarity with tests. Categorizing the data into the areas of cognitive functioning described earlier organizes the data in a meaningful way.
3. Hypothesis testing:
   a. We instruct the fellows to test the hypotheses they have developed, based on their clinical questions. Does the testing refute or confirm their hypothesis? Do the conclusions make sense? Is the information sufficient to answer their question?
4. Formulating and making Recommendations:
   a. Trainees are encouraged to include the neuropsychological data in their biopsychosocial formulation. This creates a useful

case summary, which can then be used clinically in an ongoing way.

b. Recommendations that follow this formulation will thus be similarly coherent and trackable.

Integrative Seminar

The integrative seminar takes place in a small group and gives us the opportunity to provide more in-depth teaching. The first session focuses on reading disorders, where the emphasis is on the evaluation, nosology, and remediation of reading disorders. The second session focuses on the neuropsychology of ADHD and executive function disorders. The third session is devoted to Asperger's disorder and nonverbal learning disabilities. In this last session, we compare and contrast the disorders, explaining commonalities and differences seen through the lens of neuropsychological assessment.

Drop-In Supervision

Drop-in supervision is offered bi-weekly and offers an opportunity to consolidate learning. The child psychiatrist and neuropsychologist consult on cases presented and review recommendations. This group supervision gives fellows an opportunity to see testing from a variety of settings such as school-based, medical center, and private practice evaluation settings. By reviewing each other's cases, residents have the opportunity to evaluate more cases and to act as peer supervisors. Over the course of the year, residents hear about a wide variety of cases.

CONCLUSION

Pediatric neuropsychological evaluations provide child psychiatrists an additional, empirically based lens through which to view and understand a child's development. Research in cognitive development, neurobiology, and brain–behavior relationships has led to the development of instruments that shed light on commonly observed disorders of childhood. Like psychiatry, the field of neuropsychology is rapidly changing; it requires a lifelong approach to understanding neuropsychological data. Effective collaboration between neuropsychologists and child psychiatrists has the potential to improve clinical care and result in more efficient use of health care and educational resources.

REFERENCES

Achenbach, T. M., & Rescorla, L. A. (2001). *Manual for the ASEBA school-age forms and profiles*. Burlington, VT: University of Vermont, Research Center for Children, Youth and Families.

Ambrosini, P. J. (2000). Historical development and present status of the Schedule for Affective Disorders and Schizophrenia for School-Age Children (K-SADS). *Journal of the American Academy of Child and Adolescent Psychiatry, 39,* 49–58.

Bayley, N. (2005) *Bayley scales of infant development* (3rd ed.) San Antonio, TX: Psychological Corporation.

Beery, K. E., Buktencia, N. & Beery, N. A. (2005). *The Beery-Buktencia developmental Test of Visual–Motor Integration* (5th ed.). Minneapolis, MN: NCS Pearson.

Bellak, L., & Abrams, D. M. (1997). *The T.A.T., C.A.T., and S.A.T. in clinical use* (6th ed.). Needham Heights, MA: Allyn and Bacon.

Bender, L. (2003). *Bender Visual-Motor Gestalt Test* (2nd ed.). San Antonio, TX: Psychological Corporation.

Bengtson, M. L, & Boll, T. J. (2001). Neuropsychological assessment of the child. In C. E. Walker & M. C. Roberts (Eds.), *Handbook of clinical child psychology* (3rd ed.). New York: Wiley.

Braaten, E. B., & Felopulos, G. (2004). *Straight talk about psychological testing for kids.* New York: Guilford Press.

Brownell, R. (2000). *Expressive-One Word Picture Vocabulary Test.* Novato, CA: Academic Therapy.

Conners, C. K. (1994). *The Conners Continuous Performance Test.* Toronto, Canada: Multi-Health Systems.

Conners, C. K., Sitarenios, G., Parker, J. D. A., & Epstein, J. N. (1998). The revised Conners Parent Rating Scale (CPRS-R): Factor structure, reliability, and criterion validity. *Journal of Abnormal Child Psychology, 26,* 257–268.

Delis, D. C., Kramer, J. H., Kaplan, E., & Ober, B. A. (2000). *The California Verbal Learning Test* (2ed ed.). San Antonio: Psychological Corporation.

Dunn, L. M., & Dunn, L. M. (1997). *Peabody Picture Vocabulary Test* (3rd ed.). Circle Pines, MN: American Guidance Service.

Elliot, C. D. (2006). *Differential Ability Scales—Second edition (DAS–II) Adminstration and scoring manual.* San Antonio, TX: Psychological Corporation.

Exner, J. E., Jr., & Weiner, I. B. (1995). *The Rorschach: A comprehensive system: Assessment of children and adolescents* (Vol. 3, 2nd ed.). New York: Wiley.

Fletcher, J. M., & Taylor, H. G. (1997). Children with brain injury. In E. J. Mash & L. G. Terdal (Eds.), *Assessment of childhood disorders* (3rd ed., pp. 453–480). New York: Guilford Press.

Frick, P. J., & Kamphaus, R. W. (2001). Standardized rating scales in the assessment of children's behavioral and emotional problems. In C. E. Walker & M. C. Roberts (Eds.), *Handbook of clinical child psychology* (3rd ed.). New York: Wiley.

Gioia, G. A., Isquith, P. K., Guy, S. C., & Kenworthy, L. (2000). *Behavior Rating Inventory of Executive Function: Professional manual.* Lutz, FL: Psychological Assessment.

Hooper, H. E. (1958) *The Hooper Visual Organization Test manual.* Los Angeles, CA: Western Psychological Service.

Kamphaus, R. W., & Frick, P. J. (1996). *Clinical assessment of child and adolescent personality and behavior.* Boston: Allyn and Bacon.

Katz, L. J., & Slomka, G. T. (1990). Achievement testing. In G. Goldstein & M. Hersen (Eds.), *Handbook of psychological assessment* (2nd ed.). New York: Pergamon.

Kaufman, A. S., & Kaufman, N. L. (2004). *Administration and scoring material for the Kaufman Assessment Battery for Children* (2nd ed.). Circle Pines, MN: American Guidance Service.

Lindamood, P. C., & Lindamood, P. (2004). *Lindamood Auditory Conceptualization Test: Examiner's manual.* Austin, TX: Pro-Ed.

Luciana, M. (2003). Computerized assessment of neuropsychological function in children: Clinical and research applications of the Cambridge Neuropsychological Testing Automated Battery (CANTAB). *Journal of Child Psychology and Psychiatry, 44,* 649–663.

McArthur, D. S., & Roberts, G. E. (1982). *Roberts Apperception Test for Children: Manual.* Los Angeles, CA: Western Psychological Services.

Mullen, E. M. (1995). *Mullen Scales of Early Learning* (AGS ed.). Circle Pines, MN: American Guidance Service.

Murray, H. A. (1943). *Thematic Aperception Test manual.* Cambridge, MA: Harvard University Press.

Phelps-Terasaki, D., & Phelps-Gunn, T. (2007). *Test of Pragmatic Language-2.* San Antonio, TX: Psychological Corporation.

Rey, A. (1941). "L'examen psychologique dans les cas d'encephalopathie traumatique." *Archives de Psychologie, 28,* 215–285.

Reynolds, C. R., & Kamphaus, R. W. (2004). *The clinician's guide to the Behavior Assessment System for Children* (2nd ed.). New York: Guilford Press.

Roid, G. H. (2003). *Stanford Binet Intelligence Scale* (5th ed.). Chicago: Riverside.

Semel, E., Wiig, E. H., & Secord, W. A. (2003). *Clinical evaluation of language fundamentals* (CELF-4). San Antonio, TX: Psychological Corp.

Sheslow, D., & Adams, W. (2003). *Wide range assessment of memory and learning* (2nd ed.). Lutz, FL: Psychological Assessment Resources.

Stone, M. H., Jastak, S., & Wilkinson, G. (1995). *Wide Range Achievement Test-3.* Wilmington, DE: Jastak Assessment Systems.

Talley, J.L. (1990). *Children's Auditory Verbal Learning Test.* Odessa, FL: Psychological Assessment Resources.

Tiffin, J. (1968). *The Purdue Pegboard.* Chicago: Research Associates.

Trites, R. L. (1977). *Neuropsychological test manual.* Ottawa, Ontario, Canada: Royal Ottawa Hospital.

Wagner, R. K., Torgesen, J. K., & Rashotte, C. A. (1999). *Comprehensive test of phonological processing* Austin, TX: PRO-ED.

Wechsler, D. (2002). *Wechsler Preschool and Primary Scale of Intelligence* (3rd ed.). San Antonio, TX: Psychological Corporation.

Wechsler, D. (2001). *Wechsler Individual Achivement Scale* (2nd ed.). San Antonio, TX: Psychological Corporation.

Wechsler, D. (2003). *Wechsler Intelligence Scale for Children* (4th ed.). San Antonio, TX: Psychological Corporation.

Wilkinson, G. S., & Robertson, G. J. (2006). *Wide Range Achievement Test* (3rd ed.). Lutz, FL: Psychological Assessment Resources.

Williams, K. T. (1997). *Expressive Vocabulary Test* (2nd ed.). Circle Pines, MN: American Guidance Service.

Wirt, R. D., Lachar, D., Klinedinst, J. E., Seat, P. D., & Broen, W. E. (2001). *Personality Inventory for Children manual* (2nd ed.). Los Angeles: Western Psychological Services.

Woodcock, R. W., McGrew, K. S., & Mather, N. (2001). *Woodcock-Johnson III Test.* Itasca, IL: Riverside Publishing Company.

7

Neuropsychology and Pediatric Medicine

ELLEN B. BRAATEN AND ELLEN O'DONNELL

Pediatric neuropsychologists diagnose the cognitive and behavioral problems of the developing child as related to the child's neurological status. The goal of the pediatric neuropsychological evaluation is to provide an in-depth understanding of a child's functional strengths and weaknesses and to make recommendations for short- and long-term treatment planning. This type of evaluation can be extremely important to the overall well-being and care of a child or adolescent, and this can be particularly true for children experiencing a medical crisis or a chronic disease. In fact, neuropsychologists are increasingly playing an important role in the care of children within pediatric medical settings.

As part of a multidisciplinary team that provides children with integrated care, the neuropsychologist can bring to the team an orientation that combines psychological, cognitive, and medical concerns. For example, we have both been affiliated with the Pediatric Multiple Sclerosis Center at Massachusetts General Hospital. Team members include a pediatric neurologist, clinical psychologist, clinical nurse specialist, educational diagnostician, social worker, as well as a pediatric neuropsychologist. In addressing patients' needs, each member of the team addresses salient features of his or her examination. The pediatric neuropsychologist is in a unique position in that he or she can discuss intellectual ability, determine whether a learning disability or psychiatric illness may be comorbid with the medical issue, determine the neuropsychological sequelae of the medical illness itself, and shed light on possible psychological or psychiatric difficulties the patient might be exhibiting.

There are many factors and various challenges that children with an acute medical crisis or a chronic illness may exhibit or experience. Many of the factors are a result of the illnesses themselves, whereas other factors (such as psychosocial factors) can be the result of missing school because of frequent hospitalizations, difficulties socializing with peers because of illnesses, and problems participating in normal activities, such as sports, because of the medical condition. Neuropsychological testing can be useful for a host of medical conditions and illnesses, but within this chapter we will focus on how neuropsychological testing can be useful for some of the more common pediatric medical conditions.

EARLY DEVELOPMENTAL PROBLEMS

Pediatricians are often the first professionals that parents encounter when they suspect a problem in their child's development. Children vary widely in the age at which they reach developmental milestones, and this variability may be difficult for pediatricians to interpret without more specific data. Furthermore, delays in specific areas of development may be markers of more specific pathologies. Thus, requesting neuropsychological testing of young children who are suspected of having developmental delays is becoming more common. This type of testing is quite useful in answering the following questions:

- Is the child's cognitive development and learning progressing at a normal rate?
- What is the child's cognitive standing relative to his/her peers?
- What are the child's cognitive strengths and weaknesses?
- Is there a specific etiology/diagnosis that can explain the child's pattern of cognitive deficits?
- How can the child's cognitive/academic weaknesses be addressed in a therapeutic or educational setting?

- How can the child utilize his/her strengths to compensate for areas of cognitive weakness?
- How effective is treatment (monitoring functioning over time)?

Although children do not typically receive neuropsychological testing much before the age of $2^{1}/_{2}$ to 3 years, there are a number of measures that can be performed with children that can provide the pediatrician and assessing psychologist with information about the child's development from birth. These include:

Bayley Scales of Infant and Toddler Development –Third Edition (*Bayley-III*; Bayley, 2005). The Bailey can be used to assess children as young as 1 month of age and can be used to assess children up to 42 months of age. Children are assessed in five key developmental domains: cognition, language, social–emotional, motor, and adaptive behavior. Growth scores can be used to chart intervention progress.

Developmental Profile 3 (*DP-3*; Alpern, 2005). The DP-3 can be used to screen for developmental delays in five key areas (physical, adaptive behavior, social–emotional, cognitive, and communication) in children from birth to 12 years of age.

Developmental Assessment of Young Children (*DAYC*; Voress & Maddox, 1998). The DAYC can be used to identify children (ages birth to 5.11 years) with possible delays in cognition, communication, social–emotional development, physical development, and adaptive behavior.

Psychoeducational Profile, Third Edition (*PEP-3*; Schopler, Lansing, Reichler, & Marcus; 2005). The PEP-3 assesses the skills and behaviors of children with autism and communicative disabilities who function between the ages of 6 months to 7 years.

Merrill-Palmer-Revised Scales of Development (*Merrill-Palmer-R*; Roid & Sampers, 2004). The Merrill-Palmer-R was designed to assess cognitive, language, motor, self-help, and social–emotional domains in children ages birth to 6.5 years.

Peabody Developmental Motor Scales, Second Edition (*PDMS-2*; Folio & Fewell, 2000). The PDMS-2 can be used to assess the motor skills of children ages birth to 5 years.

Once the child reaches the age of 3 years, a more comprehensive test battery is typically suggested that includes measures of cognition, pre-academic skills, language, visual motor skills, memory, attention, and executive functions. The goal of the testing is to provide an in-depth understanding of the child's functional strengths and deficits, while providing useful recommendations for short-term and long-term treatment planning.

EPILEPSY

Epilepsy has been found to occur in 1 to 2% of the population (Hynd & Willis, 1988). Children with epilepsy are at great risk for academic and social difficulties (Austin, Huberty, Huster, & Dunn 1998; Fastenau et al., 2004; Mitchell, Chavez, Lee, & Guzman, 1991; Sillanpaa, Jalava, & Kavela, & Shinnar, 1998; Westbrook, Silver, Coupey, & Shinnar, 1991). Pavone et al. (2001) examined the cognitive deficits in children with absence epilepsy and found lower scores on measures of general cognitive functioning and visuospatial skills as compared to controls. Impairment in nonverbal memory was also noted and children whose seizures began at an earlier age had more severe cognitive deficits. Fastenau et al. (2004) found that although academic underachievement is common in pediatric epilepsy, these effects are moderated by family factors. In other words, when children's homes were more organized and supportive, academic achievement was less affected.

Because the neuropsychological effects of epilepsy are well documented, a neuropsychological evaluation is critical in understanding the effect of epilepsy on a child's academic and psychological functioning. In fact, providing regular neuropsychological assessments of a child's neuropsychological, cognitive, and psychosocial functioning is very useful in measuring the long-term effects of chronic seizure disorders and medication. Ideally, the measurement of a child's functioning is done in the context of a multidisciplinary team, which would include a pediatrician, pediatric neurologist, child psychologist, and an educator. Because data has indicated that negative reactions by peers and teachers to the child's behavior can have a negative impact on a child's school attainment (Dreifuss, 1994), collaboration with the school is important. Educating teachers and students about epilepsy may help mitigate some of the negative images that they might hold. The neuropsychologist can be an important source of information since he or she can discuss the particular behaviors that a child might exhibit. For example, a child with absence seizures may appear *spacey*, inattentive, or willfully defiant when in actuality he is experiencing seizure activity. Similarly, the pediatrician and neurologist can be helpful in educating teachers and students about the behavioral changes frequently observed before, during, and after seizures.

In terms of educational interventions, it is crucial that the school be aware of the diagnosis and have a plan of action for working with the child, both medically and academically. Monitoring seizure activity and the effect of medication on a child's performance is important and, thus, educating the teacher on the behaviors that might be observed (lethargy, hyperactivity, sleepiness, confusion, and clumsiness) is key. It is also important that the school develop a plan of action that will be taken in the event the child has a seizure at school. Because children with seizures do not fit a typical neuropsychological profile, there is no "one size fits all" list of recommendations that need to be followed. Instead, the neuropsychological evaluation can be used to develop an individualized comprehensive intervention program for the child. This program should not only address cognitive and academic issues, but also psychosocial stressors that the child may be experiencing. Finally, helping children develop normal peer relationships in the context of a chronic illness is important, and the roles that various members of the treatment team can play in helping peers understand the child's needs and possible unusual behaviors should not be underestimated.

MULTIPLE SCLEROSIS

Multiple sclerosis (MS) is a chronic, most often progressive, demyelinating disease of the central nervous system that is associated with cognitive dysfunction, depression, and psychosocial problems in adults. Over the past 10 years neurologists have increasingly begun to recognize MS in pediatric patients. An estimated 2 to 5% of MS patients experience onset prior to age 16 (Duquette et al., 1987; Ghezzi et al., 1997), and MS has been diagnosed in children as young as 3 years old. Pediatric MS patients tend to be disproportionately female with onset between 8 and 14 years old (Ness et al., 2007). There is an additional group of children and adolescents who experience demyelinating diseases (e.g., acute disseminated encephalomyelitis or ADEM) that have effects on their functioning similar to MS, without meeting full criteria for the disease. Although relatively little is known about the long-term prognosis for these children (see Ness et al., 2007, for a review), we know a fair amount about the likely impact of MS on their functioning at home and in school.

Some of the more obvious symptoms impacting pediatric MS patients include severe fatigue, changes in vision, and motor impairment. Less obvious, but also problematic (especially for children), are the more subtle neuropsychological impairments associated with MS. Slowed processing speed, decreased fine motor skills, problems with organization, problem-solving, and executive functions, and impairments in attention and memory frequently affect academic functioning and daily life for children and adolescents with MS. If these dysfunctions are not addressed, they have the potential to limit cognitive, social, and academic development. A study of 10 pediatric MS patients found that all 10 experienced impairments on at least one test of a standard neuropsychological battery, with most experiencing impairments on multiple tests (Banwell & Anderson, 2005). Another study of 37 children with MS (MacAllister et al., 2005) found that one third had impairments on two or more neuropsychological tests. An interesting finding was that children in both studies more often showed deficits on neuropsychological batteries than on commonly used assessments of intelligence and academic achievement. This is important because it implies that the neuropsychological symptoms of pediatric MS are not likely to be detected on standard assessments (e.g., the Wechsler Scales) used in school-based testing. As a result, children and adolescents with a diagnosis of MS or other demyelinating conditions should be referred for comprehensive neuropsychological testing either in place of or as a supplement to a school assessment.

Although pediatricians, neurologists, and parents might be inclined to wait for a child with a demyelinating disease to show cognitive impairments or a decline in school performance to refer the child for neuropsychological testing, earlier screening is often warranted. The limited longitudinal data on the course of pediatric MS suggests that at least some children will show a continuous decline in cognitive functioning (MacAllister et al., 2005). It is important for these children to have a baseline assessment of cognitive functioning at diagnosis for later comparison. Even for children who do not show obvious cognitive symptoms of MS or a significant decline in functioning, a careful neuro-psychological assessment can identify areas of weaknesses and suggest interventions for home and school. Children and adolescents with MS often benefit from a reduced workload (especially when they experience a flare-up of symptoms), a scribe or access to a word processor to limit fine motor demands, preferential seating, accommodations to maximize attention in school, occupational therapy, and instruction in strategies to maximize retention of newly learned material.

JUVENILE DIABETES

Type 1, insulin-dependent diabetes mellitus (IDDM) is one of the most chronic illnesses of childhood, affecting approximately 1.7 per 1000 children under the age of 19 in the United States with an estimated 13,000 new cases diagnosed each year (Centers for Disease Control, n.d.). Type I diabetes is an autoimmune disease affecting pancreatic beta cells that produce insulin, a hormone essential to the metabolization of glucose, and has associated functional and structural effects on the central nervous system. Children may be at particular risk for negative cognitive sequelae of type 1 diabetes because their increased energy needs make the young brain especially vulnerable to metabolic insult (Taylor & Alden, 1997). Poorly controlled diabetes is characterized by persistent hyperglycemia or elevated blood glucose, and is particularly problematic among adolescents, who frequently struggle with increas-ingly poor control of their diabetes (Helgeson, Siminerio, Escobar, & Becker, 2009; Leonard, Jang, Savik, & Plumbo, 2005). Chronic hyper-glycemia is associated with neuronal loss, slowed nerve conduction, altered neurochemistry, and cerebral atherosclerosis (Northam et al., 1998). Acute hyperglycemia can lead to ketoacidosis and coma. Even when well controlled with insulin treatment, children and youth with diabetes are vulnerable to episodes of hypoglycemia or low blood sugar. Acute hypoglycemia alters cerebral blood flow to the frontal and hippo-campal regions of the brain and is associated with transient reductions in mental efficiency. Evidence from research over the past several decades suggests that repeated episodes of severe hypoglycemia, and even more mild fluctuations in blood glucose that occur over a lifetime of living with type I diabetes, are associated with weaknesses in attention, processing speed, memory, new learning, and executive functions (Holmes, O'Brien, & Greer, 1995; Ryan et al., 1990).

The most common areas of neuropsychological functioning affected in type 1 diabetes seem to be those associated with the left frontal and temporal regions of the brain—memory, attention, processing speed, and new learning, as well as executive functions such as self-monitoring, problem-solving, and organizational abilities (Auer & Siesjo, 1988; Chalmers et al., 1991; Jarjour, Ryan, & Becker, 1995; Northam et al., 1998). A recent meta-analysis of 15 studies found effects of type 1 diabetes on visuospatial abilities, motor speed and writing, sustained attention, reading, and subtle effects on full, verbal, and performance IQ (Naguib, Kulinskaya, Lomax, & Garralda, 2009). A study comparing children with type 1 diabetes with a history of severe hypoglycemia, children with type 1 without a history of severe hypoglycemia, and normal controls found that those with type 1 diabetes and severe hypoglycemia had more neuropsychological deficits, increased incidence of learning difficulties, and needed more special education services than either of the other two groups (Hannonen, Tupola, Ahonen, & Riikonen, 2003). Furthermore, children who had experienced severe hypoglycemia had weaker verbal short-term memory and phonological processing skills than healthy children. Children with diabetes have been found to have poorer school achievement, especially in reading and spelling, and research suggests that boys with type 1 diabetes may be especially likely to experience learning difficulties (Holmes, Dunlap, Chen, & Cornwell, 1992). The negative impact of IDDM on cognitive and neuropsychological functioning seems to increase over time, especially among those children with an early age of onset (less than 5 years old) and it has been suggested that early onset may disrupt verbal skills acquisition (Northam et al., 1998), possibly because of more frequent episodes of severe hypoglycemia.

Although pediatricians, parents, and school personnel may be well aware of the transient effects of hypoglycemia, or low blood sugar, on children's cognitive functioning, they are much less likely to be knowledgeable about the possible chronic and long-term cognitive and neuropsychological effects of the disease. Oftentimes, children and adolescents with diabetes struggle in school and their difficulties are attributed to the stresses of living with the disease and frequent absences from class as a result of visits to the school nurse or for doctors' appointments. As a result, learning disabilities or subtle neuropsychological weaknesses that can affect functioning and academic achievement may be missed. We have also seen problems with processing speed and visual-spatial weaknesses mistakenly attributed to poor vision, secondary to diabetic retinopathy, by school psychologists when no retinopathy exists. In fact, slowed processing speed is one of the most consistent findings among children and youth with type I diabetes and is apparently a central processing deficit that cannot be explained by retinopathy or peripheral neuropathy alone (Northam et al., 1998).

A comprehensive neuropsychological evaluation can be critical to teasing apart the source of subtle impairments in cognition among children and adolescents with diabetes and to informing appropriate interventions. Although there are numerous resources available to parents and schools for developing 504 plans for students with diabetes, which include accommodations for visits to the nurse, checking blood sugar and administering insulin during the school day, and allowing for frequent doctors' visits (e.g., http://www.childrenwithdiabetes.com/504/), there is less available to guide the development of individualized intervention programs for children who experience neuropsychological weaknesses. A pediatric neuropsychologist can draw on his or her expertise in working with children with language processing difficulties, visual-spatial processing weaknesses, and poor executive functioning to help pediatricians, endocrinologists, parents, and schools develop individualized plans for children and adolescents with diabetes. Oftentimes, such plans should include suggestions for helping children and adolescents manage the day-to-day tasks involved in living with diabetes since, in our experience, weaknesses in skills like self-monitoring, planning, and organization can impact a child's ability to successfully negotiate the intensive diabetes management regimens that are currently recommended. Because the Diabetes Control and Complications Trial (DCCT, 1996), the standard of care for type 1 diabetes is an intensive daily schedule of blood sugar checks, insulin administration, and carbohydrate counting. Problems with cognitive function, including weak memory skills, have been found to impact adherence (Holmes et al., 2006) and may be especially problematic when adolescents are expected to take on more of these responsibilities independently.

WHY A NEUROPSYCHOLOGICAL EVALUATION IS NEEDED

In addition to the benefits discussed of having a neuropsychological evaluation completed by a psychologist who is a part of a multidisciplinary team for children affected by illness, there are several reasons why a comprehensive neuropsychological evaluation may be especially critical for children with acute or chronic pediatric conditions. A neuropsychological evaluation is more likely than a school assessment to include a careful screening of possible symptoms of depression, anxiety or behavioral problems that are often associated with epilepsy, MS, diabetes, and other pediatric conditions. A clinical neuropsychologist will also have access to medical and psychosocial information that a school psychologist might not be aware of and that might be impacting both a child's functioning and his or her adherence to recommended treatments. Furthermore, many of the neurocognitive deficits associated with chronic pediatric conditions are subtle. For example, in type 1 diabetes, children have been found to have lower average IQ scores than their healthy peers, but scores that are still within the normal range for their age (Gaudieri, Chen, Greer, & Holmes, 2008). Although not hugely significant, these kinds of subtle weaknesses can be especially problematic for a child who already has to deal with the stress, demands on time, and frequent absences from school that accompany living with a chronic illness, but they may be overlooked as part of a general school evaluation. The subtle weaknesses in executive functioning associated with pediatric MS are much less likely to be captured as part of a school evaluation that will rarely include measures of executive functioning. Even subtle weaknesses can impact a child academically, especially if he is in a competitive or increasingly challenging environment. We have often seen older children who have struggled in school for some time because their cognitive and academic difficulties were overlooked in the context of more pressing medical concerns. When a comprehensive neuropsychological assessment is included as part of a child's medical care, it can identify areas of weakness early and the psychologist can make recommendations not only for school, but also to support a family coping with a child who has developmental delays and acute or chronic illness. The following case examples are drawn from our experience working with both the pediatric MS and pediatric endocrine clinics at Massachusetts General Hospital.

Case Presentation: Juvenile Diabetes

Matthew was a 16-year-old young man referred for a neuropsychological evaluation by his pediatric endocrinologist and his treating psychologist. Matthew's early developmental and medical history were unremarkable, but at age 7 years, he was diagnosed with type 1 insulin-dependent diabetes and liver disease, and subsequently had a liver transplant 4 years later. At the time of the assessment, Matthew had been on insulin-pump therapy for 3 years and was taking antirejection medication daily. Although he consistently took his oral medication, his parents reported that his compliance with management of his diabetes had always been poor and had become worse since he started high school and was increasingly required to be responsible for checking his blood sugar and taking insulin. As a result, he had recently been referred to the pediatric psychologist affiliated with the endocrine clinic for behavioral therapy aimed at improving adherence and control of his diabetes. His psychologist reported that his poor diabetes control was mostly a result of his forgetting to take insulin to cover his frequent meals and snacks. Matthew would reportedly plan to bolus insulin with his pump, but was easily distracted and would frequently fail to follow through on his plan.

In terms of school history, Matthew had reportedly begun having academic difficulty in elementary school. Problems with reading and math had been noted and he was evaluated through his school system for special education services, at his parents' request, when he was in the 6th grade, shortly after his transplant surgery. The results of the school's evaluation indicated that Matthew's intellectual skills were in the average range overall. He showed minor weaknesses on arithmetic skills and tasks assessing alertness to visual detail and spatial reasoning and logic. Some difficulties with organization, attention, and planning were noted in qualitative observations, but the school evaluator reported no significant problems with distractibility. At the time, his parents did not indicate enough symptoms of an attention deficit on a parent rating scale for Matthew to meet criteria for a diagnosis of attention-deficit/hyperactivity disorder (ADHD). Academic testing indicated that Matthew's school achievement was below expected grade level, a fact that was attributed at the time to his having missed a significant amount of school because of his medical problems, and he began receiving additional educational supports.

When he was referred for behavioral therapy, Matthew was in the 11th grade. He and his parents reported to his psychologist that he had continued to struggle in school and his grades were poor. In addition to difficulty remembering the tasks necessary to take care of his diabetes, Matthew reported having difficulty paying attention in his classes, especially in the afternoon. He attributed this to frequently experiencing high blood sugar after lunch. His parents reported that they often had to repeat instructions to Matthew, but that he had never been what they would consider hyperactive. His psychologist suspected that Matthew might have an undiagnosed attention deficit that interfered both with his performance in school and his ability to follow his diabetes care regimen. However, in listening to his history and in consultation with his endocrinologist, there were a number of confounding factors (e.g., effects of chronic and episodic fluctuations in blood sugar on attention and executive functions, possible side effects of antirejection medication, and a significantly disrupted school history) and concerns about starting Matthew on a trial of stimulant medication (because of a possible effect on appetite and blood sugar control) that warranted a referral for a comprehensive neuropsychological evaluation before deciding on treatment.

Matthew was evaluated at the hospital assessment clinic and testing again indicated that he possessed intellectual skills in the average range for his age. However, he scored in the low average range for his age on tests of working memory (the ability to retain and mentally manipulate novel information for short periods of time and for problem solving). His simple directed attentional ability was below average as evidenced by his ability to repeat only 5 digits forward and 4 digits backward on the Digit Span subtest of the *WISC-IV*, and his sustained attentional abilities were far below expectations on a number of other neuropsychological measures (e.g., the Connor's Continuous Performance Test and Wisconsin Card Sort). Although his mother continued to report few difficulties in executive functioning on a questionnaire measure, test results and observational data indicated significant problems with working memory and attention, organizational difficulties, and impulsive responding consistent with an ADHD. Overall, testing suggested that Matthew's difficulties with executive functioning were significant enough to negatively affect his ability to problem-solve in everyday life, to use strategic thinking and planning, to recognize cause and affect relationships, and to maintain goal-directed behavior, especially in unstructured situations. Achievement testing also indicated that Matthew continued to fall below grade level across a number of areas and met criteria for learning disabilities in reading and math. Specific suggestions were made to support Matthew in school and in therapy, and a trial of stimulant medication was recommended and started.

Matthew continues in treatment with his psychologist and has made significant gains in his academic performance and in his ability to independently manage his diabetes. His case is illustrative in several ways of why a pediatrician or pediatric specialist might refer a child for neuropsychological assessment and why assessment by a trained neuropsychologist is often preferable to school-based assessment among children and adolescents with chronic medical conditions. What was likely an underlying attention deficit that impacted Matthew's academic achievement had been dismissed as a consequence of having had significant medical problems and frequent absences from school in the critical early elementary years. It is also possible that the difficulties Matthew was having with attention by the 11th grade had been exacerbated by a history of poor glycemic control. In either case, the measures used in a standard school-based assessment were not comprehensive enough to notice and diagnose an attention deficit that, irrespective of its cause, was significantly impacting Matthew's school achievement and health.

Case Presentation: Multiple Sclerosis

Lilian was a 17-year-old female who was a senior in high school at the time of the evaluation. This was a reevaluation for Lilian, as her first evaluation occurred 18 months prior, after her initial diagnosis of relapsing-remitting multiple sclerosis. Lilian's first evaluation indicated cognitive abilities in the average range with similar verbal and nonverbal performance. Academic achievement in reading, spelling, and math were commensurate with expectations based on her cognitive ability. Tests of language were within the average range, although tests of auditory memory indicated variable performance with rote memory skills (e.g., WAIS-III Digit Span [Wechsler, 1997], WRAML Sentence Memory [Adams & Sheslow, 2003]) and performance on a list-learning task were mildly impaired. Lilian was referred for a reevaluation because she had been having trouble focusing and she felt she was struggling in a number of courses. She had a number of psychosocial stressors, most notably that her father had recently been in a car accident. Although he had completely recovered, he was out of work for 3 months.

Lilian received care through an integrated team approach at Massachusetts General Hospital. This team included neurologists, nurses, psychologists, rehabilitation therapists, and educators. The treatment team felt an additional neuropsychological evaluation was warranted given Lillian's increased symptoms. They were particularly concerned as Lillian was planning to attend college in the fall, which was only 6 months away. It is interesting to note that the reevaluation indicated no loss of functioning as compared to her previous evaluation, although processing speed was more fully evaluated during the second evaluation and was noted to be an area of weakness. All academic areas were within normal limits, although she did demonstrate difficulty on a timed reading test (which was not administered in the prior battery). The majority of her neuropsychological functions were intact, including attention, executive functions, language functions, and visual-spatial functions. Consistent with her previous test results, she did exhibit difficulty retrieving information from memory, although memory storage was intact. In contrast, Lillian did report symptoms of depression and anxiety on measures of psychological functioning. Despite the relatively benign neuropsychological findings, she was reporting "real world" problems with set-shifting, planning/organization, and task completion. Her difficulties were more in the psychological realm, and she was referred to the staff psychologist for counseling and support. One major issue that was uncovered was Lillian's fear of going to college. Although she was quite excited, she was also experiencing anxiety with regard to whether she would be able to monitor her medication in a dorm room, or be able to get her medication delivered to her on time. She was nervous that she would not find a treatment team that would care for her near her college and was worried about what would happen if she had a relapse far from home. Thus, a consultation with the nursing staff (to help plan for medication management) and a social worker (to help find competent local medical care) was pursued. In addition, her neurologist evaluated the effect her medication might be having on her mood (Lillian was taking interferon) and made adjustments accordingly. The staff psychiatrist evaluated the possibility of medication for her symptoms of depression. The neuropsychologist made recommendations regarding course-load selection and assistance from the learning center. Happily, with the support of her treatment team and her parents, Lillian made a very successful transition to college and is pursuing a degree in nursing.

REFERENCES

Adams, W., & Sheslow, D. (2003). *Wide range assessment of memory and learning.* San Antonio, TX: Psychology Corporation

Alpern, D. (2005). *Developmental Profile 3.* Los Angeles: Western Psychological Associates.

Auer, R. N., & Siesjo, B. K. (1988). Biological differences between ischemia, hypoglycemia, and epilepsy. *Annals of Neurology, 24,* 699–707.

Austin, J. K., Huberty, T. J., Huster, G. A., & Dunn, D.W. (1998). Academic achievement in children with epilepsy. *Developmental Medicine & Child Neurology, 40,* 248–55.

Banwell, B. L., & Anderson, P.E. (2005). The cognitive burder of multiple sclerosis in children, *Neurology, 64,* 891–894.

Bayley, N. (2005). *Bayley Scales of Infant Development* (3rd ed.). San Antonio, TX: Psychological Corporation.

Center for Disease Control and Prevention. (n.d.). *Diabetes projects.* Retrieved May 11, 2009, from http://www.cdc.gov/diabetes/projects/cda2.htm

Chalmers, J., Risk, M., Kean, D., Grant, R., Ashworth, B., & Campbell, I. (1991). Severe amnesia after hypoglycemia. *Diabetes Care, 14,* 922–925.

Diabetes Control and Complications Trial. (1996). Effects of intensive diabetes therapy on neuropsychological function in adults in the diabetes control and complications trial. *Annals of Internal Medicine, 124,* 379–388.

Dreifuss, F. E. (1994). Partial seizures (focal and multifocal). In K. Swaiman (Ed.), *Pediatric neurology* (pp. 509–530). St. Louis, MO: Mosby.

Duquette, P., Murray, T. J., Pleines, J., Ebers, G. C., Sadovnick, D., Weldon, P., et al. (1987). Multiple sclerosis in childhood: Clinical profile in 125 patients. *Journal of Pediatrics, 111,* 359–363.

Fastenau, P. S., Shen, J., Dunn, D. W., Perkins, S. M., Hermann, B. P., & Austin, J. K. (2004). Neuropsychological predictors of academic underachievement in pediatric epilepsy: Moderating roles of demographics, seizure, and psychosocial variables. *Epilepsia, 45,* 1261–1272.

Folio, M. R., & Fewell, R. R. (2000). *Peabody Developmental Motor Scales* (2nd ed). San Antonio, TX: Harcourt Assessment.

Gaudieri, P. A., Chen, R. C., Greer, T. F., & Holmes, C. S. (2008). Cognitive function in children with Type 1 diabetes. *Diabetes Care, 31*(9), 1892–1897.

Ghezzi, A., Deplano, V., Faroni, J., Grasso, M. G., Liguori, M., Marrosu, G., et al. (1997). Multiple sclerosis in childhood: Clinical features of 149 cases. *Multiple Sclerosis, 3,* 43–46.

Hannonen, R., Tupola, S., Ahonen, T., & Riikonen, R. (2003). Neurocognitive functioning in children with type-1 diabetes with and without episodes of severe hypoglycaemia. *Developmental Medicine and Child Neurology, 45,* 262–268.

Helgeson, V. S., Siminerio, L., Escobar, O., & Becker, D. (2009). Predictors of metabolic control among adolescents with diabetes: A 4-year longitudinal study. *Journal of Pediatric Psychology, 34,*(3m) 254–270.

Holmes, C. S., Chen, R., Streisand, R., Marschall, D. E., Souter, S., Swift, E. E., & Peterson, C. C. (2006). Predictors of youth diabetes care behaviors and metabolic control: A structural equation modeling approach. *Journal of Pediatric Psychology, 31*(8), 770–784.

Holmes, C. S., Dunlap, W.P., Chen, P. S., & Cornwell, J. M. (1992). Gender differences in the learning status of diabetic children. *Journal of Consulting and Clinical Psychology, 60*(5), 698–704.

Holmes, C. S., O'Brien, B., & Greer, T. (1995). Cognitive functioning and academic achievement in children with insulin dependent diabetes mellitus (IDDM). *School Psychology Quarterly, 10*(4), 329–345.

Hynd, G. W., & Willis, W. G. (1988). *Pediatric neuropsychology.* Orlando, FL: Grune & Stratton.

Jarjour, I. T., Ryan, C. M., & Becker, D. J. (1995). Regional cerebral blood flow during hypoglycaemia in children with IDDM. *Diabetologia, 38,* 1090–1095.

Leonard, B. J., Jang, Y. P., Savik, K., & Plumbo, M. A. (2005). Adolescents with Type I diabetes: Family functioning and metabolic control. *Journal of Family Nursing, 11,* 102–121.

MacAllister, W. S., Belman, A. L., Milazzo, M., Weisbrot, D. M., Christodoulou, C., Scherl, W. F., et. al. (2005). Cognitive functioning in children and adolescents with multiple sclerosis. *Neurology, 64,* 1422–1425.

Mitchell, W. G., Chavez, J. M., Lee, H., & Guzman, B. L. (1991) Academic under-achievement in children with epilepsy. *Journal of Child Neurology, 6,* 65–72.

Naguib, J. M., Kulinskaya, E., Lomax, C. L., & Garralda, M. E. (2009). Neuro-cognitive performance in children with Type I diabetes: A meta-analysis. *Journal of Pediatric Pscyhology, 34*(3), 271–282.

Ness, J. M., Chabas, D., Sadovnick, A. D., Pohl, D., Banwell, B., & Weinstock-Guttman, B. (2007). Clinical features of children and adolescents with multiple sclerosis, *Neurology, 68,* 37-45.

Northam, E. A., Anderson, P. J., Werther, G. A., Warne, G. L., Adler, R. G., & Andrewes, D. (1998). Neuropsychological complications of IDDM in children 2 years after disease onset. *Diabetes Care, 21*(3), 79–384.

Pavone, P., Bianchini, R., Trifiletti, R. R., Incorpora, G., Pavone, A., & Parano, E. (2001). Neuropsychological assessment in children with absence epilepsy. *Neurology, 56,* 1047–1051.

Roid, G. H., & Sampers, J. L. (2004). *Merrill-Palmer—Revised scales of development.* Wood Dale, IL: Stoelting.

Ryan, C. M., Atchison, J., Puczynski, S., Puczynski, M., Arslanian, S., & Becker, D. (1990). Mild hypoglycemia associated with deterioration of mental efficiency in children with insulin dependent diabetes mellitus. *Journal of Pediatrics, 117,* 32–38.

Schopler, E., Lansing, M. D., Reichler, M. D., & Marcus, L. M. (2005). *Psychoeducation profile* (3rd ed.). Austin, TX: Pro-Ed.

Sillanpaa, M., Jalava, M., Kaleva, O., & Shinnar, S. (1998). Long-term prognosis of seizures with onset in childhood. *New England Journal of Medicine, 338,* 1715–1722.

Taylor, H. G., & Alden, J. (1997). Age-related differences in outcomes following child-hood brain insults: An introduction and overview. *Journal of the International Neuro-psychological Society, 3,* 555–567.

Voress, J. K., & Maddox, T. (1998). *Developmental assessment of young children.* Austin, TX: Pro-Ed.

Wechsler, D. (1997). *Wechsler Adult Intelligence Scale* (3rd ed.). San Antonio, TX: Psychological Corportation.

Westbrook, L. E., Silver, E. J., Coupey, S. M., & Shinnar, S. (1991). Social characteristics of adolescents with idiopathic epilepsy: A comparison to chronically ill and non-chronically ill peers. *Journal of Epilepsy, 4,* 87–94.

8

Neuropsychology and Speech/Language Therapy

CHRISTINE L. CASTILLO

The fields of clinical neuropsychology and speech–language therapy, also known as speech–language pathology, are distinct though complementary disciplines. Regardless of the specific population (pediatric, adult, or geriatric) served by these professionals, neuropsychologists and speech–language pathologists are likely to interact more frequently and share more common knowledge than any other medical or mental health professionals on a hospital inpatient treatment or rehabilitation team. This chapter discusses the boundary lines between neuropsychology and speech–language therapy. Training guidelines, tenets of professional ethics and standards, as well as state law and clinical practice issues all help distinguish between these two disciplines (see Table 8.1 for a brief overview of these distinctions). Distinctions between neuropsychology and speech–language therapy are important to understand so that both disciplines are utilized appropriately for the benefit of individuals who undergo evaluation or participate in rehabilitation services. Although only neuropsychologists are qualified to administer certain evaluation measures, both neuropsychologists and speech-language pathologists rely on the data in a comprehensive neuropsychological evaluation to deliver comprehensive care. For both disciplines, neuropsychological test data can reveal a tremendous amount of information on ways in which a person's individual strengths and weaknesses in expressive and/or receptive language may impact daily functioning in other domains, such as memory and learning. Two case studies, one of a toddler and one of an 18-year-old young man, help demonstrate the depth and breadth of neuropsychological evaluation and illustrate how the results of such an evaluation can be used in treatment planning and intervention, especially in the realm of speech–language pathology; names have been changed to protect confidentiality of each patient. Finally, this chapter provides a general discussion on the ways in which neuropsychological test data leads to the development of speech–language therapy goals and objectives.

TRAINING GUIDELINES

Neuropsychologists and speech–language pathologists share in the study of the relationship between brain function and behavior. However, they differ in terms of their scope of evaluation. As a result, the training guidelines are different for neuropsychologists than for speech–language pathologists.

Speech–Language Pathologists

The American Speech–Language–Hearing Association (ASHA) is the sole certification group for speech–language pathologists (Paul-Brown & Ricker, 2003). In order to obtain the ASHA Certification of Clinical Competence (CCC), speech–language pathologists must first obtain a master's or doctoral degree. The master's degree must be from a program that is accredited by the Council on Academic Accreditation in Audiology and Speech–Language Pathology (CAA), with specific academic coursework that reflects a program involving study of the biological/physical sciences, behavioral/social sciences, and issues specific to the treatment of speech, language, hearing, and related disorders. Following completion of a sufficient amount of coursework, students complete clinical practica, during which they complete at least 25 hours of clinical observation and 350 hours of supervised evaluation and treatment of individuals with speech and language disorders. Within 2 years after the completion of their coursework and clinical practica, individuals must pass the national examination offered by ASHA.

Table 8.1

TRAINING AND PRACTICE GUIDELINES

	NEUROPSYCHOLOGISTS	SPEECH/LANGUAGE PATHOLOGISTS
	TRAINING AND SUPERVISION	
Minimum Academic Degree	Doctor of Philosophy (PhD) or Doctor of Psychology (PsyD) in a health service delivery area, such as Clinical Psychology or School Psychology	Master of Arts (MA) or Master of Science (MS) in a program in Speech-Language Pathology, Communication Sciences and Disorders, or Communication Disorders.
Supervised Clinical Practica	Varies according to graduate program requirements for graduation, practica site, and predoctoral internship admission standards.	$\geq$ 25 hours of clinical observation, and $\geq$ 350 hours of supervised evaluation and treatment
Internship	The equivalent of 1 calendar year of full-time supervised clinical training in a predoctoral internship is required for award of the doctorate. Enrollment in the predoctoral internship occurs following completion of doctoral-level coursework; predoctoral internships with an emphasis in clinical neuropsychology are available.	This is included in the $\geq$ 350 hours of practica, but individual graduate program requirements vary. Enrollment in the internship occurs following completion of coursework and clinical practica.
Postgraduate Supervised Clinical Work	The equivalent of 1 calendar year of full-time supervised postdoctoral training and experience is required for general licensure in most but not all states. For specialty training in neuropsychology, the equivalent of 2 calendar years of full-time, supervised training in neuropsychology is the "aspirational" requirement expressed in the Houston Conference Guidelines.[1]	The equivalent or greater than 9 months of full-time experience is required for licensure in most states.
Accrediting Bodies	American Psychological Association (APA) Association of Psychology Postdoctoral and Internship Centers (APPIC) Canadian Psychological Association (CPA)	Council on Academic Accreditation in Audiology and Speech-Language Pathology (CAA)

(continued)

Table 8.1 *(continued)*

	NEUROPSYCHOLOGISTS	SPEECH/LANGUAGE PATHOLOGISTS
	LICENSURE AND CERTIFICATION	
Licensure	For licensure at the Independent Practice Level, individual states define the criteria required for satisfactory completion of the doctorate, which includes satisfactory completion of the predoctoral internship, satisfactory completion of all postdoctoral training hours if any required by the state in which general licensure is sought, and a passing score on the Examination of Professional Practice in Psychology (EPPP). Consult individual state requirements for specific details regarding licensure requirements for psychologists at the independent practice level.	Licensure is required in most states and required by most insurance companies to qualify for reimbursement. Individual States typically require 300 to 375 hours of supervised clinical experience prior to graduation, 9 months of postgraduate professional clinical experience, and a passing score on the Praxis Series Specialty Area Tests in Speech Language Pathology. Consult individual state requirements for specific details.
Required National Exam	Examination of Professional Practice in Psychology (EPPP); individual states define the EPPP passing score required for licensure in that state.	Praxis Series Specialty Area Tests in Speech-Language Pathology; individual states define the Praxis passing score required for licensure in that state.
Additional Exam Requirements by State	In addition to a passing score on the EPPP, some states have requirements for licensure that include a state-based jurisprudence exam and/or an oral examination. Individual states also determine passing levels on jurisprudence and oral exams.	In addition to a passing score on the Praxis, some states have requirements for licensure that include additional examinations on state-based legal regulations. Consult individual state requirements for passing levels and specific details.

Table 8.1 *(continued)*

	NEUROPSYCHOLOGISTS	SPEECH/LANGUAGE PATHOLOGISTS
	LICENSURE AND CERTIFICATION	
Specialty Certification	Board certification in neuropsychology is optimal but not required for practice in neuropsychology *as long as* the licensed psychologist's training meets the criteria for specialty training outlined in the Houston Conference Guidelines, which were intended to be "aspirational" in nature.	ASHA Certification of Clinical Competence (CCC) can be obtained if the individual has obtained a graduate degree from an accredited university, completed 400 hours of supervised clinical experience, completed a 36-week postgraduate clinical fellowship under the supervision of an individual holding the ASHA CCC, and passed the Praxis; in many cases completion of these requirements will fulfill state licensure requirements.
	CLINICAL PRACTICE	
Scope of Practice	Determined by state law,[2] APA Ethical Principles of Psychologists and Code of Contact, and any specialty guidelines that apply	Determined by state law[3] and ASHA guidelines
Scope of Diagnoses	Adjustment disorders Behavior disorders Cognitive disorders Developmental disorders Language disorders Learning disorders Mood and anxiety disorders Personality disorders Psychotic disorders	Speech delay/disorders Language delay/disorders Voice disorders Fluency disorders Swallowing disorders
Interventions	Psychotherapy Consultation with patient and family Consultation with other professionals Cognitive rehabilitation related to aspects of scope of practice for neuropsychologists outlined above	Speech/language/swallowing therapy Consultation with patient and family Consultation with other professionals Cognitive rehabilitation related to scope of practice for Speech and Language outlined above

(continued)

Table 8.1 *(continued)*

	NEUROPSYCHOLOGISTS	SPEECH/LANGUAGE PATHOLOGISTS
	CLINICAL PRACTICE	
Confidentiality	Health Insurance Portability and Accountability Act (HIPAA) governs disclosure of medical information and medical records.	Health Insurance Portability and Accountability Act (HIPAA) governs disclosure of medical information and medical records.
	State law governs privacy. Communications between patient (as in an individual who consults a psychologist for the purpose of diagnosis and treatment) and licensed psychologists, including those specializing in neuropsychology, are privileged as defined by state laws. Consult state law for the exact language as it applies to privileged communication between psychologist and patient.	State law governs privacy. Communications between patient (as in an individual who consults a speech-language pathologist for the purpose of diagnosis and treatment) and licensed speech-language pathologists are privileged as defined by most state laws. Consult state law for the exact language as it applies to privileged communication between speech-language pathologist and patient.

[1]For details on the Houston Conference Guidelines on Specialty Education and Training in Clinical Neuropsychology, consult any of the following Web sites: <www.appcn.org>; <www.div40.org>; <www.nanonline.org>; or <www.theaacn.org>.
[2]State laws prohibit any individual from using the words "psychologist," "psychological" or "psychology" to describe services or competencies, unless the individual is licensed as a psychologist. Any person not licensed as a psychologist pursuant to state law, but who otherwise represents himself or herself as a psychologist, risks monetary fine(s), imprisonment or both. Consult state law for specific guidelines.
[3]State laws prohibit any individual from using the words "speech–language pathologist" or "speech–language pathology" or other variations of those words to describe services or competencies, unless the individual is licensed as a speech–language pathologist. Consult state law for specific guidelines.

Finally, receipt of the CCC is dependent on completion of a clinical internship (also known as the clinical fellowship year), which requires an equivalent of at least 36 hours per week of full-time professional experience, which has to be completed within no more than 36 consecutive months and no more than 4 years following completion of coursework and practica. It is typically completed in 9 months and is supervised by another speech–language pathologist who has had their CCC for a minimum of 3 years.

It is important to note that the CCC is not sufficient for a speech–language pathologist to practice independently and supervise the practice of individuals who do not yet hold the certification, including trainees and other personnel. Each state has different licensure requirements. For example, the State Board of Examiners for Speech–Language Pathology and Audiology is the main licensure and governing body for speech–language pathologists in the state of Texas. Requirements for licensure are very similar to those for receiving the CCC. As in most states, licensure in Texas requires individuals to have passed the PRAXIS examination in speech–language pathology.

Neuropsychologists

Due to the wide breadth and depth of knowledge needed in order to provide evaluation and treatment to a very large patient catchment, neuropsychologists carry a greater education and training demand than do speech–language pathologists. It is essential to understand that neuropsychologists are first psychologists. A doctoral-level education program is required, most of which are broad in scope and based in one of the three license-eligible programs of clinical, counseling, or school psychology. However, individuals who desire to specialize in the field of neuropsychology typically take additional classes in their area of specialization. Following completion of the doctoral program, which includes multiple short-term clinical practica and 1 year of full-time clinical internship, graduates must complete supervised postdoctoral training prior to applying for licensure as a psychologist. Most states require 1 year of full-time postdoctoral experience, as well as successful completion of the Examination for Professional Practice in Psychology (EPPP), a state jurisprudence examination, and in some states, an oral exam. Following successful completion of these steps, individuals will be licensed as a psychologist (not as a neuropsychologist), regardless of any additional specialty training; only Louisiana provides a specialty license in clinical neuropsychology.

In 1997, select neuropsychological educators and clinicians convened in order to discuss education and training guidelines for clinical neuropsychology. The results of this gathering, now known as the

Houston Conference Guidelines (Hannay et al., 1998), provide aspirational goals with regard to education, training, and clinical experiences for individuals who wish to specialize in neuropsychology. The Guidelines include expectations for essential knowledge and skills, doctoral education in clinical neuropsychology, internship training in clinical neuropsychology at an approved American Psychological Association (APA) or Canadian Psychological Association (CPA) site, postdoctoral training to produce an advanced level of competence in clinical neuropsychology for an equivalent of 2 years of full-time training, and continuing education in neuropsychology.

The Guidelines suggest that these expectations will lead an individual to seek board certification. There are several different methods to board certification in neuropsychology, the most prominent being the examination process offered by the American Board of Clinical Neuropsychology (ABCN), which is a specialty board of the American Board of Professional Psychology (ABPP). Additional boards include the American Board of Professional Neuropsychology (ABPN), American Board of Pediatric Neuropsychology (ABPdN), and even the American Board of School Neuropsychology (ABSN). It is important for the public, as well as other professionals in the medical and mental health field to realize that certain unscrupulous individuals might call themselves neuropsychologists, even when their training is not aligned with the aspirational goals of the Houston Conference Guidelines. Therefore, it is recommended that caution be used when selecting a specialty caregiver, with the understanding that board certification is not a required condition of employment in most circumstances.

PRACTICAL ISSUES

For the public and medical professionals alike, there is often confusion about how a neuropsychologist differs from a speech–language pathologist, especially when they often work in the same venues, see the same patients, interact in the context of inpatient multidisciplinary teams, and use the same assessment instruments.

Places of Employment

It is not uncommon for individuals who require services from a neuropsychologist to also receive evaluation or treatment from a speech–

language pathologist at some point in their inpatient and/or outpatient treatment. The primary reason for this service overlap is the complex and inseparable nature of cognition and language, both of which can be assessed, at least to some degree, by neuropsychologists or speech–language therapists. As a result, individuals who endure an injury or suffer a particular disease process within their central nervous system may have resulting weaknesses that can be identified and treated by a team of professionals, which includes neuropsychologists and speech–language therapists, in addition to many other medical and rehabilitation specialists. This occurs most frequently when neuropsychologists and speech–language therapists are an embedded part of a comprehensive rehabilitation team in a medical environment, such as pediatric and veteran's affairs hospitals, or within tertiary care centers such as rehabilitation facilities and nursing homes.

Overlap between neuropsychologists and speech–language therapists may also occur on an outpatient basis. For instance, a child who has a medical history significant for a traumatic brain injury may receive speech, occupational, and physical therapy on an outpatient basis in their community or school shortly after discharge from the hospital. Neuropsychology services are not always the first service to be requested, perhaps because of a lack of awareness of what the child needs during the acute stage of injury, and therefore referrals are often made to speech, occupational, and physical therapies as immediate intervention methods. In addition to the lack of awareness of neuropsychology by community hospitals and primary care physicians, availability of neuropsychology services may also impact an individual's interaction with this service. Because of the very specialized nature of neuropsychology, there are limited resources in many communities, resulting in long waiting lists. Regardless of the reason, neuropsychological evaluation does not always immediately follow the acute stage of injury, and thus may occur some time after evaluation by other rehabilitation professionals and the initiation of rehabilitation services. In this case, evaluation data and intervention information from the speech–language pathologist, as well as the physical and occupational therapists, is often requested and used as a supplement to the comprehensive neuropsychological evaluation battery.

Shared Patient Groups

Individuals who sustain traumatic brain injuries or experience strokes, seizures, brain tumors, or neurological disease (e.g., meningitis, encephalitis) often require evaluation by inpatient treatment teams, as well as professionals who evaluate and provide treatment for patients on an outpatient basis. Because of the resulting impact that these injuries or processes may have on the central nervous system, neuropsychologists and speech–language therapists are consulted by neurologists, neuro-oncologists, and other medical health professionals to help determine a patient's current level of functioning, and to identify appropriate goals to assist with treatment planning and eventual discharge or discontinuation of treatment.

For instance, an adult patient who has suffered a stroke in the left hemisphere may have varying levels of Broca's aphasia (i.e., significant difficulties with expressive language) and/or Wernicke's aphasia (significant difficulties with language comprehension), which may also include dysnomia (i.e., word finding difficulties). Left-hemisphere stroke patients may also suffer from dysarthria, also known as apraxia of speech, which is a difficulty in pronouncing words that may be caused by damage to the primary motor cortex in the brain or their connections to the oral-motor muscles. In addition to these concerns that are directly related to the comprehension of language, production of words, and expressive communication, injuries and disease processes such as described above may also cause higher-order cognitive difficulties, which may include inattention, problem solving difficulties, trouble with sequencing of multiple-step behaviors (i.e., getting dressed), and even memory difficulties. These weaknesses are all within the purview of neuropsychologists and speech–language therapists.

Inpatient Team Participation

For individuals with acquired brain injury, including traumatic brain injury, stroke, brain tumor, or progressive neurological process, a collaborative multidisciplinary team is essential. As previously mentioned, neuropsychologists often work closely with speech–language pathologists, occupational therapists, and physical therapists, especially when based in a medical setting such as a hospital or rehabilitation facility. In fact, according to recent guidelines set forth by the Joint Committee on Interprofessional Relations Between the ASHA and Division 40 of the APA (2007), multidisciplinary teams should include "at least a clinical neuropsychologist and speech–language pathologist...when cognitive, communication, emotional, and psychosocial domains are affected" (p. 4). Additional members of a multidisciplinary team may include neurologists, surgeons, psychiatrists, social workers, child life specialists, nurses, dieticians, respiratory therapists, and others. In inpatient rehabilitation settings, physiatrists (i.e., physicians who specialize in the rehabilitation of patients following injury or illness) are typically involved in a patient's multidisciplinary team. Family members and patients are also essential members of the rehabilitation team.

There is some information to suggest that the significant overlap between members of a multidisciplinary team could indeed foster territorial feelings, insecurity with regard to the professional's perceived role on the team, and confusion for patients and colleagues (Booth & Hewison, 2002). Specifically for neuropsychologists and speech–language pathologists, confusion may arise as a result of the different terminology used to describe level of functioning or impairment and the different assessment measures used to evaluate similar domains of functioning (Wertheimer et al., 2008). In previous research, it has been found that speech–language pathologists perceive the neuropsychologist as playing a *consultant role* and participating primarily in the evaluation stage of rehabilitation; the neuropsychologist perceives the speech–language pathologist as providing assessment and treatment across functional domains (Sander, Raymer, Wertheimer, Paul, & Brown, 2006).

In an ideal world, neuropsychologists and speech–language pathologists, who are interacting within the context of an inpatient multidisciplinary team, will collaborate prior to completing any evaluation or assessment of the patient. This would allow for reduced redundancy of testing and ensure that all functional domains are evaluated appropriately between the two services. However, this luxury is not typically available as a result of the significant demands placed upon each professional's time. In fact, according to the results of some recent focus groups, these service providers typically complete evaluations independent of one another, but were often able to collaborate regarding the results (Wertheimer et al., 2008).

Evaluation

As has been previously mentioned, there is quite a bit of overlap with regard to the patients seen by neuropsychologists and speech–language pathologists, as well as the scope of each service's evaluation. That is, speech–language pathologists are concerned about speech functions (e.g., articulation, dysarthria), language and communication skills (e.g., syntax, semantics, pragmatics, literacy), swallowing and other oral-motor functions, fluency (e.g., stuttering), and voice quality (e.g., pitch, nasality, loudness) (ASHA, 2007). They are also concerned with cognition as it relates to an individual's ability to demonstrate language skills, which may sometimes include qualitative assessment of attention, memory, problem solving, and executive functioning (ASHA, 2007).

Comparatively, neuropsychologists usually complete a very broad evaluation that includes many different domains of functioning. A comprehensive evaluation would likely include formal evaluation of cognition, learning and memory, attention and concentration, visual-motor and perceptual skills, and sensorimotor skills. Evaluations also typically include assessment of general psychological functioning (i.e., mood, behavior, emotional functioning) and executive functioning skills, which are a broad set of higher-order cognitive skills that are important and necessary in carrying out everyday tasks. Some of these skills include behavioral and emotional regulation (i.e., inhibition) and monitoring, planning and organization, flexibility of thinking, processing speed, and working memory (i.e., receiving information via auditory or visual channels and manipulating it to produce a result), among others. For children, adolescents, and sometimes even adults, assessment of the patient's academic achievement may also be included in the evaluation.

Similar to speech–language evaluations, comprehensive neuropsychological evaluations often include assessment of the individual's language and communication skills. This may include evaluation of the patient's naming skills, phonological processing, receptive and expressive language, and verbal fluency. Neuropsychological evaluations do not typically use quantitative measures to evaluate certain speech functions and voice quality, but observations of these issues are typically documented. For instance, a child whose speech is difficult to understand due to phonemic substitutions or deletions will be indicated to have articulation difficulties or dysarthria, but very specific information about the phonemic errors are not typically delineated in detail. Similarly, for a child who has a very hoarse voice or limited prosody (e.g., atypical voice intonation and rhythm), these issues will be noted but not expounded upon. Neuropsychologists are not trained to assess swallowing or other oral-motor functions specifically, but observational data may be included in neuropsychological evaluation reports about these issues (such as an excessive tongue thrust while speaking).

In the context of evaluation, neuropsychologists and speech pathologists alike have the responsibility of providing accurate diagnoses for their patients. Unlike speech–language pathologists who provide diagnoses only with regard to speech, language, voice, and swallowing disorders, neuropsychologists' responsibility for diagnosis is much larger. Specifically, neuropsychologists have the ability to diagnose the presence of mental retardation, adjustment disorders, pervasive developmental disorders (e.g., autistic disorder, Asperger's disorder), learning disabilities, behavior disorders (e.g., attention-deficit/ hyperactivity disorder, conduct disorder), mood disorders (e.g., major depressive disorder, bipolar disorder), anxiety disorders (e.g., social phobia, generalized anxiety disorder), personality disorders (e.g., borderline personality disorder, obsessive-compulsive personality disorder), psychotic disorders (e.g., schizophrenia, delusional disorder), and numerous other disorders. Language disorders, including expressive language disorder, mixed receptive-expressive language disorder, phonological disorder, and communication disorder not otherwise specified can be diagnosed by neuropsychologists and speech–language pathologists. The *Diagnostic and Statistical Manual of Mental Disorders* (*DSM-IV-TR*; American Psychiatric Association, 2000) provides guidelines for the diagnoses of these aforementioned disorders. Although labeling may be looked at unfavorably by some, accurate diagnoses are essential for appropriately identifying the needs of patients and efficiently communicating that information to other professionals who may provide services for the patient. Diagnosis is also important in that it may help patients access certain services that would not otherwise be available to them.

Interpretation of Evaluation

It is interesting to note that previous research has identified that speech–language pathologists have a tendency to take on more of a process approach, in contrast to the use of normative data by neuropsychologists (Wertheimer et al., 2008). In fact, speech–language pathologists may refer to the Rancho Los Amigos Cognitive Scale (Hagen, Malkmus, & Durham, 1972; revised by the primary author in 1997) in order to describe an individual's cognitive responsiveness, ranging from "No

Response" and therefore requiring total assistance, to "Purposeful, Appropriate." This functional description method is quite a difference compared to a neuropsychologist's use of standard scores to describe level of impairment in light of injury to the brain, or to broadly describe an individual's relative strengths and weaknesses.

The quite variable nature of each service's differences in interpretation may in turn, impact treatment and intervention (Wertheimer et al., 2008). For example, a speech–language pathologist may interpret the language difficulties exhibited by an adolescent with a traumatic brain injury as aphasia (i.e., difficulty speaking or comprehending language), whereas additional or alternative assessment measures used by the neuropsychologist may in fact reflect impairments of executive functioning and working memory. Although there is likely some truth in each interpretation, this variability can impact which goals and objectives are identified for treatment, and even the selected treatment methods.

Intervention and Rehabilitation

For many speech–language pathologists, their clinical practice is divided into screening, evaluation, and treatment. Although provision of direct intervention is more common for speech–language pathologists than it is for neuropsychologists, there are some neuropsychologists who have the opportunity to engage in varying levels of intervention and cognitive rehabilitation, also known as cognitive remediation or retraining (Paul-Brown & Ricker, 2003). Although cognitive rehabilitation is not exactly the same as the interventions provided during speech–language therapy, both methods are based on the idea that the brain, and thus the individual, is able to change and improve given certain interventions; this idea was originally proposed by Alexander Luria in 1948. Together, speech–language therapy and cognitive rehabilitation techniques can provide individual patients with techniques that will help accommodate their weaknesses. In fact, some recent research (Cicerone et al., 2005) indicates that broad cognitive rehabilitation techniques can impact numerous functional domains, including cognitive-linguistic skills, functional communication (i.e., pragmatic language, gestural training, language formulation), visuospatial ability, memory, attention, visual scanning, reading comprehension, and problem solving.

Research has indicated that rehabilitation should "facilitate and guide natural recovery, reinforcing positive compensation, and suppressing maladaptive behaviors" (Salazar et al., 2000, p. 3080). There are two basic methods for rehabilitation of skills that occurs during speech–language therapy and cognitive rehabilitation: restoration and compensation. In general, rehabilitation methods are thought to be best employed in a multidisciplinary manner so that all involved individuals are actively engaged in the intervention. Notably, Braga, Da Paz Júnior, and Ylvisaker (2005) discovered that children with TBI participating in a cognitive rehabilitation program demonstrated greater physical and cognitive improvements when it was implemented in the context of their everyday life, rather than in a clinical environment.

Although it would be ideal for neuropsychologists to facilitate a program of cognitive rehabilitation for individuals who have suffered loss or impairment of skills, it is unfortunately very difficult for this specialty service to obtain authorization and eventual reimbursement from insurance companies for such services. However, speech–language pathologists fortunately are able to implement some very similar strategies to facilitate recovery in these patients, all in the context of speech–language therapy (Paul-Brown & Ricker, 2003). This follows Paul-Brown and Ricker's assertion very well, in that "attempts to separate tests and interventions into two mutually exclusive proprietary domains are destined to fail in the provision of the highest quality of service to the patient" (p. 9).

Pediatric Case Example

This case study details the course of diagnosis and treatment for a 3-year-old little girl who was diagnosed with a brain tumor. It illustrates the acute cognitive, language, and behavioral changes associated with surgical resection for certain types of brain tumors, and how neuropsychological evaluation can help determine current levels of functioning and appropriate services, especially addressing the sudden onset of expressive language difficulties.

Initial Evaluation

Maggie Holliday was a little girl who experienced a normal gestation, neonatal, and toddler period, with achievement of motor and language developmental milestones at appropriate ages. She had been developing normally without any medical or early learning difficulties until shortly after her third birthday, when she began experiencing occasional morning vomiting. The morning vomiting increased in frequency over the course of the next 6 months and, because physicians were unsure of the cause of her emesis, she underwent exploratory abdominal surgery. Surgery revealed a small intestine hematoma (i.e., blood collected around an organ because of an injury or rupture of the blood vessel), which was corrected.

Following surgery, Maggie experienced fewer episodes of vomiting, but she became more clumsy and developed strabismus (i.e., crossing of the eyes). These neurological symptoms were cause for concern, and her physicians ordered a magnetic resonance imaging (MRI) of her brain a month following her abdominal surgery. The MRI revealed a tumor in the posterior fossa region of her brain (near the brain stem and cerebellum), in addition to obstructive hydrocephalus (i.e., blockage of cerebrospinal fluid causing buildup of fluid in the ventricles and increased pressure on the brain). Two days following the MRI, Maggie underwent neurosurgery to remove the tumor. Following surgery, Maggie developed cerebellar mutism. She also continued to demonstrate right eye esotropia (i.e., inward turning of the eye) and gait ataxia (i.e., staggering and unsteadiness while walking). Craniospinal radiation and chemotherapy were initiated a few days after surgery.

Cerebellar mutism is a somewhat common result of resection of midline posterior fossa tumors, especially medulloblastomas (as Maggie had), due to the brain region (i.e., cerebellum) affected during surgery. The cerebellum is essential in the coordination of voluntary movements, including walking, talking, manipulating things with the hands, and focusing the eyes. It typically develops immediately after surgery, with onset occurring usually within one week of surgery and lasting somewhere between one week and several years. Although the term *cerebellar mutism* implies lack of expressive speech, it has a broader constellation of symptoms that includes weaknesses in gross and fine motor coordination (e.g., gait ataxia), hypotonia (i.e., low muscle tone), and increased emotional lability (Kotïl, Eras, Akcetïn, & Bïlge, 2008; Robertson et al., 2008).

Approximately 3 weeks following surgery, Maggie underwent a brief neuropsychological evaluation consisting of parent interview and brief play-based observation. Her parents also completed a behavioral rating scale and an adaptive rating scale. Due to her tender age (3 years, 8 months), the Mullen Scales of Early Learning (Mullen, 1995) was the only quantitative measure administered directly to Maggie.

During the interview with Mrs. Holliday, Maggie played easily with her older sister. She readily explored a toy box that was provided to her. During the direct evaluation with Maggie, she seemed to enjoy the interaction and was quite playful. In fact, on several occasions when she was asked to point to something, Maggie purposefully pointed to the incorrect item while grinning in an apparent attempt to fool the psychologist. When the direction was repeated, Maggie promptly pointed to the correct item. Although Maggie's attention began to wane over the course of the evaluation, her level of attention and concentration was appropriate for her age. Overall, she demonstrated appropriate activity levels and did not exhibit any atypical patterns of behavior or emotional functioning.

Based on her performance on the Mullen Scales of Early Learning, Maggie performed in the average range on tasks measuring her Visual Reception, which required her to match by shape and size, sort by category, and remember single pictures or objects. Her fine motor skills were delayed, as she was unable to use her right hand for anything except stabilization of objects while she manipulated items primarily with her left hand. Although she was able to complete many of the tasks with her left hand (e.g., placing pennies in a bank, building with blocks), she was unable to complete any of the bimanual tasks (e.g., stringing beads, or screwing a cap on a jar). Also, while walking to and from the evaluation room, Maggie required assistance from her mother due to her ataxic gait. In fact, when she was required to travel long distances by foot, her parents pushed her in a stroller even though she did not require use of a stroller prior to her surgery.

With regard to language functioning, Maggie demonstrated moderate difficulty with receptive language, and severe difficulty with expressive language. Specifically pertaining to receptive language, Maggie was able to understand spatial commands (e.g., on, under, behind) and action words (e.g., drinking, writing), identify object functions, and follow single unrelated commands. However, Maggie was unable to demonstrate understanding of length or size concepts, and had difficulty following directions that involved more than one step. It should be noted that the Receptive Language subtest on the Mullen Scales of Early Learning also asks children to demonstrate general knowledge by briefly answering questions such as "What is your name?" and "How old are you?" Because Maggie was unable to answer any of these questions except for her age (she correctly held up three fingers), her score in the receptive language domain was likely an underestimate of her true functioning in this area.

With regard to expressive language, Maggie had significant difficulty. She made numerous vocalizations (e.g., giggling) and produced single phoneme (i.e., /d/) and double phoneme sounds (i.e., /th/), but was unable to produce any recognizable words. It was especially difficult for Mrs. Holliday to witness Maggie's performance, as Mrs. Holliday reported that her daughter was previously a very loquacious and humorous little girl.

According to Mrs. Holliday's responses to the *Adaptive Behavior Assessment System—Second Edition* (*ABAS-II;* Harrison & Oakland, 2003) and the *Behavior Assessment System for Children—Second Edition* (*BASC-II;* Reynolds & Kamphaus, 2004), Maggie was having significant difficulty with communication skills. Her mother's responses also led to mild concerns with Maggie's ability to perform daily living and self-care tasks, due to her poor fine and gross motor skills.

Based on the information gleaned from the evaluation, it was recommended that rehabilitation services, including speech–language, occupational, and physical therapy, be initiated as soon as possible. Although cerebellar mutism resolves in most children (Robertson et al., 2008), some difficulties may remain even after expressive language skills return and ataxia diminishes. In addition to the immediate participation in rehabilitation services recommended for Maggie, several other things were also suggested. Since Maggie's safety was of utmost importance, her parents were instructed to obtain an identification bracelet with Maggie's name and birthday, as well as the family's contact information. In the case that she should become lost or separated from her parents, having this information readily available would be invaluable, especially given Maggie's inability to verbally communicate any of this important information.

Mr. and Mrs. Holliday were also educated about the behaviors that may arise as a result of Maggie's inability to express her wants and needs. That is, some children like Maggie who have acute loss of expressive language skills may become extremely frustrated about their inability to effectively communicate. Children in this situation may demonstrate a tendency to withdraw from situations during which communication is very important, such as play groups and sibling play time. In addition to this social withdrawal, children may also become irritable, and possibly even physically aggressive, even when they never previously demonstrated these behaviors, especially when they have something especially salient to express. Mr. and Mrs. Holliday were strongly urged to engage Maggie by attempting the following:

1. Make and maintain eye contact with Maggie prior to initiation of directions or requests.

2. Keep instructions and directions short, simple, and concrete. Limit requests to single commands and convey as much meaning as possible using only a few words. Pair instructions with demonstrations.
3. Break complex tasks down into smaller components or steps.
4. Repeat instructions. Do not assume that she understands what she has been told to do because she nods her head "yes" when asked if she understands.
5. Monitor Maggie while she is carrying out the request and provide support as needed.

In addition to these recommendations provided to Mr. and Mrs. Holliday, it was proposed that Maggie's speech–language therapist help Maggie and her parents develop alternative means of expressive communication. Because of the increased likelihood of Maggie experiencing frustration and withdrawal, it was suggested that these methods be implemented as soon as possible. One of the common means of supplemental communication is through use of a Picture Exchange Communication System (PECS; Frost & Bondy, 1994). Essentially, the PECS is an augmentive system that was initially used with children and adults with autism and severe language impairments. However, it is currently used with a wide variety of individuals with language difficulties. It is a system of pictures that allows a child to use that picture to visually represent what they would otherwise be able to verbally communicate; the pictures can also be placed in front of the child or lined up to represent the next activity or an entire daily schedule. For instance, dozens of pictures may be used to represent all facets of a child's day, including meal choices (e.g., juice box, hamburger), activities of daily living (e.g., toothbrush, bathtub), and leisure time activities (e.g., blocks, television).

Finally, Mr. and Mrs. Holliday were instructed to work closely with all of Maggie's therapists in order to generalize the skills learned during therapy to her broader environment. If a PECS was developed for Maggie during her therapy, it should be used consistently. If Maggie was encouraged to use her right hand for fine motor tasks during therapy, her parents should also encourage these same behaviors at home.

Reevaluation

Approximately 6 months after the initial neuropsychological evaluation, Maggie returned for a follow-up evaluation. Since the initial visit, Maggie had undergone radiation, and continued to receive chemotherapy treatment. No additional medical issues were noted during that time, and Maggie had reacted as expected to chemotherapy treatments, with mild levels of nausea.

She had been participating in outpatient speech-language, occupational, and physical therapy on a regular basis.

During the evaluation, Maggie initially seemed interested in the tasks presented to her, but quickly became frustrated. She began crying on two separate occasions on relatively simple tasks, one of which the psychologist had asked her to pick out seven blocks from a set. When this occurred, Maggie and her mother took a 5-minute break and explored the area surrounding the clinic. When they returned, Maggie appeared happy and ready to participate. Although she did not demonstrate increased levels of inattention, it was apparent that Maggie was becoming quite fatigued after extended periods of testing. Her level of impulsivity and hyperactivity were appropriate for her age.

To determine progress since the initial evaluation, the Mullen Scales of Early Learning was again administered to Maggie. She had made tremendous progress in three of the four domains, with her performance on the fine-motor, receptive language, and expressive language subdomains falling in the average range for her age. On tasks measuring her visual reception, Maggie performed slightly above the average range. Although she had regained skill in her right arm and hand, she continued to demonstrate greater preference for use of her left hand in fine motor tasks. She demonstrated awareness of her right hand and often used it to assist her left hand by grasping objects or holding a paper while she wrote or drew shapes. Her gross motor skills had not yet returned to premorbid levels, but she was able to ambulate with greater independence than she was able to during the initial evaluation.

One of the most notable gains demonstrated by Maggie was in her expressive language skills. She demonstrated excellent naming skills and answered questions appropriately. However, she demonstrated very poor speech articulation. That is, when Maggie initiated a topic of conversation that was not in the context of an ongoing task, it was extremely difficult to determine the content of her speech. Nevertheless, Mrs. Holliday's responses on the ABAS-II and BASC-II did not reveal any concerns.

Given the information from the reevaluation, it was apparent that some of Maggie's previously impaired skills were improving. However, it was apparent that the cerebellar mutism continued to have an impact on her speech articulation, right arm and hand, and gait. Although a modified PECS had been put in place with the help of Maggie's speech–language therapist, its use was reduced once she began to regain verbal communication skills. This decision was supported, with a suggestion to help Maggie attempt tasks on her own first, with assistance provided as needed in order to foster independence and self-esteem. Additionally, it was recommended that Maggie continue to participate in all three of the rehabilitation therapies, with continued emphasis on remediation and accommodation for her weaknesses. Relatedly, Mr. and Mrs. Holliday were encouraged to contact the public school to request consideration for special education services in the context of a prekindergarten environment. This was recommended not only so Maggie may be provided with rehabilitation therapies, but also so that she could be exposed to a structured educational environment. This is important, especially considering the additional weaknesses (e.g., inattention, slow processing speed, continued fine motor weaknesses) that Maggie may encounter as she develops due to her complex treatment regimen.

Adolescent/Young Adult Case Example

This case study details the impact that ongoing clinical and subclinical seizure activity had on a young man's neurocognitive, memory, and language functioning. Specific recommendations will be provided on how to accommodate this young man's weaknesses in order to increase his functional skills in various settings.

Simon Harding was an 18-year-old right-handed young man who had a history of complex partial seizures since 12 years of age. His developmental history did not indicate any significant contributing factors, with development of language and motor skills at appropriate ages. He was prescribed Depakote and Lamictal. At the time of evaluation, Simon had not experienced any seizures for approximately 6 months.

Just prior to the neuropsychological evaluation, Simon underwent a full neurological evaluation on the Epilepsy Monitoring Unit (EMU) at his local medical center. During his hospitalization on the EMU, one seizure was recorded. The ictal (i.e., during a seizure) electroencephalography (EEG) showed seizure onset in the left frontotemporal region of his brain, with fast spreading to the entire left hemisphere. An MRI of Simon's brain did not indicate any signs of mesial temporal sclerosis (i.e., neuron loss and tissue scarring in the brain's temporal lobe, a common cause of temporal lobe epilepsy), but showed mild prominence of the sulci (the grooves/fissures in the brain) within the left posterior frontal region, consistent with mild atrophy.

Simon was completing his senior year in high school, a year behind his peers because he was retained in sixth grade. Because of chronic academic difficulties, Simon had undergone several psychoeducational evaluations for determination of continued eligibility for special education services. In tenth grade, he was administered the *Gray Oral Reading Tests—Third Edition* (*GORT-III*; Wiederholt & Bryan, 1992), on which he performed in the "very poor" range on reading comprehension and rate. That same year, his performance on the *California Achievement Test—Fifth Edition* (*CAT-V*; CTB Macmillan/McGraw-Hill, 1992) revealed grade equivalents ranging from the second-grade level in reading to the third-grade level in mathematics.

In eleventh grade, Simon underwent further evaluation at his school. His performance on the *Woodcock-Johnson Tests of Cognitive Ability—Third Edition* (WJ-III; Woodcock, McGrew, & Mather, 2001b) revealed Verbal Ability in the borderline range; Thinking Ability in the low average range; Cognitive Efficiency in the borderline range; and a General Intellectual Ability score in the borderline range. On the *Wechsler Individual Achievement Test—Second Edition* (WIAT-II; Psychological Corporation, 2002), Simon received a Reading Composite standard score of 80 (low average); a Mathematics Composite score of 72 (borderline) and a Written Language Composite score of 79 (borderline).

Functionally, Simon was living at home with his mother and father. He was not employed and did not have a driver's license, but expressed the desire to obtain his license once his neurologist gave him clearance to do so, which is usually a minimum of at least 2 years without any seizure activity. His parents expressed concerns about Simon's self-care skills, noting that he fails to take his medications unless reminded and relies on his parents to wake him up for school each morning. Primary concerns for Simon noted by Mr. and Mrs. Harding at the time of the evaluation included the lack of initiation for independent living skills, poor frustration tolerance, poor memory skills, impulsivity, and increased anxiety.

Both of Simon's parents accompanied him to the evaluation. He appeared friendly and rapport was easily developed and maintained throughout the evaluation. He demonstrated a euthymic mood with notable anxiety about his performance. For instance, when Simon was unsure of an answer that he was required to express verbally, he was extremely reluctant to admit that he did not know. Instead of stating that he did not know the answer, Simon often spent large amounts of time trying to formulate an appropriate response. In between formal assessment tasks, he was quite talkative and engaged the psychologist in much spontaneous conversation. However, his thought processes were somewhat incoherent and scattered. He had difficulty clarifying his statements when requested to do so by the psychologist. Also, it was apparent that Simon had difficulty understanding instructions and directions, and frequently requested repetition or clarification. He did not evidence any difficulty with speech articulation, but had significant word finding difficulties on tasks that required specific answers.

Simon's level of attention and concentration were appropriate for the situation, and he was not easily distracted by extraneous stimulation. However, he was easily fatigued when required to work over extended periods of time, requesting breaks during the evaluation. Simon's level of behavioral inhibition was adequate. In fact, he had the tendency to have delayed initiation, taking much longer to begin tasks or provide answers than expected.

In order to further evaluate his cognitive skills, Simon was administered the *Wechsler Adult Intelligence Scale—Third Edition* (*WAIS-III*; Wechsler, 1997a). He obtained scores in the low-average range on tasks measuring his Perceptual Organization and Working Memory skills, with standard scores of 85 and 83, respectively. On tasks measuring his Verbal Comprehension and Processing Speed skills, Simon performed in the borderline range, with standard scores of 73 and 76, respectively. These results were very consistent with his previous performance on the WJ-III Tests of Cognitive Ability administered approximately 1 year prior.

Numerous tasks were administered to Simon in order to evaluate aspects of his executive functioning skills. On tasks of working memory, Simon demonstrated better developed nonverbal working memory skills than auditory working memory skills, with scores generally falling within the borderline range for the latter. On tasks measuring his cognitive flexibility, he demonstrated significant difficulty across verbal and nonverbal domains. For example, on a letter-number sequencing task, he completed it very slowly, having difficulty maintaining the correct sequence in his mind. In fact, he often repeated the alphabet sequence in order to correctly identify each subsequent letter.

On verbal fluency tasks, although Simon was able to perform within the low-average range when presented with phonemic cues (i.e., words that start with a specific letter), he had significant difficulty when asked to name words that belonged to specific categories. It should be noted that for individuals with involvement of the left frontal or temporal region of the brain like Simon, the pattern demonstrated (Category Fluency better than Letter Fluency) is not unusual, given that category fluency requires more organization and effort to search for appropriate lexical items, and dysnomia can impact word retrieval.

Another task was administered to Simon in order to identify his ability to inhibit overlearned (i.e., automatic) verbal responses to produce a conflicting response. On the initial tasks that required Simon to name patches of color on a page, and then read color words printed in black ink, he performed in the average range. However, when he was required to name the ink color rather than reading the word (e.g., the word *yellow* printed in orange ink), he had significant difficulty. This reflected Simon's difficulty with inhibition of automatic responses.

The final task measuring Simon's executive functioning skills was administered in order to identify strengths and weaknesses in his spatial planning, rule learning, and inhibition of impulsive responses. This task required him to build a tower by manipulating up to five disks across three pegs to match a target tower, all of which must be done by moving only one disk at a time and never placing a larger disk on a smaller disk. Although Simon was able to complete most of the towers within the time limit, he did so with great inefficiency, haphazardly moving the disks across the pegs, appearing to hope that the disks would somehow end up looking like the target.

To gain more ecologically valid information about Simon's daily demonstration (or lack of) executive functioning skills, his parents and two of his teachers completed the *Behavior Rating Inventory of Executive Function* (BRIEF; Gioia, Isquith, Guy, & Kenworthy, 2000). There was consensus regarding significant concerns with regard to Simon's cognitive flexibility, task initiation, working memory, and planning and organization skills.

To determine the extent of Simon's memory difficulties, as reported by his parents, the *Wechsler Memory Scale—Third Edition* (WMS-III; Wechsler, 1997b) was administered to him. When presented with photographs of faces to remember, he performed in the average range after their initial presentation. After a 30-minute delay, he correctly recognized 95% of the faces he correctly recognized during the immediate trial, indicating good retention of information he originally learned. On another visual memory task in which Simon was shown four scenes and was asked to verbally describe the details of each scene, he performed in the mildly impaired range after they were initially shown to him and after a 30-minute delay. During this task, Simon expressed feeling overwhelmed by the amount of information he was being asked to remember.

On an initial auditory memory task, two stories were read to Simon, and he was asked to repeat each story immediately after it was read. His first recall of the stories fell in the borderline range. Approximately 30 minutes later, he performed in the mildly impaired range when asked to recall each story. He required a prompt about the first story, but was only able to recall one correct fact about the story. He did not require a prompt for the second story, but only recalled 11 correct facts. When asked to answer yes/no questions about the two stories, Simon correctly answered 21 of the 30 questions. Of the nine questions he answered incorrectly, he had provided the correct answer for only one of them during the delayed recall, suggesting he had not originally encoded most of the information he was being asked about.

On the final memory task, Simon was asked to learn a list of eight word pairs. He recalled two word pairs of the list after it was read to him the first time, obtaining a score in the average range. After the list was read to him four times and he was asked to provide the second word of the pair after the psychologist provided the first word, he demonstrated a low average learning slope, failing to increase the number of pairs recalled after each trial as expected for his age. When asked to recall the word pairs after a 30-minute delay, he recalled only two pairs, which is in the impaired range. Compared to his recall of four words during Trial 4, Simon demonstrated a somewhat greater than expected amount of retroactive interference (i.e., learning new information interferes with recall of old information). Furthermore, when given the opportunity to recognize word pairs from the list among distracters, he identified 12 of the 12 word pairs as part of the original list; he did not misidentify any nontargets. Overall, his recognition of auditory information is better developed than his ability to freely recall it.

A broad assessment of Simon's language skills was completed, given the difficulty with understanding directions and expressing his thoughts observed during the initial part of the evaluation. With regard to his receptive vocabulary as measured by the *Peabody Picture Vocabulary Test—Third Edition* (*PPVT-III*; Dunn, Dunn, & Dunn, 1997), Simon performed in the borderline range, obtaining a standard score of 73. On the *Expressive Vocabulary Test* (*EVT*; Williams, 1997), Simon had even more notable difficulty, obtaining a standard score of 53, which is in the impaired range. Based on the administration of the Understanding Directions subtest of the *Woodcock-Johnson Tests of Achievement—Third Edition* (WJ-III, Achievement; Woodcock, McGrew, & Mather, 2001a), Simon obtained a standard score of 72. On the *Clinical Evaluation of Language Fundamentals—Fourth Edition* (*CELF-IV*; Semel, Wiig, & Secord, 2003), he obtained a score in the impaired range on the Recalling Sentences subtest, which required him to repeat increasingly longer sentences. Simon also obtained a score in the borderline range when asked to formulate sentences when given a word and picture on which to base his sentence.

Throughout the evaluation, Simon expressed feelings of inadequacy about his performance at school. He also spoke of feeling the heavy weight of his parents' expectations. He divulged that he did not have any close friends, and that he has difficulty making himself understood by others. His responses

on the BASC-II revealed mildly elevated levels of social stress, attention problems, and inadequacy. His locus of control was somewhat more external than
expected, which is not surprising given the level of supervision and support
provided to him by his parents. He denied concerns with depression or anxiety,
and his responses led to adequate levels of self-esteem. Conversely, his parents
and teachers reported mild concerns with symptoms of anxiety and depression.
They also noted significant levels of attention problems, and severe communication difficulties.

Given information gleaned from the evaluation, it was apparent that Simon
was demonstrating significant weaknesses in language. These weaknesses
were affecting him in many functional domains, including social relationships,
memory, and academic achievement. It is important to note that individuals
with involvement of the left frontotemporal region of their brain may demonstrate some of the weaknesses shown by Simon. That is, the left posterior
region of the frontal lobe (i.e., Broca's area) is heavily implicated in naming
skills and expressive language. The left temporal lobe, specifically the superior
temporal gyrus (i.e., Wernicke's area), is implicated in receptive language
skills. Although Simon had not had any apparent seizure activity for over 6
months prior to the evaluation, individuals with a history of seizures may still
demonstrate neuropsychological weaknesses based on the location of previous
seizure onset. Additional weaknesses such as poor problem solving skills,
slower processing speed, limited cognitive flexibility, and diminished working
memory capacity further impacted Simon's ability to communicate effectively
and verbally recall previously learned information.

As a result of Simon's primary language impairment, accommodating
and remediating his language skills was the focus for intervention. Several
recommendations were provided to Simon, his parents, and the special education team at his school. First, Simon and his parents were reminded that he
will likely experience difficulty naming specific objects or items, resulting in
frustration. Instead of trying to express his thoughts using single word answers,
he was reminded to explain or "talk around" the idea to express his thoughts.

During class, there are numerous things that school personnel can do to
facilitate more interaction between Simon, the teacher, and his fellow students.
For example, when asked to answer questions orally, Simon will need additional time to formulate his answer. They were instructed to avoid broad, open-
ended questions such as, "What was the main theme of the last chapter you
read in *The Great Gatsby*?" Instead, Simon's parents and school staff were
instructed to provide questions with several possible options, in order to rely
on his much better developed recognition memory, rather than his recall

memory, which is significantly impacted by his poorly developed expressive language skills.

Alternatively, to prevent extended pauses between the time the teacher asks Simon a question and the time it takes him to gather his thoughts to respond, the teacher may prepare him in advance for a question or set of questions that might be asked of Simon. For example, prior to reviewing the chapter in *The Great Gatsby* that was read the day before, Simon's teacher may approach him while the other students are transitioning from a different task. The teacher can tell Simon that she is going to ask questions about the main issues in the chapter, the characters involved, and the possible events that may occur in the next chapter. The teacher can then instruct Simon to raise his hand and be reassured that he will be called on to answer. With this preparation, Simon can begin thinking of the answers and participate in the class discussion, rather than be left out because he does not generate responses as quickly as other students.

Finally, some additional recommendations were made to facilitate Simon's successful completion of high school and transition to adulthood. He was first encouraged to make sure he devotes all of his attention to individuals when they are providing instructions or information to him. Reiterating or rephrasing this information to the individual will help Simon clarify anything that he may have not initially understood. Also, utilizing an organizer or schedule book was strongly encouraged because of his weaknesses in planning and organizational strategies, which affect his ability to independently carry out daily living tasks. This book should include a list of all necessary daily care activities, including necessary medication, medical appointments, homework assignments, and job interviews. Although his parents would likely have to supervise his use of this tool at the outset, they were instructed to slowly take away support and provide only occasional reminders to Simon.

DEVELOPMENT OF INTERVENTIONS

As demonstrated by discussion of the previous two case studies, a comprehensive neuropsychological evaluation can reveal a tremendous amount of information about how an individual's weaknesses in expressive and/or receptive language may impact their functioning in other domains. Information about a child's level of nonverbal cognitive ability, or information about an adult's learning and memory skills in the auditory and visual domains, can assist with development of appropriate goals and objectives for speech–language therapy. This information can also assist in the determination of appropriate accommodation strategies, such as Simon's aforementioned organizer.

Broad goals and short-term objectives will vary widely for individuals participating in speech–language therapy. For instance, Maggie's participation in therapy after her first neuropsychological evaluation would have included goals to regain a certain level of expressive language (e.g., 10 words in 4 months). Because she initially was not able to demonstrate any recognizable words, the short-term objective would have been to increase use of phonemes and approximations of single syllable words (e.g., yes, no, eat). Another short-term objective may have been to increase Maggie's use of nonverbal signals to supplement her then current lack of expressive language, possibly through use of the PECS and/or by developing certain hand signals or signs. After the 6-month reevaluation, Maggie's speech therapy goals would have changed quite dramatically. Although she regained expressive language skills, she demonstrated significant articulation difficulties. Therefore, goals for speech–language therapy would have focused on articulation and pronunciation of words.

Conversely for Simon, he had no difficulty with speech articulation. Instead, his ability to understand complex directions was impaired, and he therefore required training on how to improve his ability to understand directions. If he were to participate in speech–language therapy, he would have been given direct training on how to implement some of the recommendations offered to him and his caregivers, including focusing his attention and reiterating instructions to give the speaker opportunity for clarification.

In general, a comprehensive neuropsychological evaluation would likely provide the reader information about an individual's current (and possibly premorbid) cognitive ability, learning and memory skills, and executive functioning skills. This information is very valuable, as it assists the speech–language therapist in designing an appropriate plan for therapy. Specific information about an individual's cognitive processing speed may alter the expectations for therapy, as those with language impairments and slower processing speed may need additional or more intense supports and services than those with language impairments and average processing speed. Difficulties with task initiation and behavioral inhibition are especially common for certain individuals with brain injuries, sometimes co-occurring within the same individual, and are often detected through neuropsychological evaluation. Without this information, a speech–language therapist may initially approach an individual with expectations of socially appropriate behavior and timely responses. However, given this information beforehand, the therapist would possibly change their methods and therapeutic plan somewhat, in order to accommodate for these weaknesses and provide intervention to address them.

SUMMARY

A comprehensive treatment team with members who fully understand and appreciate the expertise of other team members is a serendipitous thing. Treatment teams that employ physicians, psychiatrists, neuropsychologists, and rehabilitation specialists (e.g., speech–language pathologists) may sometimes fail to collaborate regarding an individual's care, thus repeating unnecessary procedures and evaluation measures; thus, treatment may not be fully informed. It is reminiscent of "The Blind Men and the Elephant," a poem by John Godfrey Saxe that is based on an original fable. In this poem, there are six blind men who each encounter a different part of an elephant. As a result, each man describes the elephant as something altogether different and separate from the parts encountered by each of the other men. For example, one man describes the trunk as a snake, and another man describes the tusk as a spear. In the end, each man maintains their position, continuing to dispute that their interpretation of the elephant is correct. It is hoped that this is a rare occasion within comprehensive treatment teams. The practices of neuropsychologists and speech–language pathologists are not so distinct that each professional can claim special rights to cognitive or language functioning. However, their distinct areas of specialty can certainly benefit the individuals whom they serve, especially with helping to develop appropriate accommodations in the academic, social, and vocational environments.

REFERENCES

American Psychiatric Association. (2000). *Diagnostic and statistical manual of mental disorders* (4th ed., text rev.). Washington, DC: American Psychiatric Press.

American Speech-Language-Hearing Association (ASHA). (2007). *Scope of practice in speech-language pathology* [Scope of practice]. Retrieved October 20, 2008, from www.asha.org/docs/html/SP2007-00283.html

Booth, J., & Hewison, A. (2002). Role overlap between occupational therapy and physiotherapy during in-patient stroke rehabilitation: An exploratory study. *Journal of Interprofessional Care, 16*, 31–40.

Braga, L. W., Da Paz Júnior, A. C., & Ylvisaker, M. (2005). Direct clinician-delivered versus indirect family-supported rehabilitation of children with traumatic brain injury: A randomized controlled trial. *Brain Injury, 19*, 819–831.

Cicerone, K. D., Dahlberg, C., Malec, J. F., Langenbahn, D. M., Felicetti, T., Kneipp, S., et al. (2005). Evidence-based cognitive rehabilitation: Updated review of the literature from 1998 through 2002. *Archives of Physical Medicine and Rehabilitation, 86*, 1681–1692.

CTB Macmillan/McGraw-Hill. (1992). *California Achievement Test* (5th ed.). Monterey, CA: Author.

Dunn, L. M., Dunn, L. M., & Dunn, D. M. (1997). *Peabody Picture Vocabulary Test* (3rd ed.). Circle Pines, MN: American Guidance Service.

Frost, L. A., & Bondy, A. S. (1994). *The picture exchange communication system training manual.* Cherry Hill, NJ: Pyramid Educational Products.

Gioia, G. A., Isquith, P. K., Guy, S. C., & Kenworthy, L. (2000). *Behavior Rating Inventory of Executive Function.* Lutz, FL: Psychological Assessment Resources.

Hagen, C., Malkmus, D., & Durham, P. (1972). *Levels of cognitive functioning.* Downey, CA: Rancho Los Amigos Hospital.

Hannay, H. J., Bieliauskas, L. A., Crosson, B. A., Hammeke, T. A., Hamsher, K. deS., & Koffler, S. P. (1998). Proceedings of the Houston Conference on Specialty Education Training in Clinical Neuropsychology. *Archives of Clinical Neuropsychology, 13*, 157–250.

Harrison, P., & Oakland, T. (2003). *Adaptive behavior assessment system* (2nd ed.). San Antonio, TX: Psychological Corporation.

Joint Committee on Interprofessional Relations Between the American Speech-Language-Hearing Association and Division 40 (Clinical Neuropsychology) of the American Psychological Association. (2007). *Structure and function of an interdisciplinary team for persons with acquired brain injury.* Retrieved on September 25, 2008, from www.asha.org/docs/html/GL2007-00288.html

Kotïl, K., Eras, M., Akçetïn, M., & Bïlge, T. (2008). Cerebellar mutism following posterior fossa tumor resection in children. *Turkish Neurosurgery, 18*, 89–94.

Mullen, E. M. (1995). *Mullen Scales of Early Learning.* Minneapolis, MN: Pearson.

Paul-Brown, D., & Ricker, J. H. (2003). *Evaluating and treating communication and cognitive disorders: Approaches to referral and collaboration for speech-language pathology and clinical neuropsychology* [Technical Report]. Retrieved on September 25, 2008, from www.asha.org/docs/html/TR2003-00137.html

Psychological Corporation. (2002). *Wechsler Individual Achievement Test* (2nd ed.). San Antonio, TX: Author.

Reynolds, C. R., & Kamphaus, R. W. (2004). *Behavior Assessment System for Children* (2nd ed.). Minneapolis, MN: Pearson.

Robertson, P. L., Muraszko, K. M., Holmes, E. J., Sposto, R., Packer, R. J., Gajjar, A., et al. (2008). Incidence and severity of postoperative cerebellar mutism syndrome in children with medulloblastoma: A prospective study by the Children's Oncology Group. *Journal of Neurosurgery, 105*(6 Suppl. Pediatrics), 444–451.

Salazar, A. M., Warden, D. L., Schwab, K., Spector, J., Braverman, S., Walter, J., et al. (2000). Cognitive rehabilitation for traumatic brain injury: A randomized trial. *Journal of the American Medical Association, 283,* 3075–3081.

Sander, A. M., Raymer, A. M., Wertheimer, J., Paul, D., & Brown, S. (2006). Perceived roles of neuropsychologists and speech-language pathologists in rehabilitation. *Clinical Neuropsychologist, 20,* 583.

Semel, E., Wiig, E. H., & Secord, W. A. (2003). *Clinical Evaluation of Language Fundamentals* (4th ed.). San Antonio, TX: Harcourt Assessment.

Wechsler, D. (1997a). *Wechsler Adult Intelligence Scale* (3rd ed.). San Antonio, TX: Psychological Corporation.

Wechsler, D. (1997b). *Wechsler Memory Scale* (3rd ed.). San Antonio, TX: Psychological Corporation.

Wertheimer, J. C., Roebuck-Spencer, T. M., Constantinidou, F., Turkstra, L., Pavol, M., & Paul, D. (2008). Collaboration between neuropsychologists and speech-language pathologists in rehabilitation settings. *Journal of Head Trauma Rehabilitation, 23,* 273–285.

Wiederholt, J. L., & Bryan, B. R. (1992). *Gray Oral Reading Tests* (3rd ed.). Austin, TX: Pro-Ed.

Williams, K. T. (1997). *Expressive Vocabulary Test.* Circle Pines, MN: American Guidance Service.

Woodcock, R. W., McGrew, K. S., & Mather, N. (2001a). *Woodcock-Johnson Tests of Achievement* (3rd ed.). Itasca, NY: Riverside.

Woodcock, R. W., McGrew, K. S., & Mather, N. (2001b). *Woodcock-Johnson Tests of Cognitive Ability* (3rd ed.). Itasca, NY: Riverside.

9

Using Neuropsychological Instruments in School Settings: Possibilities and Limitations

DAVID L. WODRICH, ARA J. SCHMITT, AND JOY GOLDBERG

This chapter presents important information for consumers of neuropsychological testing. It is potentially important for reasons that already may be obvious to some readers: (a) current mandates require that all children succeed in school (exemplified in the United States by the No Child Left Behind legislation) and (b) some degree of intact neuropsychological functioning is required for this success. Besides the obvious importance of central nervous system integrity in school learning, claims about the value of neuropsychological examinations are sometimes excessive, and the same is true of the entire neuroscience–education interface (see Varma, McCandliss, & Schwartz, 2008, for a discussion of "educational neuromyths"). Furthermore, important issues related to local policies and traditions exist in all of today's schools that may influence the diagnosticians' ability to conduct neuropsychological assessments and discuss the concepts that they attempt to measure. This chapter addresses some of these issues and provides practical information. In doing so, it is our hope that this chapter provides a balanced summary of what can and cannot be accomplished. This chapter provides background information about neuropsychological test use in schools, concrete examples of the application of those techniques among children with and without obvious brain impairment, as well as a summary and concluding comments.

BACKGROUND ISSUES IN SCHOOL NEUROPSYCHOLOGICAL TEST USE

To understand school-based evaluations in general (including those that may include neuropsychological aspects) requires the reader to grasp three points: (a) how the referral process works in schools, (b) the schools' key purpose in conducting formal evaluations, and (c) the credentials and training of the school professionals who conduct these evaluations. First, school-based evaluations that involve psychologists almost always represent the culmination of a multistep process. Preevaluation steps are designed to see whether a teacher's (or parent's) presenting concern (e.g., poor reading) is ameliorated by simple steps, such as requesting extra help, or by straightforward classroom adjustments. Simple steps like these may avoid expensive formal testing and prevent labeling (e.g., reading learning disability). Second, formal psychological (or neuropsychological) testing typically concerns special education eligibility. Carefully spelled out rules exist to guide the evaluation process and inform school personnel who does or does not qualify for special education help. Of the existing 13 special education categories, psychological and neuropsychological testing are most often involved when the following are at issue: specific learning disability, mental retardation, autism, speech–language disability, other health impairment, and traumatic brain injury (some, but not all, of these categories will be mentioned later in this chapter). Whereas schools have a habitual concern with eligibility, parents, physicians, or other professionals may want psychometric testing to be conducted simply to better understand the nature of a student's problem or to plan for him/her. Crucially, evaluation requests that do not concern special educational eligibility may not be honored. When schools do honor such requests, the ensuing evaluations sometimes only address eligibility (e.g., "Yes, your son or daughter does qualify for services because of a learning disability"), potentially disappointing those seeking answers to more fundamental questions regarding the nature of a child's problem or what to do about it (see Wodrich, Pfeiffer, & Landau, 2008). Third, school evaluations are often conducted by teams (i.e., school psychologist, speech pathologist, special educator), whose training and practice may be less concerned about brain function than their counterparts who work in hospitals or clinics. For example, roughly 75% of "school psychologists" employed in schools do not hold the doctoral degree (Carlson, Demaray, & Hunter-Oehmke, 2006), and, unlike most clinic-based colleagues, most are not licensed for practice outside of school settings (e.g., in hospitals, clinics, or private office settings). The minimum training standard advocated by the National Association of School Psychologists (2000) is a 60-hour graduate program, followed by a year-long supervised internship. Regarding neuropsychological conditions, which are this book's chief concern, few school psychologists possess formal training in neuropsychological assessment, and most profess none of the special knowledge of brain–behavior relationships claimed by neuropsychologists. For instance, in 1999, Walker, Boling, and Cobb found that only 23% of school psychology training programs required a semester-long course in neuropsychology. As seen later, school psychologists often use briefer test batteries than out-of-school neuropsychologists. In fact, in some schools formal evaluations have become rare with the advent of *response-to-intervention*, a procedure described below.

Fortunately, school-based evaluations hold some potential advantages over clinic-based evaluations. First, all school personnel are familiar with child development and all are accustomed to working with children. This contrasts with some clinic-based neuropsychologists whose practices extend from pediatric to geriatric patients, and who lack much training or experience with children. Second, school psychologists enjoy access to students in their natural environments, and they can assess potentially invaluable school records and teachers' reports. Thus, schools' ecologically rich data sometimes offsets limited psychometric testing, especially when referrals are for so-called developmental problems (see below). Third, some children lack health insurance coverage needed for clinic-based neuropsychological evaluations. The insurance barrier does not exist in public schools if school personnel initiate or consent to complete an evaluation.

Consumers of neuropsychological testing may find it helpful to consider three types of suspected problems for which students are referred for evaluation. This distinction may be helpful, even though school personnel rarely think of these divisions. Students in one group comprise those with academic failures for which there is no suspected underlying brain damage or frank brain disorder. Children in this first group have *developmental* problems. Children in a second, much smaller, group have health histories implying brain impairment arising before or shortly after birth. These children have known or suspected *congenital* problems, such as genetic syndromes and birth-related impairment. Children in a third group, which is also relatively small, experience *acquired* brain impairments, such as those that result from trauma, stroke, or unavoidable negative effects of medical treatment (e.g., treatment for brain tumor or leukemia). Children with congenital and acquired conditions are particularly well suited to the use of neuropsychological tests, either conducted inside or outside of schools. The remainder of this chapter discusses these three types of conditions and provides practical examples to help readers understand how school-based evaluations that use neuropsychological tests are potentially valuable.

EVALUATION OF DEVELOPMENTAL LEARNING PROBLEMS

Among psychologists who work in schools, a primary and highly valued role is to evaluate students for the presence of academic skill problems that are developmental in nature. Although the suspected academic skills problem sometimes proves to arise from autism or mental retardation, more often it is a specific learning disability (SLD), the most commonly identified disability in the schools (U.S. Department of Education, 2005). Current federal special education law is embodied in the far-reaching and detailed 2004 Individuals with Disabilities Act (IDEA). IDEA requires schools that receive public funds to evaluate for special education eligibility when a severe problem is present and a basic reading, reading fluency, reading comprehension, math calculation, math reasoning, listening comprehension, and/or oral expression SLD is suspected. Reading and math disabilities are discussed below as examples of how tests, including neuropsychological tests, can sometimes add valuable diagnostic and treatment-planning information to SLD evaluations.

Available Options for School-Based Evaluation of Developmental Academic Problems

Current state and federal rules allow school districts to adopt one of three procedures for formal identification of SLD, but not all of them involve testing. The first procedure has historically been employed by school psychologists, and, for most children, includes psychological and educational, but not neuropsychological, tests. According to Schmitt and Wodrich (2008), neuropsychological tests can be defined as "those that were devised, often with a neuropsychological theory as their basis, to assess brain–behavior relationships, or after their development have been used for this task" (p. 827). The second option is permitted by recent federal legislation and relies on evidence of poor response to intervention, without mandatory psychometric testing, to establish SLD eligibility. The third is more comprehensive, and includes use of selective neuropsychological tests.

The Traditional Testing Option for SLD Assessment

The first, *traditional*, method identifies SLD primarily by the presence of a "severe discrepancy between intellectual ability and achievement" (*Federal Register*, 2006, p. 46786). Readers may notice that this method, which was the sole method available prior to IDEA 2004, is aligned with the *learning disorders* definition in the *Diagnostic and Statistical Manual of Mental Disorders* (*DSM-IV-TR*; American Psychiatric Association, 2000). As a result, many psychologists in and out of the schools have long routinely adopted a bare-bones battery comprised of a standardized intelligence measure (IQ) and an individually-administered academic achievement test (to produce standardized scores in areas such as reading, arithmetic, and writing). If the goal is merely to document a statistically significant ability (IQ)/achievement gap, then this test battery suffices. However, it is so limited that it risks shedding little light on the underlying cause(s) of the learning failure, information that may help in planning effective postassessment interventions.

How, then, do psychologists working in schools implement the ability/achievement discrepancy method to identify SLDs? They begin with an individually adminstered, norm-referenced IQ test. IQ tests provide a *quantitative* estimate of a child's general ability (i.e., overall reasoning and problem solving). For example, the *Wechsler Intelligence Scales for Children, Fourth Edition* (*WISC-IV*; Wechsler, 2003), the most commonly used IQ test in the schools (Prifitera, Saklofske, Weiss, & Rolfhus, 2005), possesses excellent evidence that it measures overall (general) ability, and some evidence that it measures more delimited linguistic and visual-spatial abilities that are distinct from overall general ability. There is less evidence that it measures aspects of working memory and cognitive speed, although separate scores for these domains arise from routine use of the WISC-IV (called the working memory and processing speed index scores; Watkins, Wilson, Kotz, Carbone, & Babula, 2006). Most composite IQ-test scores (such as WISC-IV full-scale IQ) are reported as standard scores, with an average of 100 and a standard deviation of 15. Scores between 85 and 115 are within 1 standard deviation of average, and if a score falls beyond this range, psychologists take notice. Scores that fall beyond 70 and 130 (2 standard deviations of average), are especially remarkable as these two scores represent the point at which an intellectual disability and giftedness, respectively, are considered.

Besides IQ testing, an individually administered, norm-referenced achievement test to obtain *quantitative* estimates of reading, math, and written expression skills may be used by a psychologist, another educational diagnostician, or a teacher. Individual achievement test scores are also reported using the same (mean = 100; standard deviation = 15) metric. Crucially, severe underachievement is then determined by comparing IQ and achievement scores, often supported by a software program that is able to determine whether IQ/achievement differences are genuine and notably large in light of complex factors such as the degree of correlation between the IQ and achievement tests and each test score's reliability (stability). When a child fails to meet IQ-score-based expectations, the presence of a SLD is considered.

IQ and achievement tests, and the differences between them, are only part of a complex, rule-driven process. Unlike evaluations conducted in clinics, those in schools routinely document the results of prereferral strategies, classroom observations, the referred child's skills levels within his/her general curriculum, and data used to rule out competing explanations for the reported reading, arithmetic, or writing problems (e.g., lack of quality instruction, presence of an emotional disability, vision or hearing impairment, etc.). These are all required by law. Thus, data obtained from psychometric testing in isolation is never sufficient to identify SLD. As seen below, however, these traditional evaluations often fail to address why a child is not learning as expected.

The Response-to-Intervention Option for SLD Assessments

Consumers of children's neuropsychological tests should recognize that the traditional SLD method (e.g., IQ/achievement testing only) has been critiqued for its limited contribution to intervention planning and instructional decision making (e.g., see Gresham, 2007). Consequently, the 2004 reauthorization of IDEA permitted SLD to be identified by "a process based on the child's response to scientific, research-based intervention" (p. 46786), not just ability/achievement discrepancy. This procedure is commonly referred to as response to intervention (RTI; see Jimerson, Burns, & VanDerHeyden, 2007, for details).

States adopting RTI typically use three levels or *tiers* comprising intervention and careful progress monitoring prior to formal SLD identification. Tier one involves implementation of scientifically supported curricula (e.g., a reading program documented to be efficacious in a randomized controlled study) and high quality instructional strategies for all students, not just those suspected of SLD. Tier-two services are provided to only a subset of students whose learning rate and acquired academic skills fall below grade-level expectations. These struggling children are often selected via low test scores on school wide achievement testing or poor performance on short reading or math probes that match each state's curriculum, sometimes called curriculum-based measurement (CBM). This group of students receives evidence-based treatment (typically in small groups outside of special education), classroom accommodations (e.g., key terms highlighted, use of word processor or calculator), and frequent monitoring of learning rate. Tier-three (most intensive) services are reserved for those students who are clearly unresponsive to second tier interventions; each is reasoned to need the most highly individualized, intensive interventions and the most scrupulous progress monitoring. The reader should note that in the RTI scheme, lack of response to multiple tiers of intervention itself may result in SLD identification. Thus, some students can be identified without any psychometric (IQ, individual achievement, neuropsychological) testing at all.

The Comprehensive Option for SLD Evaluations That Include Neuropsychological Tests

Should a consumer of neuropsychological tests be satisfied upon encountering an evaluation report describing either a traditional (i.e., IQ and achievement only) or a simply RTI approach? The answer is likely "no" for two critical reasons. First, skills not tapped by IQ tests and environmental factors often better explain specific academic performance than does IQ (Gresham, 2007). Second, performance on neuropsychological instruments may reveal the nature of a student's learning problem and help select the best intervention. Similarly, neuropsychological instruments may help explain why previous intervention attempts have been unsuccessful (Hale, Kaufman, Naglieri, & Kavale, 2006). Even psychologists who contend that standardized assessment data adds little to the understanding of learning problems acknowledge that a reading SLD is most easily identified by testing for deficits in neuropsychological abilities that predict academic reading problems. An example of this is that dyslexia (a type of SLD characterized by poor word recognition) is assuredly detected via tests of phonological awareness (a neuropsychological ability) and word decoding skills (Wodrich & Schmitt, 2006). In contrast, IQ tests alone principally measure overall ability, which may not prove helpful for identification or selection of an intervention (i.e., known interventions exist for students with phonologically related dyslexia). For example, after identifying phonological awareness deficits, Torgesen et al. (2001) implemented *The Lindamood Phoneme Sequencing Program for Reading, Spelling, and Speech* (Lindamood & Lindamood, 1998) to improve the word-reading skills of 60 elementary students. After the intensive, 8-week intervention period, 40% of the students no longer required basic reading services. This is just one example of how neuropsychological tools sometimes inform intervention.

Several recent publications address the utility of neuropsychological assessment as part of school-based evaluation of learning problems (see D'Amato, Fletcher-Janzen, & Reynolds, 2005; Hale & Fiorello, 2004; Wodrich & Schmitt, 2006). Whereas school neuropsychological assessment batteries may vary, generally covered are: global cognitive ability, language, visual–spatial ability, memory, attention, executive function (e.g., organization, planning, mental flexibility), motor skills, academic achievement, and the social–emotional realm (Fletcher-Janzen, 2005). To work most efficiently, however, school psychologists often use a problem-solving approach during which neuropsychological test components are used selectively. For example, only when questions about general ability have been addressed would more fine-grained neuropsychological instruments be used (see Wodrich & Schmitt, 2006, for a comprehensive approach). Assessment of domains such as those previously cited are of interest to individuals who argue for the inclusion of comprehensive assessment, even when RTI procedures are used (Flanagan, Ortiz, Alfonso, & Dynda, 2006; Hale, Kaufman, Naglieri, &

Kavale, 2006; Ofiesh, 2006; Wodrich, Spencer, & Daley, 2006). A review of how select skills within these domains apply to the evaluation of reading and math disorders follows.

Comprehensive Evaluations That Include Neuropsychological Tools for Reading Problems (Dyslexia).   The rationale for including neuropsychological instruments in reading (developmental) evaluations is that their inclusion creates a more comprehensive battery, which in turn may help in understanding *why* a child is not reading up to expectations. To appreciate the value of these tools, a synopsis of the psychology of reading is necessary. Perhaps the most thorough review compiled to date concerning the requisite cognitive underpinnings of reading was published by the National Reading Panel (NRP; 2000), an expert subcommittee. The panel identified (a) phonemic awareness, (b) phonics, (c) fluency, (d) vocabulary, and (e) comprehension as skills essential for competent reading and as appropriate targets for intervention (available at http:// reading.uoregon.edu [University of Oregon, 2004]). For the purpose of this chapter, it is important to recognize that these neuropsychologically supported skills (Fletcher, Lyon, Fuchs, & Barnes, 2007; Hale & Fiorello, 2004) are largely untapped by most tests of general cognitive ability (IQ). In order to fully explore why dyslexia, or deficient word reading, occurs despite normal IQ and an optimal environment (Shaywitz, 2003) it is necessary to assess phonological skills (Siegel, 2003). Examples of neuropsychological tasks and instruments follow.

Assessment of phonemic awareness (the ability to detect sounds) and phonics (the ability to link sounds to symbols and employ the *alphabetic* principle) is essential, as robust empirical findings link deficits in these skills to virtually all subtypes of reading problems (e.g., Morris et al., 1998). *A Developmental Neuropsychological Evaluation–2* (*NEPSY-2*; Korkman, Kirk, & Kemp, 2007) is an example of a comprehensive neuropsychological battery that includes subtests (of which there are two) designed to detect phonological problems. The first *NEPSY-2* subtest is entitled Phonological Processing. This subtest, considered by most to be a test of phonological awareness, rather than phonics, requires a child to delete a phoneme(s) from a verbally presented word and then state the new word (e.g., say the word "pat" without saying the /p/ "pat;" the correct response is "at"). It also includes more difficult items in the same subtest in which a word is said, a single phoneme deleted from it, and another phoneme inserted to create a new word that must finally be spoken. Another subtest called Repetition of Nonsense Words, assesses the child's ability to repeat nonsense words presented via audiotape.

The NEPSY-2 also includes a subtest that appears to tap skills that undergird phonics, or the ability to apply the alphabetic principle by linking sounds to print. The NEPSY-2 The Memory for Names subtest requires memorization of names associated with faces. In this sense it is akin to learning to read by requiring associations between patterns that are seen and sounds (or words) that are spoken. Even though this is not a measure of phonics per se (as letters and their associated sounds are not used) children with poor word-reading skills are known to have difficulty with the task. For example, Schmitt and Wodrich (2004) discovered that this subtest, as well as the Phonological Processing subtest, on the first edition of the NEPSY (Korkman, Kirk, & Kemp, 1998), discriminated school-age children referred for evaluation largely because of reading failure from children in a normal control group. The differences in the two groups remained even after the effect of IQ was controlled. That is, the Memory for Names and Phonological Processing subtests explained differences between the two groups in a way that IQ alone could not. Therefore, the administration of the NEPSY-2 is likely to provide data beyond that of a test of global IQ.

Regarding reading, consider the double-deficit hypothesis (Wolf & Bowers, 1999). This is a contemporary neuropsychological theory asserting that deficits in both phonological processing and rapid naming (e.g., rapid oral identification of visually presented stimuli) are hallmarks of dyslexia. Research shows that both skills may be necessary to learn to read and that each accounts for unique variance in reading ability (Cronin & Carver, 1998; Fletcher, Lyon, Fuchs, & Barnes, 2007; Morris et al., 1998). For example, rapid naming ability is associated with reading competence, particularly by the middle school years (Kirby, Parrila, & Pfeiffer, 2003) when fluent reading is necessary to handle a rapidly presented and complex curriculum. In the Schmitt and Wodrich (2004) investigation, the predominantly reading–disabled group again performed more poorly than controls on the NEPSY Speeded Naming subtest. This subtest requires oral labeling of figures that vary on several dimensions (e.g., size or color). Again, the referred children received poorer scores than controls on this task, even after controlling for the influence of IQ. Taken together, NEPSY-2 subtests of Phonological Processing, Memory for Names, and Speeded Naming may provide more information than sole use of IQ measures, like the *WISC-IV*, and thus are sometimes used in reading referrals. Thus, use of selective *NEPSY-2* subtests, or those from other neuropsychological instruments, may be warranted when a reading problem is under investigation.

Before leaving a discussion of IQ and neuropsychological batteries, an additional note is in order. At least one comprehensive, integrated test battery measures overall ability and phonological skills. This is the *Woodcock-Johnson III Normative Update Tests of Cognitive Ability* (*WJ-III NU TCA*; Woodcock, McGrew, & Mather, 2007). The *WJ-III NU TCA* produces both a General Ability Index (IQ-like score) that comprises seven subtests and a cluster called Phonemic Awareness that is made of up of two subtests: Sound Blending and Incomplete Words. Sound Blending requires recognizing and repeating an English word that has been presented in fragments on an audiotape. The Incomplete Words subtest requires a child to recognize an English word presented on audiotape with one of its phonemes missing. Some psychologists also look at scores on a subtest called Visual-Auditory Learning. This subtest, like the *NEPSY-2* Memory for Names subtest, is a means to assess phonics/the alphabetic principle by linking sounds to symbols. The *WJ-III NU TCA*, also contains a subtest called Rapid Picture Naming that taps the known reading fluency correlate of rapid naming. Under time constraints, this subtest presents children with color illustrations of common objects/stimuli, and the examinee must correctly label the objects/stimuli (e.g., when presented the pictures, name "bird, tree, knife, rock").

Rather than using lengthy test batteries or complex, multipart tests (e.g., *WISC-IV, NEPSY-2*), psychologists sometimes rely on special ability tests to understand reading failure. For example, focusing on just phonological skills, Wagner, Torgesen, and Rashotte (1999) developed a 12-subtest *Comprehensive Test of Phonological Processing*. Besides basic phonemic awareness and sound blending, this test measures auditory memory and rapid naming, which have been found to predict phonics-based oral reading deficits. In-depth measures of phonological processing can be used when necessary to confirm underlying problems in the face of diagnostic uncertainty or to explore fully the nature of suspected phonological deficits (e.g., distinguish limited ability to detect sounds from limited ability to rapidly access known sounds) and guide intervention planning.

Finally, we would also like the reader of this chapter to appreciate that the complexity of individually administered academic achievement tests is increasing with our burgeoning understanding of the deficits associated with various SLDs. Thus, besides documenting the presence of deficient word-reading skills among students with normal IQ, performance on achievement tests may also be used to understand the underlying cause of the reading failure. For example, with respect to dyslexia, both the *Wechsler Individual Achievement Test–Second Edition* (*WIAT-II*; Wechsler, 2001) and *Woodcock Johnson Normative Update Tests of Achievement* (*WJ-III-NU-TA*; Woodcock, McGrew, & Mather, 2007) contain inventive subtests to tap the phonics/alphabetic principle. When an achievement test merely requires recognition of an English word, the examiner is unsure if success arose from decoding skills or simple word recognition (i.e., as a "sight word"). To bypass exposure effects, the *WIAT-II* and the *WJ NU-TA* contain subtests that require examinees to decode nonsense words (where straightforward word recall from memory alone will never produce a correct response). For example, the child must use his or her phonics skills to decode (sound out) nonsense words like "zop," "frun," or "pirn." Supplementing the typical achievement test battery with this subtest, along with the previously mentioned phonological and rapid naming measures, can sometimes help psychologists identify students for whom intact phonological awareness is present, but who nonetheless have failed to master the alphabetical principle and acquire phonics competence. Such information can guide efforts to teach the student to read better.

Comprehensive Evaluations That Include Neuropsychological Tools for Mathematics Problems (Dyscalculia). Knowledge of the brain's contribution is less well understood for math than reading, where imaging techniques have pinpointed inefficient use of specific left hemisphere functions among poor readers (see Shaywitz, 2003). In turn, the cognitive correlates of reading disorders that may be targeted for intervention are better established than those for math disorders. Regarding math, general education initiatives have spurred increased interest in this academic skill, apparently with just cause. The National Center for Educational Statistics (NCES) in 2005 reported that only 30% of U.S. eighth graders attained minimal proficiency in math. When math failure occurs, assessment is complicated by the diverse nature of math tasks that might be involved. The NCES (2005) identified (a) number properties and operations, (b) measurement, (c) geometry, (d) data analysis and probability, and (e) algebra as distinct competencies. That being said, IDEA identifies just two domains of potential math deficits in its SLD position and, consistent with this notion, evaluation and research efforts have traditionally focused on math calculation and math reasoning, defined as a *transfer challenge* that requires the application of "knowledge, skills and strategies to novel [math] problems" (Fuchs & Fuchs, 2003, p. 307). The function of neuropsychological tools within the evaluation of what Rourke and Conway (1997) termed "developmental dyscalculia," an academic disorder marked by abnormal inability to make math calculations despite adequate cognitive ability, will be reviewed.

As with evaluation of reading disabilities, a routine ability/achievement battery has dominated the traditional evaluation of math disabilities. IDEA 2004, as reviewed earlier, allows school districts to identify math calculation and math reasoning SLDs by, in part, establishing the presence of an ability/achievement discrepancy. If a school district employs this procedure, a measure of general cognitive ability (IQ) and individually administered math achievement subtests are administered. Likewise, school districts may elect to employ RTI procedures to identify math disabilities with or without the inclusion of neuropsychological tools. Understanding the theoretical and factual cognitive correlates of dyscalculia reveals how, by excluding neuropsychological assessment tools, the nature of a student's math failure and the scope of necessary intervention may not be fully appreciated.

Review of the literature suggests there are at least two subtypes of math disability linked to dyscalculia (e.g., Geary, 1993, 2003; Geary, Hoard, & Hamson, 1999; Mazzocco, 2001; Rourke & Conway, 1997). First, it appears as though some children with dyscalculia may possess the same cognitive deficits seen among children with dyslexia. For example, a subgroup of children with dyscalculia demonstrate poor accuracy and fluency in identifying numbers and retrieving answers to math facts, or phonological memory problems. The reader can now appreciate that these academic skills are very similar to reading in that the formation and retrieval of sound-print linkages (phonemic awareness and phonics) are required for both. Given its association with dyslexia, it is not surprising that data show phonological decoding has been linked to arithmetic and calculation performance in the general population (Fuchs et al., 2006). What neuropsychological tools exist to assess for the presence of phonological decoding related to mathematics?

The same subtests of the *NEPSY-2* mentioned earlier can be used when a mathematics deficit is at issue and more pervasive problems with general ability or lack of adequate instruction have been ruled out. As with the assessment of dyslexia, poor performance on the Phonological Processing Memory for Names, and Speeded Naming, *NEPSY-2* subtests may indicate this type of problem when poor accuracy and fluency in identifying numbers and retrieving answers to math facts is present. Likewise, subtests of the *WJ-III NU CTA* discussed earlier, may be used.

Another math disability subtype linked to developmental dyscalculia mimics the cognitive deficits seen in children with Turner's syndrome, a genetic disorder discussed in the next section. This visual-spatial subtype is characterized by (a) difficulty using spatial skills to make the mental representations necessary to complete problems and (b) trouble negotiating problems involving spatially presented information and concepts (Geary, 2003). Most tests of intelligence such as the *WISC-IV* and *WJ-III NU TCA* may be of assistance in identifying this problem as visual-spatial reasoning tasks are almost always included in these instruments. For example, the *WISC-IV* contains subtests that require examinees to manipulate colored blocks to mirror complex designs, identify patterns within complex figures, and identify missing elements of objects/scenes.

The evaluator may also be interested in how a child with a math disability approaches visual-spatial tasks that are free of much problem-solving (i.e., tasks that more purely measure visual-perception). For example, the *NEPSY-2* Arrows' subtest may be administered to this end. This subtest requires matching of arrows to targets at varying levels of difficulty. Also measuring visual perception, the Block Construction subtest of the *NEPSY-2* requires examinees to stack red blocks to mimic a pattern presented on a stimulus card. Finally, *NEPSY-2* also contains a Design Copying subtest that involves the child using a pencil to copy designs of increasing complexity. Although this subtest does involve visual-spatial skills, it also requires fine-motor skills (an important component skill for handwriting). In brief, regarding assessment for dyscalculia, neuropsychological tools may be used to explore if phonological memory deficits and/or visual-spatial deficits are contributing to the inability to make math calculations as expected. Once determined, interventions that align with each may be identified (e.g., Cover-Copy-Compare versus use of graph paper when making calculations).

EVALUATION OF CHILDREN WITH CONGENITAL AND ACQUIRED DISORDERS AFFECTING THE BRAIN

Almost all school-based evaluations concern academic (developmental) problems, such as in reading and math. Some students, however, encounter problems more directly linked to impaired brain functioning. In some cases, the brain-related impairment has existed since birth (congenital). In other cases, it arose later in life, such as after a particular event (acquired). Consumers will first learn how neuropsychological tests are sometimes helpful for congenital and second for acquired disorders (Table 9.1 provides additional details regarding use of such tests with some particular disorders for illustrative purposes).

Congenital Disorders and Neuropsychological Testing

One illustrative congenital disorder is Turner syndrome (TS). TS results from a chromosomal abnormality that occurs in approximately 1/2500 female births when one female (X) chromosome is absent (Christopoulos, Deligeoroglou, Laggari, Christogiorgos, & Creatsas, 2008). TS is often suspected based on physical features (e.g., short stature, webbed neck); however, TS can also affect psychological functioning, behavior, social interactions, and includes learning disabilities. Girls with TS usually have normal intelligence, but risk learning difficulties, particularly in mathematics. Interestingly, many also experience spatial deficits, such as in map reading or visual organization. Research also confirms selective memory and attention difficulties. From reading the material on developmental problems above, the reader may anticipate the role of neuropsychological testing. If referred for evaluation, girls with TS may have a math problem confirmed (or ruled out) by straightforward achievement testing or by an approach that includes RTI. Furthermore, IQ testing (such as use of the *WISC-IV*) can rule out overall cognitive delay. However, none of these techniques is precisely designed to detect circumscribed problems with sense of space and direction or with visual attention. In contrast, selected neuropsychological tests are designed to measure just these abilities. For example, the *NEPSY-2* Visuomotor Precision and Visual Attention subtests, as well as the Visual-Motor Integration Test and Bender-Gestalt Test (Reynolds, 2007), seek to measure visual organization, sense of space and direction, and/or visual attention. Therefore, these tests appear to target the areas determined

Table 9.1

EXAMPLES OF NEUROPSYCHOLOGICAL TESTS APPLIED TO ILLUSTRATIVE CONGENITAL DISORDERS

DIAGNOSIS	AREA OF RISK	EXAMPLES OF NEUROPSYCHOLOGICAL TESTS (OR SUBTEST)	EXAMPLES OF TEST ITEMS
Turner syndrome	Inattention, math, visuospatial, social deficits, impaired facial recognition, anxiety, depression	NEPSY-II Memory for Faces	Several trials requiring selection of recently seen children's face from a group of faces
		NEPSY-II Visual Attention	Two trials requiring children to scan for specific items among a group of other items (scanning for essential visual information)
		Test of Visual-Motor Integration; Bender-Gestalt Test	Copying geometric shapes with a pencil
		Behavior Assessment System for Children-2; Beck Youth Inventories; Children's Depression Inventory	Questionnaires completed by parent/teacher/student that assess behavior and socio-emotional functioning
Klinefelter syndrome	Expressive language, ST/LT verbal and spatial memory, attention, math, fine motor, reading, and writing	One-Word Expressive and Receptive Vocabulary Tests	Name pictures (with one word); point to picture matching a word spoken by examiner
		NEPSY-II Comprehension of Directions	Follow one-step to multistep directions with visual cues
		WRAML II-Story Memory	Comprehend and remember details of a story and then re-tell it
		WRAML II-Verbal Learning	Encode a verbally presented word list and then recall those words
		Conners' Continuous Performance Task	Attend to closely and respond to a screen flashing stimuli

to be most at risk in group research on TS. For example, the Visuomotor Precision subtest requires a child to quickly draw a line through a maze-like path while staying within an allotted space. The Visual Attention Task subtest entails quick scanning of pages to locate various matching objects (i.e., faces, animals) in space. The VMI and Bender-Gestalt each assess ability to copy shapes and objects in a planned and organized manner, and sense of direction and spatial alignment are reflected in scoring criteria. Recognizing whether the typical problems (e.g., those with space and math) are present in a particular child helps teachers, parents, and students to understand, and this understanding can begin the planning process. Extra math drills may be required, perhaps using relative strengths, such as intact verbal abilities. Visual-spatial demands may need to be assessed in class and steps taken to circumvent or avoid them (such as minimizing expectations that learning can depend on graphs or figures).

Another example of a congenital disorder with its own neuropsychological risk pattern is Klinefelter syndrome (KS). KS is a relatively common (1/500, 1/1000) syndrome caused by an extra X chromosome in males, leading to an XXY karyotype (Gerschwind & Dykens, 2004). Commonly reported problems include mild cognitive delays, significant language-based learning disabilities, and executive dysfunction (Gerschwind & Dykens, 2004). Similarly, studies have reported that boys with KS often experience intact nonverbal reasoning coupled with relative deficits encoding verbal information into working memory (Fales et al., 2003). In addition, diminished reading and spelling skills are often observed (Berch & Bender, 2000). KS has also been associated with difficulties in executive functioning and with specific and consistent difficulties regarding inhibition (Manning & Hoyme, 2002). If referred for evaluation, boys with KS may express difficulties with language-based academic skills (e.g., reading comprehension, spelling), which are sometimes identified by straightforward achievement testing or by an RTI-related approach. Again, IQ testing (such as the *WISC-IV*) can rule out overall problems with cognitive delay. However, these traditional techniques may miss more narrow problems with verbal reasoning and verbal memory, although differences between composite verbal and non-verbal *WISC-IV* scores sometimes can be detected (Ross et al., 2008). The potential for enhanced sensitivity of neuropsychological tests is exemplified by the Story Memory and Verbal Learning subtests of the *Wide Range Assessment of Memory and Learning (WRAML-*

II; Adams & Sheslow, 2003), which necessitate repeating details and themes heard in stories or remembering words from a list that has been presented aloud. Problems with behavior and lack of inhibition are sometimes assessed via rating scales (Behavior Assessment System for Children Rating Scale-2; BASC-2) or psychometric tests of attention and impulse control (e.g., the *Conner's Continuous Performance Task; CCPT*).

There are many other congenital conditions able to impact schooling. These include fetal alcohol syndrome (and prenatal exposure to other toxins), prenatal stroke, delay associated with prematurity, or other risk factors surrounding birth (neonatal hypoxia, delivery complications), and an assortment of genetic disorders, such as Down and fragile X syndromes. Each of these represents a cause (or a risk) of impaired brain functioning. In turn, each is associated with a possibility of delayed general cognitive development, for which IQ tests are quite helpful, or selective impairments, such as in language or memory, for which neuropsychological tests may be required. For many of these conditions, however, no hallmark pattern exists (such as is true with the examples of TS and KS). Thus, a neuropsychological battery that taps many domains helps guarantee that a deficit(s) requiring classroom accommodations or remedial instruction is not missed. One final point is in order regarding assessment of congenital disorders: the natural history of these disorders may mimic developmental disorders. That is, these children are often found to have impairments (or to be impairment free) when tested early in life, and the same or similar patterns then persist over time. Although this is true for affected children with many conditions, there are exceptions. For example, some research has shown that boys with fragile X experience cognitive growth trajectories that plateau at or near puberty (Hodapp, Dykens, Hagerman, & Schreiner, 1990). This information can be useful in planning and keeping any apparent changes in developmental trajectory in context.

Acquired Disorders and Neuropsychological Testing

Of course, not all brain impairments commence at birth. Some are acquired later in life following a period of typical development. As with congenital disorders, acquired ones often include features that entreat neuropsychological test use. Three types of acquired brain impairments are presented for illustrative purposes.

Traumatic Brain Injury

Traumatic injuries to the head are common among school children, with the Centers for Disease Control estimating 435,000 annual emergency room visits for traumatic brain injury (TBI). Research confirms that pediatric TBI can produce an array of initial and long-term negative school outcomes (Yeates & Taylor, 2006). Degree and duration of impairment are somewhat related to injury severity, which can be measured by the presence and severity of coma and length of post-injury memory impairments (Yeates & Taylor, 2006). For purposes of this chapter, however, the most pertinent question is how potential negative effects of TBI are determined or, conversely, how their absence is established. As before, general cognitive testing (IQ) is a logical starting place. Regarding head injury, moderate and severe TBI is sometimes associated with IQ loss; the more severe the injury, the greater the degree and duration of loss (Hawley, Ward, Magnay & Mychalkiw, 2004). The presence of this predictable IQ–brain relationship means that IQ tests meet some criteria that define neuropsychological tests. In practice, consumers of psychological testing may see reports of IQ testing after injuries. Furthermore, unlike their use in developmental evaluations, IQ tests may be repeated in fairly short order subsequent to TBI (e.g., within months of prior testing following a severe injury). A postinjury IQ falling within the average range (or one unchanged from preaccident level) is a positive sign that the TBI may not exert lasting effects; an IQ score that drops then trends upward is another positive sign.

Traditional (developmental) evaluation procedures, such as IQ and achievement testing, may be insufficient, however. For example, research documents that regardless of severity, pediatric TBI can be associated with difficulty retaining and retrieving newly learned information (Hawley et al., 2004). Thus, traditional SLD-related batteries may be insensitive (i.e., miss true cases) to some important post-injury impairments. Two neuropsychological domains, and associated representative tests, are discussed here to illustrate how neuropsychological testing is sometimes useful concerning TBI.

Executive function is a first domain known to be affected by TBI. Executive function includes "effortful and flexible organization" as well as "strategic planning;" its measurement often taps the following elements: responding to a stimulus after a delay; internal representation (of a schema or action plan); response inhibition; efficient and consistent responding; effortful responding with active strategies; use of flexible strategies (Denckla, 1994). One reason that executive function problems are so common in TBI is that many pediatric head injuries occur to the front of the head (such as riding a bicycle into a parked car or hitting one's forehead on a car's dashboard). Consequently, the front of the brain is easily damaged, owing simply to its immediate trauma and to its housing inside a particularly bony part of the skull. Regarding post-injury executive deficits, Levin and colleagues (1994) found that among 6 to 16 year-olds with TBI, the size of frontal lobe lesions, but not non-frontal lesions, was strongly related to performance on a classic executive function test (the Tower of London). Similarly, working memory impairment, another frontal/executive dysfunction, was shown in a school-aged TBI group compared to controls (Mandalis, Kinsella, Ong, & Anderson, 2007). The brain's frontal lobes, located in this area, are known to support executive functions, among other abilities. Thus, psychologists working in schools sometimes use all or part of Delis-Kaplan Tests of Executive Functioning (Delis, Kaplan, & Kramer, 2001), which includes a tower and working memory tests (among others). The former task requires an individual to create a plan, hold it in memory, and follow it step by step without becoming distracted or responding too impulsively. The latter requires holding material in mind briefly, an obvious challenge that depends upon maintaining focus and ignoring distractions. Other neuropsychological tests for children and teens also include executive tests, such as the NEPSY-2 *Trail Making Test for Children* (Reitan, 2003), *Stroop Color and Word Test* (Golden, Freshwater, & Golden, 2003), and *Wisconsin Card Sorting Task* (Heaton, Chelune, Talley, Kay, & Curtis, 1993).

Declarative memory is a second domain associated with TBI. It is the ability to recall facts and events over time, which is distinct from working memory (i.e., briefly maintaining and manipulating information). Nonetheless, both types of memory appear to be at risk in TBI. In a study of youngsters (6 to 16 years old) who had suffered a TBI, injury severity was associated with ability to learn and retain in memory verbally presented lists of words (i.e., declarative memory; Warschausky, Kay, Chi, & Donders, 2005). This association existed even when the effects of IQ were removed, thus implying that IQ alone may miss some post-injury memory impairments. The NEPSY-2 includes measures of memory related to stories, word lists, and faces. Other pediatric memory scales are the *Children's Memory Scale* (CMS; Cohen,

1997) and the *Wide Range Assessment of Memory and Learning* (WRAML-2; Sheslow & Adams, 2003), which require children to *memorize* visual and verbal information delivered via lists of words, stories, or pictures.

Stroke

A second example of an acquired disorder, albeit rare in school-age children, is stroke (sudden interruption of blood supply to the brain due to a block or hemorrhage). A stroke's neuropsychological effects depend on its location. For example, deficient writing or motor planning may arise from a right hemisphere stroke. Conversely, left-hemisphere strokes particularly jeopardize comprehending directions and expressing thoughts (i.e., verbal skills), although overall IQ may be preserved in both left (and right) side strokes (Max, 2004). To add sensitivity to traditional techniques (IQ, RTI, academic tests), selected neuropsychological tests can be used. For example, regarding right-hemisphere strokes especially, the *Grooved Pegboard* task (Trites, 2002) and Test of Visuomotor Precision from the *NEPSY-2* can sometimes detect problems with efficient and accurate motor performance. The former does so by measuring manual dexterity (placing pegs in a form board while timed) for the preferred and nonpreferred hands (and comparing performance between the two); the latter assesses the ability to complete a paper–pencil task quickly and accurately by drawing a line through a maze. Beyond the verbal subtests included in most IQ assessments (e.g., WISC-IV), verbal fluency and expressive vocabulary tasks such as the Controlled Oral Word Association (COWA/FAS) and *Boston Naming Test* (Kaplan, Goodglass, & Weintraub, 1983), may assist in identifying specific language difficulties, such as those especially at risk in left hemisphere strokes. The COWA/FAS requires a child to quickly specify as many words as possible that begin with a certain letter (verbal fluency), whereas the *Boston Naming Test* requires aloud naming of everyday items (confrontation naming). Questionnaires, such as the *Behavior Assessment System for Children Rating Scale-2* (BASC-2; Kamphaus & Reynolds, 2004) or *Social Skills Rating Scale* (Gresham & Elliot, 1990), can measure behavioral status and coping, at risk from many acquired impairments, including those arising from stroke.

Brain Tumor

A third illustrative acquired disorder is brain tumor, which is also rare in children (e.g., Packer, 1999, estimates 2.5–4/100,000 children per year). As with strokes, pediatric brain tumors produce effects so heterogeneous that comprehensive evaluations are typically warranted for school-planning purposes. Neuropsychological outcomes vary by age at diagnosis, site of tumor, type of treatment, and reoccurrence, among other factors (Aarsen et al., 2006). Visual-spatial deficits were more common in one study, which used an earlier version of the WISC (Poggi et al., 2004). The current WISC-IV lacks some of the visual-spatial demands of its predecessor, which may imply the need for supplemental neuropsychological testing in this area. Because long-term follow-up of children treated for brain tumors generally reveals outcomes characterized by poor overall functioning and severe cognitive, social and behavioral deficits (Aarsen et al., 2006), a comprehensive battery, either administered in a school setting or at the treating clinic or hospital, is generally warranted (see above for elements comprising a comprehensive evaluation).

Special Education Services for Congenital and Acquired Diagnoses

Just as with students who have developmental learning problems, many of those with congenital and acquired conditions also qualify for special education services. One relevant IDEA (Individuals with Disabilities Education Act, 2004) category is Other Health Impairment (OHI), which is used for students with

> a limited strength, vitality, or alertness, including a heightened alertness to environmental stimuli, that results in limited alertness with respect to the educational environment, that—(a) is due to chronic or acute health problems such as asthma, attention deficit disorder or attention deficit hyperactivity disorder, diabetes, epilepsy, a heart condition, hemophilia, lead poisoning, leukemia, nephritis, rheumatic fever, and sickle cell anemia; and (b) adversely affects a child's educational performance. (§ 300.8 [c; 9])

This list of diagnoses is not exhaustive; therefore, children with congenital disorders are sometimes deemed eligible for OHI services. Little research, however, has been conducted on this topic (see Wodrich & Spencer, 2007; Wodrich & DuPaul, 2007). Furthermore, when a congenital disorder is expressed primarily as academic failure, then

SLD, not OHI, designation may be used (e.g., a girl with Turner syndrome and a math problem). Other examples are students with strokes or brain tumors (or an array of other acquired disorders). Qualifying a student for special education may be less equivocal, however, if he or she has sustained a TBI. TBI is its own special education category, defined in IDEA (2004) as an

> acquired injury to the brain caused by an external physical force, resulting in total or partial functional disability or psychosocial impairment, or both, that adversely affects a child's educational performance. The term applies to open or closed head injuries resulting in impairments in one or more areas, such as cognition; language; memory; attention; reasoning; abstract thinking; judgment; problem-solving; sensory, perceptual, and motor abilities; psychosocial behavior; physical functions; information processing; and speech. The term does not include brain injuries that are congenital or degenerative, or brain injuries induced by birth trauma. (§ 300.8 [c; 12])

It may be easy for the reader to see the role of specialized neuropsychological testing in assessing the integrity of memory, attention, and judgment not only in cases such as TBI, but also when other acquired or congenital disorders are present. As a result, many psychologists in and out of the schools supplement traditional IQ and achievement psychometric batteries in these instances. In doing so, they have acknowledged need for greater breadth of assessment tools to understand and then to assist in the education of children with more distinct diagnoses.

Some Things School-Based Evaluations Can't/Shouldn't Do

Generally, more complete evaluations enable greater insights than less complete ones; the systematic examination of areas of function (e.g., memory, motor control) permits otherwise missed problems to be detected; a more complete array of information means that hypothesized deficits and strengths can be well verified. In this chapter, we reflect the belief held by some psychologists that tests often referred to as *neuropsychological* add to the completeness of information that psychologists have to work with. These advantages notwithstanding, two temptations often follow from such complete evaluations. The first is the error of test score over-interpretation. Many test scores are too unreliable to make interpretations that low (especially only slightly low) scores confirm a true deficit. By the same token, their limited reliability means that differences between two test scores may fail to truly document relative strengths and weaknesses. Thus, psychologists' descriptions of subtle impairments regarding discrete aspects of language, memory, or attention that depend on repeated and necessarily precise parsing of test results can be erroneous. For example, a psychologist's evaluation of an elementary student may reveal average scores when constructing geometric shapes with blocks (such as is required of the *WISC-IV* Block Design subtest) and recognizing patterns (such as is required of the *WISC-IV* Matrix Analogies subtest), but low scores when copying shapes (e.g., Bender Gestalt designs) and searching for matching designs (e.g., *NEPSY* Visual Matching). It may be enticing to cite this information alone as evidence for intact visual perception when confronting *organized* visual space but deficient visual processing when confronted with *unstructured* visual arrays. Such interpretations, however, run the risk of reaching beyond the assessment data because no known research supports them. Of course, additional support from classroom observations might strengthen any potential interpretation like this, which should nonetheless probably be offered only as a working hypothesis. Accordingly, consumers of neuropsychological reports are justified in proceeding cautiously upon encountering reports filled with subtle interpretations.

A second related risk is the use of neuropsychological tests in schools to draw specific inferences about brain functioning. For example, a student recovering from a TBI with extremely low scores on all language measures, but intact visual spatial skills (perhaps, also with better left than right hand motor speed) might be said to suffer a left hemisphere impairment. After all, most right handed individuals' language functioning is localized to their brain's left hemisphere (and right hand motor speed as well, depends on left hemisphere integrity). Crucially, however, the decision-rules that psychologists should access to infer left hemisphere impairment in the presence of such scores are seldom spelled out. Furthermore, most school psychologists lack the training to make such inferences about brain functioning regardless of the conspicuousness of the scores at their disposal. Faulty conclusions about brain impairment are a looming possibility when practices like these are undertaken. Equally important, reference to potential lesion sites generally is irrelevant for educational planning. A student who, after an injury, is both unable to consistently understand what is said to her and unable to fully express her thoughts to others, may warrant assistance with speech–language therapy, classroom accommodations to reduce the risk of confusing directions, and reduced demands for oral explanations. Educational programming of this type generally requires understanding of functional skills, abilities, and disabilities and is rarely informed by references to potential left hemisphere impairment.

SUMMARY

The prospective use of neuropsychological tests in school is an interesting, if somewhat odd, topic. On the one hand, few psychologists practicing in school settings possess training in clinical neuropsychology. Furthermore, most school-based evaluations concern students for whom academic failure is the prime issue and for whom references to underlying potential brain impairment are neither helpful nor appropriate. On the other hand, neuroscience research is beginning to identify the neural basis of common academic failure, such as in reading and math. Of more practical importance, some psychometric tests that are deemed neuropsychological appear to hold promise for better understanding and planning for those students with reading and math problems. Moreover, some students do in fact suffer documented brain impairments that are either congenital or acquired, and neuropsychological tests are designed to comprehensively assess the status of precisely these children and adolescents. Consumers, thus, are encouraged to recognize the role for these tests, but to appreciate the limitations expressed in this chapter.

REFERENCES

Aarsen, F. K., Paquier, P. F., Reddingius, R. E., Streng, I. C., Arts, W. F., Evera-Preesman, M., et al. (2006). Functional outcome after low-grade astrocytoma treatment in childhood. *Cancer, 106,* 396–402.

Adams, W., & Sheslow, D. (2003). *Wide range assessment of memory and learning* (2nd ed.). Wilmington, DE: Wide Range.

American Psychiatric Association. (2000). *Diagnostic and statistical manual of mental disorders* (4th ed., text rev.). Washington, DC: Author.

Beck, J. S., Beck, A. T., & Jolly, J. B. (2001). *Beck Youth Inventories.* San Antonio,TX: Psychological Corporation.

Berch, D. B., & Bender, B. G. (2000). Turner syndrome. In K.O. Yeates, M. D. Ris, & H. G. Taylor (Eds.), *Pediatric neuropsychology: Research, theory, and practice* (pp. 252–279). New York: Guilford Press.

Carlson, J. S., Demaray, M. K., & Hunter-Oehmke, S. (2006). A survey of school psychologists' knowledge and training in child psychopharmacology. *Psychology in the Schools, 43,* 623–633.

Christopoulos, P., Deligeoroglou, E., Laggari, V., Christogiorgos, S., & Creatsas, G., (2008). Psychological and behavioural aspects of patients with Turner syndrome from childhood to adulthood: A review of the clinical literature. *Journal of Psychosomatic Obstetrics & Gynecology, 29,* 45–51.

Cohen, M. J. (1997). *Children's memory scale.* San Antonio, TX: Psychological Corporation.

Conners, K. (2000). *Conners' Continuous Performance Test—II manual.* North Tonawanda, NY: Multi-Health Systems.

Cronin, V., & Carver, P. (1998). Phonological sensitivity, rapid naming, and beginning reading. *Applied Psycholinguistics, 19,* 447–461.

D'Amato, R. C., Fletcher-Janzen, E., & Reynolds, C. R. (Eds.). (2005). *Handbook of school neuropsychology.* Hoboken, NJ: Wiley.

Delis, D. C., Kaplan, E., & Kramer, J. (2001). *Delis Kaplan executive function system.* San Antonio,TX: Psychological Corporation.

Denckla, M. B. (1994). Measurement of executive function. In G. R. Lyon (Ed.), *Frames of reference for the assessment of learning disabilities: New views of measurement issues* (pp. 117–142). Baltimore, MD: Paul H. Brooks.

Fales, C., Knowlton, B., Holyoak, K., Geschwind, D., Swerdloff, R., & Gonzalo, I. (2003). Working memory and relational reasoning in Klinefelter syndrome. *Journal of International Neuropsychological Society, 9,* 839–846.

Federal Register. (2006). [34 *Code of Federal Regulations* Part 300 and 301: Assistance to states for the education of children with disabilities and preschool grants for children with disabilities; final rule]. Washington, DC: U.S. Government Printing Office.

Flanagan, D. P., Ortiz, A. O., Alfonso, V. C., & Dynda, A. M. (2006). Integration of response to intervention and norm-referenced tests in learning disability identification: Learning from the Tower of Babel. *Psychology in the Schools, 43,* 807–825.

Fletcher, J. M., Lyon, G. R., Fuchs, L. S., & Barnes, M. A. (2007). *Learning disabilities: From identification to intervention.* New York: Guilford Press.

Fletcher-Janzen, E. (2005). The school neuropsychological examination. In R. C. D'Amato, E. Fletcher-Janzen, & C. R. Reynolds (Eds.), *Handbook of school neuropsychology* (pp. 172–212). Hoboken, NJ: Wiley.

Fuchs, L. S., & Fuchs, D. (2003). Enhancing the mathematical problem-solving of students with mathematics disabilities. In H. L. Swanson, K. R. Harris, & S. Graham (Eds.), *Handbook of learning disabilities* (pp. 199–212). New York: Guilford Press.

Fuchs, L. S., Fuchs, D., Compton, D. L., Powell, S. R., Seethaler, P. M., Capizzi, A. M., et al. (2006). The cognitive correlates of third-grade skill in arithmetic, algorithmic computation, and arithmetic word problems. *Journal of Educational Psychology, 98*, 29–43.

Geary, D. C. (1993). Mathematical disabilities: Cognitive, neuropsychological, and genetic components. *Psychological Bulletin, 114*, 345–362.

Geary, D. C. (2003). Learning disabilities in arithmetic: Problem-solving differences and cognitive deficits. In H. L. Swanson, K. R. Harris, & S. Graham (Eds.), *Handbook of learning disabilities* (pp. 199–212). New York: Guilford Press.

Geary, D. C. Hoard, M. K., & Hamson, C. O. (1999). Numerical and arithmetical cognition: Patterns of functions and deficits in children at risk for a mathematical disability. *Journal of Experimental Child Psychology, 74*, 213–239.

Gerschwind, D. H., & Dykens, E., (2004). Neurobehavioral and psychosocial issues in Klinefelter syndrome. *Learning Disabilities Research and Practice, 19*, 166–173.

Golden, C. J., Freshwater, S. M., & Golden, Z. (2003). *Stroop Color and Word Test.* Wood Dale, IL: Stoelting Company.

Gresham, F. M. (2007). Evolution of the response-to-intervention concept: Empirical foundations and recent developments. In S. R. Jimerson, M. J. Burns, & A. M. VanDerHeyden (Eds.), *Handbook of response to intervention: The science and practice of assessment and intervention* (pp. 10–24). New York: Springer Publishing Company.

Gresham, F. M., & Elliot, S. N. (1990). *Social Skills Rating Scale.* Circle Pines, MN: American Guidance Service.

Hale, J. B., & Fiorello, C. A. (2004). *School neuropsychology: A practitioner's handbook.* New York: Guilford Press.

Hale, J. B., Kaufman, A., Naglieri, J. A., & Kavale, K. A. (2006). Implementation of IDEA: Integrating response to intervention and cognitive assessment methods. *Psychology in the Schools, 43*, 753–770.

Hawley, C., Ward. A. B., Magnay, A. R., & Mychalkiw, W. (2004). Return to school after brain injury. *Archives of Disease in Children, 89*, 136–142.

Heaton, R. K., Chelune, G. J., Talley, J. L., Kay, G. C., & Curtiss, G. (1993). *Wisconsin Card Sorting Test.* Odessa, FL: PAR.

Hodapp, R. M., Dykens, E. M., Hagerman, R. J., & Schreiner, R. (1990). Developmental implications of changing trajectories of IQ in males with fragile X syndrome. *Journal of the American Academy of Child and Adolescent Psychiatry, 29*, 214–219.

Individuals with Disabilities Education Act, 34 C.F.R. § 300.8(c)(9) (2004).

Jimerson, S. R., Burns, M. K., & VanDerHeyden, A. M. (Eds.). (2007). *Handbook of response to intervention: The science and practice of assessment and intervention.* New York: Springer Publishing Company.

Kamphaus, R. W., & Reynolds, C. R. (2004). *The behavior assessment system for children* (2nd ed.). New York: Pearson.

Kaplan, K., Goodglass, H., & Weintraub, S. (1983). *Boston Naming Test.* Baltimore, MD: Lippincott, Williams, and Wilkins.

Kirby, J. R., Parrila, R. K., & Pfeiffer, S. L. (2003). Naming speed and phonological awareness as predictors of reading development. *Journal of Educational Psychology, 95*, 453–464.

Korkman, M., Kirk, U., & Kemp, S. (1998). *A developmental neuropsychological assessment (NEPSY) manual.* San Antonio, TX: Psychological Corporation.

Korkman, M., Kirk, U., & Kemp, S. (2007). *A developmental neuropsychological assessment—2 (NEPSY-2) manual*. San Antonio, TX: Psychological Corporation.

Kovacs, M. (1992). *Children's Depression Inventory*. North Tonawanda, NY: Multi-Health Systems.

Levin, H. S., Mendelsohn, D., Lilly, M. A., Fletcher, F. M., Culhane, K. A., Chapman, S. B., et al. (1994). Tower of London performance in relation to magnetic resonance imaging following closed head injury in children. *Neuropsychology, 8,* 171–179.

Lindamood, P., & Lindamood, P. (1998). *The Lindamood phoneme sequencing program for reading, spelling, and speech*. Austin, TX: PRO-ED.

Mandalis, A., Kinsella, G., Ong, B., & Anderson, V. (2007). Working memory and new learning following pediatric traumatic brain injury. *Developmental Neuropsychology, 32,* 683–701.

Manning, M. A., & Hoyme, H. E. (2002). Diagnosis and management of the adolescent boy with Klinefelter syndrome. *Adolescent Medicine, 13,* 367–74.

Max, J. E., (2004). Effect of side of lesion on neuropsychological performance in childhood stroke. *Journal of the International Neuropsychological Society, 10,* 698–708.

Mazzocco, M. M. M. (2001). Math learning disability and math LD subtypes: Evidence from studies of Turner syndrome, fragile X syndrome, and neurofibromatosis type 1. *Journal of Learning Disabilities, 34,* 520–533.

Morris, R. D., Steubling, K. K., Fletcher, J. M., Shaywitz, S. E., Lyon, G. R., Shankweiler, D. P., et al. (1998). Subtypes of reading disability: Variability around a phonological core. *Journal of Educational Psychology, 90,* 347–373.

National Association of School Psychologists. (2000). *Standards for training and field placement programs in school psychology*. Retrieved October 13, 2008, from http://www.nasponline.org/standards/FinalStandards.pdf

National Center for Educational Statistics (NCES). (2005). *The nation's report card: Math highlights 2005*. Washington, DC: U.S. Department of Education.

National Reading Panel. (2000). *Teaching children to read: An evidence-based assessment of the scientific research literature on reading and its implications for reading instruction*. (NIH Publication No. 00-4754). Washington, DC: U.S. Government Printing Office.

Ofiesh, N. (2006). Response to intervention and the identification of specific learning disabilities: Why we need comprehensive evaluation as part of the process. *Psychology in the Schools, 43,* 883–888.

Packer, R. J. (1999). Brain tumors in children. *Neurological Review, 56,* 421–425.

Poggi, G., Liscio, M., Galbiati, S., Adduci, A., Massimino, M., Gandola, L., et al. (2004). Brain tumors in children and adolescents: Cognitive and psychological disorders at different ages. *Psycho-Oncology, 14,* 386–395.

Prifitera, A., Saklofske, D. H., Weiss, L. G., & Rolfhus, E. (2005). The WISC-IV in the clinical assessment context. In A. Prifitera, D. H. Saklofske, & L. G. Weiss (Eds.), *WISC-IV clinical use and interpretation: Scientist-practitioner perspectives* (pp. 3–32). New York: Elsevier.

Reitan, H. (2003). *Trail Making Test for Children*. Tucson, AZ: Reitan Neuropsychology Laboratory.

Reynolds, C. R. (2007). *Koppitz-2: The Koppitz developmental scoring system for the Bender-Gestalt Test*. Austin, TX: Pro-Ed.

Ross, J. L., Roeltgen, D. P., Stefanatos, G., Benecke, R., Zeger, M., Kushner, H., et al. (2008). Cognitive and motor development during childhood in boys with Klinefelter syndrome. *American Journal of Medical Genetics, Part A. (146A)*, 708–719.

Rourke, B. P., & Conway, J. A. (1997). Disabilities of arithmetic and mathematical reasoning: Perspectives from neurology and neuropsychology. *Journal of Learning Disabilities, 30*, 34–46.

Schmitt, A. J., & Wodrich, D. L. (2004). Validation of a developmental neuropsychological assessement (NEPSY) through comparison of neurological, scholastic concerns, and control groups. *Archives of Clinical Neuropsychology, 19*, 1077–1093.

Schmitt, A. J., & Wodrich, D. L. (2008). Reasons and rationales for neuropsychological tests in a multitier system of school services. *Psychology in the Schools, 45*, 826–837.

Shaywitz, S. (2003). *Overcoming dyslexia: A new and complete science-based program for reading problems at any level.* New York: Alfred A. Knopf.

Sheslow, D., & Adams, W. (2003). *Wide Range Assessment of Memory and Learning* (2nd ed.). Lutz, FL: Psychological Assessment Resources.

Siegel, L. S. (2003). Basic cognitive processes and reading disabilities. In H. L. Swanson, K. R. Swanson, H. L., Harris, K. R., & Graham, S. (Eds.), *Handbook of learning disabilities* (pp. 158–181). New York: Guilford Press.

Torgesen, J. K., Alexander, A. W., Wagner, R. K., Rashotte, C. A., Voeller, K. K. S., & Conway, T. (2001). Intensive remedial instruction for children with severe reading disabilities: Immediate and long-term outcomes from two instructional approaches. *Journal of Learning Disabilities, 34*, 33–58, 78.

Trites, R. (2002). *Grooved pegboard.* Lafayette, IN: Lafayette Instrument.

U.S. Department of Education. (2005). *27th annual report to congress on the implementation of the Individuals with Disabilities Education Act: Volume 2.* Washington DC: Author.

University of Oregon. (2004). *Big ideas in beginning reading.* Retrieved September 2, 2008, from http://reading.uoregon.edu/big_ideas/trial_bi_index.php

Varma, S., McCandliss, B. D., & Schwartz, D. L. (2008). Scientific and pragmatic challenges for bridging education and neuroscience. *Educational Researcher, 37*, 140–152.

Wagner, R. K., Torgesen, J. K., & Rashotte, C. A. (1999). *Comprehensive test of phonological processing.* Austin, TX: PRO-ED.

Walker, N. W., Boling, M. S., & Cobb, H. (1999). Training of school psychologists in neuropsychology and brain injury: Results of a national survey of training programs. *Child Neuropsychology, 5*, 137–142.

Warschausky, S., Kay, J. B., Chi, P., & Donders, J. (2005). Hierarchical linear modeling of California Verbal Learning Test-children's version learning curve characteristics following childhood traumatic head injury. *Neuropsychology, 19*, 193–198.

Watkins, M. W., Wilson, S. M., Kotz, K. M., Carbone, M. C., & Babula, T. (2006). Factor structure of the Wechsler Intelligence Scale-Fourth Edition among referred students. *Educational and Psychological Measurement, 66*, 975–983.

Wechsler, D. (2001). *Wechsler Individual Achievement Test* (2nd ed.). San Antonio, TX: Psychological Corporation.

Wechsler, D. (2003). *Wechsler Intelligence Scale for Children-Fourth Edition: Administration and Scoring Manual.* San Antonio, TX: Psychological Corporation.

Wodrich, D. L., & DuPaul, G. J. (2007). A survey of pediatricians regarding the other health impairment category. *Communique, 36,* 27–30.

Wodrich, D. L., Pfeiffer, S. I., & Landau, S. (2008). Contemplating the new DSM-V: Considerations from psychologists who work with school children. *Professional Psychology: Research & Practice, 39,* 626–632.

Wodrich, D. L., & Schmitt, A. J. (2006). *Patterns of learning disorders: Working systematically from assessment to intervention.* New York: Guilford Press.

Wodrich, D. L., & Spencer, M. L. S. (2007). The other health impairment category and health-based classroom accommodations: School psychologists' perceptions and practices. *Journal of Applied School Psychology, 24,* 109–125.

Wodrich, D. L., Spencer, M. L. S., & Daley, K. B. (2006). Combining RTI and psychoeducational assessment: What we must assume to do otherwise. *Psychology in the Schools, 43,* 797–806.

Wolf, M., & Bowers, P. G. (1999). The double-deficit hypothesis for the developmental dyslexias. *Journal of Educational Psychology, 91,* 415–438.

Woodcock, R. W., McGrew, K. S., & Mather, N. (2007). *Woodcock-Johnson III: Normative Update Tests of Cognitive Abilities and Tests of Achievement.* Itasca, IL: Riverside Publishing.

Yeates, K. O., & Taylor, H., G. (2006). Behavior problems in school and their educational correlates among children with traumatic brain injury. *Exceptionality, 14,* 141–154.

10

Integrating Neuropsychological Principles With Response to Intervention for Comprehensive School-Based Practice

JAMES B. HALE, CATHERINE A. FIORELLO, AND REBECCA THOMPSON

There are two practice paradigms emerging in educational settings, both of which have considerable relevance for neuropsychologists practicing in schools. These paradigms include the response-to-intervention (RTI) and school neuropsychology (SNP) approaches to school-based assessment and intervention. Although it has been suggested that RTI and SNP approaches are in opposition to each other (e.g., Reschly, 2005), the growing consensus among reasoned stakeholders is that both approaches have empirical support, and are critically needed for serving children with and without disabilities (Fuchs & Deshler, 2007; Hale, Kaufman, Naglieri, & Kavale, 2006; Kavale & Flanagan, 2007; Semrud-Clikeman, 2005). To extend the valuable knowledge and skills offered by both RTI and SNP to children, advocates of both paradigms must let go of misconceptions and limitations of past practices, and critically examine the current science for both. The thesis of this chapter is that the behavioral methods touted by RTI advocates are essential practice, but neuropsychological approaches can become an integral part of a child's educational program, especially for those children who do not respond or are treatment resistant (Fletcher-Janzen & Reynolds, 2008; Hale, Fiorello, Miller, et al., 2008).

The RTI approach is valuable in that it allows for redistribution of education funding from special education for the preventative purpose of serving children who have learning difficulty in general education (Fuchs, Deshler, & Reschly, 2004). Many of these children need supplemental instruction to attain high standards set forth by the No Child Left Behind legislation. With its roots in behavioral psychology, RTI is decidedly focused on direct assessment of child academic performance, regular progress monitoring of student curricular achievements, and increasingly intense instruction for children who are falling short of expected benchmarks (Barnett, Daly, Jones, & Lentz, 2004). Although RTI advocates see the value of direct assessment of child performance, they largely advocate curriculum-based measurement (CBM, e.g., Shinn, 2002), not assessment of cognitive and neuropsychological processing, with some fervent advocates arguing that latter assessment tools are largely irrelevant for both assessment and intervention purposes (Fletcher, Denton, & Francis, 2005; Reschly, 2005).

As RTI has become increasingly popular in school-based practice, advances in neuropsychological assessment and intervention practices for children with high incidence disorders have been equally impressive (see Hale, Fiorello, Miller, et al., 2008). With the advent of noninvasive neuroimaging techniques and sophisticated neuropsychological and psychological tests, understanding of pediatric brain–behavior relationships are no longer based on adult findings, or traumatic brain injury samples, but now use typical samples and children with disorders once considered to be outside the purview of neuropsychological research (Fiez & Petersen, 1998; Filipek, 1999; Semrud-Clikeman & Pliszka, 2005). Researchers are not only demonstrating brain–behavior relationships in children with learning disabilities, attention disorders, and other psychopathologies, but showing that assessment-intervention relationships can be established to demonstrate treatment efficacy of neuropsychological findings (e.g., Berninger et al., 2000; Chenault, Thomson, Abbott, & Berninger, 2006; Fiorello, Hale, & Synder, 2006; Gustafson, Ferreira, & Ronnberg, 2007; Hale, Fiorello, & Brown, 2005; Hale, Kaufman, Naglieri, & Kavale, 2006; Helland, 2007; Lovett, Steinbach, and Frijters, 2000; Naglieri & Johnson, 2000; Shaywitz et al., 2003; Simos et al., 2007; Smit-Glaude, van Strien, Licht, & Bakker, 2005).

Twenty years ago there were few studies that explored brain–behavior relationships in academic domains such as reading, math, or writing, or high incidence behavior disorders such as ADHD, but now there are numerous studies that show these relationships for both academic domains and psychopathologies (see D'Amato, Fletcher-Janzen, & Reynolds, 2005; Denckla, 2007; Feifer & Rattan, 2009; Hale & Fiorello, 2004; Miller, 2009). Extending this knowledge of typical and atypical child performance on neuropsychological and neuroimaging measures to children in classrooms is the next critical step. One day in the not so distant future we will see training in brain–behavior relationships as a critical component of all teacher and psychologist higher education training programs, but before this can happen people must let go of misconceptions about the utility of neuropsychological principles and practices in schools, and embrace scientific research programs designed to make brain–behavior relationships in classrooms meaningful for all children, not just children with disabilities or documented brain injury.

THE FOUNDATIONS OF CHANGE: THE RISE OF RESPONSE TO INTERVENTION

Traditional assessment practices in schools have been tied to special education eligibility under generic categories such as specific learning disability, serious emotional disturbance, or other health impaired. Because school psychologists have been traditionally identified as *gatekeepers* for disability entitlement purposes, they may have limited understanding of different disorders or disorder subtypes (Hale & Fiorello, 2004), and little experience carrying out academic or behavioral interventions (Hale, Fiorello, Miller, et al., 2008). This lack of diagnostic specificity can cause confusion and attenuate treatment results, particularly when analyzing outcomes for large heterogeneous groups (Hale et al., 2006; Kavale, Fuchs, & Scruggs, 1994).

The RTI model was primarily developed to address concerns with the traditional severe discrepancy model for identifying specific learning disabilities (SLD). This model was supported by research suggesting the global IQ was the only intelligence test score worth examining (Watkins, Glutting, & Lei, 2007), yet this belief failed to recognize that the same processing deficits that interfere with achievement also depress intellectual ability scores, making discrepancy less likely (Fiorello et al., 2007; Willis & Dumont, 2006) or that intelligence tests are best represented by individual factors, not global IQ scores (Hale, Fiorello, Kavanagh, Holdnack, & Aloe, 2007). In addition, the discrepancy model did not provide services for children until their academic problems became significant (i.e., "Wait to Fail"; Fletcher, Coulter, Reschly, & Vaughn, 2004), making prevention and early intervention unlikely (Hale et al., 2006). Although diagnostic sensitivity and specificity can be enhanced with examination of factor and subtest profiles for children with neuropsychological disorders such as SLD (Fiorello et al., 2001; Fiorello, Hale, Snyder, Forrest, & Teodori, 2008; Hale et al., 2001, 2007; Hale, Fiorello, Miller, et al., 2008; Mayes & Calhoun, 2006), this type of profile analysis has been highly criticized in the literature (McDermott, Fantuzzo, & Glutting, 1990). In addition to problems with ability–achievement discrepancy, SLD has been inconsistently operationalized across schools, districts, and states (Reschly & Hosp, 2004; Scruggs & Mastropieri, 2002), which led to high rates of SLD false positives and negatives (Hale, Fiorello, Miller, et al., 2008) and multiple studies showing little difference between those classified with SLD and those with low achievement (Fletcher et al., 1994; Fuchs, Fuchs, Mathes, Lipsey, & Roberts, 2001; Stanovich & Siegel, 1994).

The RTI model is touted as a solution to the inadequacies of past practices, as it combines academic assessment and intervention practices (Brown-Chidsey & Steege, 2005; VanDerHeyden, Witt, & Gilbertson, 2007), with some suggesting that the SLD concept is no longer useful (e.g., Gresham et al., 2005; Ysseldyke & Marston, 2000). Despite the explosion of neuropsychological research suggesting the validity of SLD (Hale, Fiorello, Miller, et al., 2008), some suggest we should move to a low achievement model, where all underachieving students would receive services (Dombrowski, Kamphaus, & Reynolds, 2004; Fletcher, Coulter, Reschly, & Vaughn, 2004; Stanovich, 1994). Although underachieving students certainly need instructional support, this should not result in a professional quid pro quo for eliminating the SLD construct, especially when overwhelming neuropsychological evidence and subtype studies attest to the validity of the SLD concept (e.g., Hale, Fiorello, Miller, et al., 2008).

Regardless, RTI was proposed and adopted in the federal Individuals with Disabilities Education Improvement Act (IDEA, 2004) as a method of special education determination. Although there are several models of RTI that have been developed (Deno, 2002; Kovaleski, 2002; O'Connor, Harty, & Fulmer, 2005; Tilly, Reschly, & Grimes, 1999; Vaughn, Linan-

Thompson, & Hickman, 2003), they all generally describe a multitiered approach in which increasingly intense instruction is provided to students who are not succeeding in the general education curriculum. First, prevention is implemented through research-supported quality instructional practices with universal screening. For those students who fail to make progress in the regular curriculum, a series of supportive interventions are implemented and the child is monitored over time to see if further intervention is needed. Although different mechanisms, such as benchmark attainment or learning slope deviations, have been proposed for eventual determination of special education eligibility (Fuchs, Fuchs, & Compton, 2004; Gerber, 2005; Marston, 2005; Speece, 2005), failure to respond is a key component.

The evidence-based teaching, early intervention, and frequent progress monitoring inherent in RTI are designed to meet the needs of all children (Hale, 2006), particularly those who do not meet traditional classification criteria for special education (Dombrowki et al., 2004). However, RTI is an intervention process, not a diagnostic procedure (Fiorello et al., 2006; Hale, Fiorello, Miller, et al., 2008; Reynolds & Shaywitz, 2009). It has limited utility in differential diagnosis of child disorders, as underachievement may be due to multiple causes (Hale, 2006; Kavale, Kaufman, Naglieri, & Hale, 2005; Mather & Gregg, 2006) and both benchmark and slope information for identification leads to high rates of false positives and negatives (Barth et al., 2008; Fuchs & Deshler, 2007; Fuchs, Fuchs, & Compton, 2004; Speece, 2005). In addition, RTI fails to meet the IDEA (2004) SLD statutory requirements, which indicate SLD is defined by an underlying processing disorder (Hale et al., 2006; Kavale et al., 2005; Schrank, Miller, Caterino, & Desrochers, 2006). Finally, there is little agreement as to whether a standard protocol or problem-solving RTI approach is best, with balanced practice models suggesting both should be included to maximize internal and external validity in the decision making process (Hale, 2006; Hale et al., 2006).

Thus, although the RTI model addresses an important need for universal and early intervention in schools, it does not address differential diagnosis of brain-based childhood disorders and special education identification and service delivery (Fletcher-Janzen & Reynolds, 2008). Many practitioners and researchers have recommended a combination of RTI and psychoeducational/neurospychological assessment to increase diagnostic sensitivity and specificity of SLD and other disorders (Hale,

Fiorello, Miller, et al., 2008; Kavale, Holdnack, & Mostert, 2005), with a growing consensus emerging that both are needed to overcome the shortcomings of both models (Willis & Dumont, 2006; Fiorello, Hale, & Snyder, 2006; Flanagan, Ortiz, Alfonso, & Dynda , 2006; Hale, 2006; Hale et al., 2006; Ofiesh, 2006; Schrank et al., 2006; Wodrich, Spencer, & Daley, 2006).

NEUROPSYCHOLOGICAL ADVANCES IN THE RTI ERA: CONVERGENCE OF NEUROPSYCHOLOGICAL AND CATTELL-HORN-CARROLL THEORY

At the same time that academics and practitioners are wrestling with the uses and limitations of RTI in schools, the fields of neuropsychology and neuroscience have shown comparable advances in theory and practice. No longer tied to research on adults with traumatic brain injury, the fields of pediatric and school neuropsychology have seen incredible advances in our understanding of typical and atypical development through use of more sophisticated assessment tools (e.g., *NEPSY-II*; Delis-Kaplan Executive Function Scale; Process Assessment of the Learner-II; Test of Memory and Learning-Second Edition) and an abundance of neuroimaging studies, all of which attest to the value of neuropsychological evaluation of children with disabilities (see Berninger & Richards, 2002; Coch, Dawson, & Fischer, 2007; D'Amato, Fletcher-Janzen, & Reynolds, 2005; Hale & Fiorello, 2004; Miller, 2007; Yeates, Ris, & Taylor, 1999). Through visual inspection of neuroimaging findings, we can see that a particular child may use multiple brain areas simultaneously to complete even a simple cognitive or academic task. However, these brain areas may differ for typical children and children with disabilities, and for those with disabilities who respond to intervention, their brain functions normalize on neuropsychological and neuroimaging measures (Coch et al., 2007; Hale, Fiorello, & Brown, 2005; Richards et al., 2006; Simos et al., 2007). These findings help us recognize that localizationist perspectives have little bearing on our modern understanding of brain function, rather we must examine interrelated brain systems in our understanding of function (Hale & Fiorello, 2004). For differential diagnosis, the answer is often not an "either-or" one, but rather a "how much," or as Goldberg (2001) suggests, a *gradiential* approach to understanding function and dysfunction.

The explosion of cognitive and neuropsychological studies seen in the last decades are paving a fascinating empirical path that demonstrates a convergence of neuropsychological (e.g., Lurian) and the cognitive-psychometric (e.g., Cattell-Horn-Carroll) theories, which adds crucial validity evidence for both approaches (Fiorello, Hale, Snyder, Forrest, & Teodori, 2008). Establishing brain–behavior relationships and their neurobiological correlates of cognitive functions (Alarcon, Pennington, Filipek, & Defries, 2000) certainly furthers our understanding of child function and dysfunction, but it also provides a crucial foundation for establishing ecological and treatment validity evidence of findings. This knowledge, combined with the enduring perspectives of A. R. Luria (1973), have resulted in a reconceptualization of both brain structure and function, especially as applied to the cerebral hemispheres (Bryan & Hale, 2001) and relationships among cortical and subcortical structures (Koziol & Budding, 2009). Although some might suggest that *cognitive* and *neuropsychological* constructs are distinct, we believe any attempt at artificial segregation of these highly related fields only serves to undermine our efforts at serving children in our schools, both those with and without disabilities.

Some of the best psychometric tools available today are considered cognitive tests, not intelligence ones. Although the debate between single factor/IQ interpretation (e.g., Watkins et al., 2007) and idiographic analysis of cognitive/neuropsychological factors (e.g., Hale et al., 2007; Hale, Fiorello, Dumont, et al., 2008) of cognitive tests will likely continue, the majority of measures available today are designed to measure multiple constructs, not IQ or a single factor "g" (Fiorello et al., 2001, 2007; Hale et al., 2006, 2007; Hale, Fiorello, Dumont, et al., 2008; Hale, Fiorello, Miller, et al., 2008). Psychometric research of cognitive factors has been primarily based on large-scale factor-analytic studies, has sought a model of cognitive functioning, culminating in Cattell-Horn-Carroll Theory (CHC Theory; McGrew & Wendling, in press). CHC Theory is a three-stratum taxonomy, with a third-stratum general term (g), between 10 and 16 broad cognitive abilities at stratum II, and upwards of 70 narrow abilities currently identified at stratum I. Although there is not an exact correspondence between the individual difference traits identified through factor analysis and the constructs identified through neuropsychological research, there is broad and uncanny convergence of the two (Fiorello et al., 2008; Fiorello, Hale, Decker, & Coleman, 2009). This convergence of theories is remarkable given that few cognitive and neuropsychological researchers are working together, or even cite each other's literature, in developing these complementary models (see Table 10.1). Using these models to identify processing deficits and develop individualized interventions shows great promise in identifying and serving children with and without disabilities.

Combining RTI With Neuropsychological Evaluations for Serving Children With Disabilities

There are many good reasons to rigorously adopt RTI principles and practices, but children with disabilities may not respond, and for these children a comprehensive cognitive/neuropsychological evaluation can be important, not only for identification, but intervention purposes as well (Hale et al., 2006). Neuropsychologists can serve this important need in the schools, either through school-based practice (school neuropsychologist) or in performing Independent Educational Evaluations in clinic or medical settings (pediatric neuropsychologist). Instead of maintaining a rigid, dogmatic position that practitioners must do RTI or comprehensive cognitive/neuropsychological assessment, many stakeholders are now arguing the value of multiple models and practices for serving children in the schools (e.g., Fletcher-Janzen & Reynolds, 2008; Hale, Fiorello, Miller, et al., 2008; Machek & Nelson, 2007; Schrank et al., 2006). More thorough evaluations using cognitive and neuropsychological measures are necessary for nonresponders, because nonresponse can happen for many reasons (Mather & Gregg, 2006). As a result, RTI is insufficient for differential diagnosis of SLD or other disorders affecting achievement and behavior in the classroom (Barth et al., 2008; Hain, Hale, & Kendorski, 2009; Hale et al., 2006; Fiorello et al., 2006; Speece, 2005). Not only is comprehensive cognitive and neuropsychological evaluation a more scientific approach to understanding disorders, but it allows one to develop truly individualized education programs, as it is clear that nonresponders do not benefit from more intense ones (see Hale, Fiorello, et al., 2008).

Our Cognitive Hypothesis Testing model (CHT; Hale & Fiorello, 2004, see Figure 10.1) provides a scientific method approach for integrating cognitive and neuropsychological assessment for children who do not respond to standard interventions. The CHT approach is similar

Table 10.1

LINKING CATTELL–HORN–CARROLL AND BRAIN–BEHAVIOR RELATIONSHIPS

CHC BROAD ABILITIES	NEUROPSYCHOLOGICAL FUNCTION	RELEVANT CORTICAL-SUBCORTICAL STRUCTURES
Fluid reasoning (Gf)	Novel/adaptive problem solving	Right frontal, especially dorsolateral circuit
Comprehension-Knowledge (Gc)	Long-term memory, crystallized ability, automaticity	Left hemisphere, particularly left temporal lobe
Short-term memory (Gsm)	Working memory	Frontal-subcortical circuits, particularly dorsolateral and dorsal cingulate circuits
Visual processing (Gv)	Visual global and visual local processing, object recognition	Occipital lobe and dorsal (global-right; local-left)/ventral (object recognition) streams
Auditory processing (Ga)	Auditory discrimination and perception	Superior temporal lobe
Long-term storage and retrieval (Glr)	Memory encoding, storage, and retrieval	Frontal-subcortical circuits, particularly dorsolateral circuit for encoding and retrieval; temporal lobe and hippocampus for storage
Processing speed (Gs)	Psychomotor speed and fluency; decision speed; sustained attention	Cingulate circuit, premotor and motor cortices, cerebellum
Reaction and decision speed (Gt)	Reaction time, timing, decision making	Cingulate and dorsolateral circuits, cerebellum

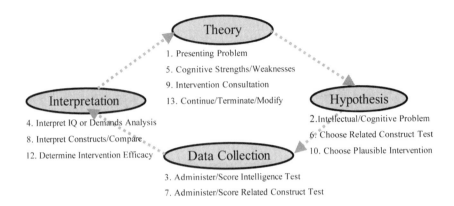

Figure 10.1 The Cognitive Hypothesis Testing model.

Source: Hale, J. B., Fiorello, C. A. (2004). *School Neuropsychology: A Practitioner's Handbook.*
New York: Guilford Press.

to RTI in that both require ongoing data-based decision-making over
time, overcoming a key criticism of some who oppose standardized
assessments of high incidence disorders (Fletcher et al., 2005). Another
criticism of cognitive and neuropsychological assessment is that it is
unrelated to intervention (Reschly, 2005), but the CHT model is specifically designed to make assessment data relevant for intervention (Hale &
Fiorello, 2004). The CHT approach has been used to document these
brain–behavior intervention relationships in children with reading (Fiorello, Hale, & Snyder, 2006), math (Hale et al., 2006), and attention
(Reddy & Hale, 2007) disorders, and is advocated for use in both
educational (Hale, Fiorello, Miller, et al., 2008) and neuropsychological
(Miller, Getz, & Leffard, 2006) settings.

In our balanced practice model that includes RTI and comprehensive
evaluation of neuropsychological processes (Hale, 2006; Hale et al.,
2006), approximately 85% of children would be served using a Tier 1
standard protocol RTI, and if children do not respond, they would be
provided with individualized problem-solving RTI at Tier 2 (serving
approximately 10% of the population, both of which happen in the
general education setting (Fiorello et al., 2006; Hale, 2006; Hale et al.,
2006). Only nonresponders at Tiers 1 and 2, about 5% of the population,

would be referred for comprehensive CHT evaluations for consideration of Tier 3 special education services. Both standardized and problem-solving protocols are necessary, because they would foster decision-making processes that take into account both external and internal validity respectively (Hale, 2006). Failure to RTI would be sufficient for SLD classification in some models (e.g., Fletcher et al., 2005; Reschly, 2005), but a comprehensive CHT evaluation is necessary, both for identification and intervention purposes at Tier 3. Neither RTI nor ability–achievement discrepancy address the statutory requirements, or differentiate SLD subtypes or SLD from other disorders, in part because there is no *true positive* in these models.

The CHT model has an advantage over traditional profile analysis in that it requires practitioners to use intellectual/cognitive tests only as screening tools; hypotheses derived from them must be tested using other cognitive or neuropsychological measures with greater specificity. Since multifactorial intellectual/cognitive subtest performance varies for multiple reasons not easily identified in large group studies (Baron, 2005), hypotheses must be confirmed or refuted using multiple data sources, not only for differential diagnoses, but also for developing individualized interventions sensitive to the child's needs (Hale & Fiorello, 2004). These interventions are developed, monitored, evaluated, and recycled until treatment efficacy is obtained (Hale & Fiorello, 2004), and single subject case study data supports the utility of such approaches (e.g., Fiorello et al., 2006; Hale et al., 2006; Reddy & Hale, 2007).

Children with brain-based disorders experience developmental deficits not delays (e.g., Castellanos et al., 2002; Francis, Shaywitz, Stuebing, Shaywitz, & Fletcher, 1996). Although using RTI approaches in providing similar intervention strategies with varying intensities (e.g., Barnett, Daly, Jones, & Lentz, 2004; Reschly, 2005) may work with children who have environmentally determined learning delay, it will not meet the academic and behavioral needs of children with brain-based disorders (Hale, Fiorello, Miller, et al., 2008). For an accurate identification of SLD and other brain-based disorders, both the statutory (i.e., disorder definition) and regulatory (disorder identification) requirements should be met according to the law (Hale et al., 2006; Kavale et al., 2005). CHT can be used with our Concordance-Discordance Model (see Figure 10.2; Hale & Fiorello, 2004) to determine if a child has a SLD, other disability, or some other cause for his or her learning and behavior

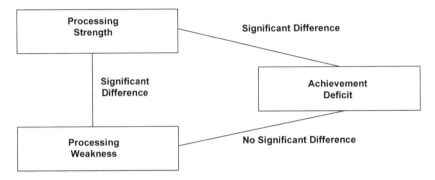

Figure 10.2 Concordance–discordance model of SLD identification.

difficulties. This model of SLD identification would comply with the "Third Method" of SLD identification specified in the federal regulations (34 C.F.R. Parts 300 and 301; *Federal Register*, 2006) "(3) May permit the use of other alternative research-based procedures for determining whether a child has a specific learning disability, as defined in §300.8(c)(10)." As with many legislative pieces, this "Third Method" is necessarily vague and nonspecific, but likely reflects similar empirically supported methods as viable alternatives to ability-achievement discrepancy and RTI (Hale, Flanagan, & Naglieri, 2008). The C-DM approach used within the CHT model ensures both the statutory and regulatory requirements for SLD identification, and with its empirical approach to assessment and intervention, could lead to better outcomes for children identified for special education services (Hale, Fiorello, Miller, et al., 2008).

NEUROPSYCHOLOGICAL PROCESSES RELEVANT FOR READING ACHIEVEMENT

Twenty years ago few neuropsychological studies had examined academic function and dysfunction. However, recent empirical advances have led to a good understanding of the brain processes involved in academic achievement, especially reading. Children don't have one brain for learning in classrooms, another for interacting with peers on the playground, and a third for completing standardized neuropsycho-

logical and academic tests. To serve the needs of children with disabilities, cognitive and neuropsychological data should be integrated with
all data sources, including academic achievement and psychosocial
functioning, if results are to be meaningful for both identification and
intervention purposes (Hale, Fiorello, Miller, et al., 2008). In this way
a neuropsychologist practicing in the schools can ensure that a child's
test results are not only useful for identification purposes, but also for
ecological and treatment validity.

Spoken language develops naturally in neurologically intact children, shifting from a right hemisphere dominance early in infancy to
left hemisphere dominance by early childhood (Goldberg, 2001; Hale &
Fiorello, 2004). Although phonological awareness seems to be critical
for reading (Shaywitz & Shaywitz, 2005; Torgesen, 2000; Vellutino et
al., 1996), multiple cognitive and neuropsychological processes that
are not specific for reading must be recruited for reading competence
(Ramus, 2004; Wolf, 2007). Children must first develop phonemic
awareness, largely a superior temporal lobe function (Breier et al., 2003;
Hale & Fiorello, 2004), and an understanding that words are made
of sounds, and then associate those sounds (phonemes) with print
(orthography) (Shaywitz et al., 2003). This mapping of sounds onto
symbols is known as the alphabetic principle (Berninger & Richards,
2002), and appears to be largely a function of the angular gyrus (Horwitz, Rumsey, & Donohue, 1998). Children who struggle with these
skills show greater activity in the homologous regions of the right
hemisphere and Broca's area, suggesting poor development of alphabetic
skills (Fiorello et al., 2006; Hale, Fiorello, Miller, et al., 2008), and
following intensive intervention, these aberrant patterns are normalized
(Simos et al., 2002).

The goal of early readers is to transfer phonetically decoded words
using phoneme–grapheme correspondence skills eventually into visual
memory so that the process becomes automatized and reading fluency
is established for subsequent comprehension (Fitch & Tallal, 2003;
Flowers et al., 2004; Hale & Fiorello, 2004; Joseph, Nobel, & Eden,
2001; Pugh et al., 2000; Richards et al., 2006; Shaywitz & Shaywitz,
2005; Shaywitz et al., 2003; Simos et al., 2005; Stein, 2001; Sunseth &
Bowers, 2002; Thomson et al., 2005; Wolf & Bowers, 1999). The automatic whole word reading occurs primarily in the occipital-temporal
ventral stream, which is likely important for rapid automatic naming
of whole words from long-term memory, which is important for reading

fluency skills and subsequent reading comprehension (Bowers, 2001; Fawcett & Nicholson, 2001; Manis & Freedman, 2001; Stein, 2001; Torgesen, Rashotte, & Alexander, 2001; Wolf & Bowers, 1999), which likely occurs in Wernicke's area (Hale & Fiorello, 2004). If the ventral stream is intact, words are read quickly and easily, freeing working memory for comprehension purposes. However, if slow and laborious dorsal stream reading continues, rapid automatic naming of words is limited (Semrud-Clikeman, Guy, & Griffin, 2000), and working memory is taxed, leading to poor reading comprehension (Gathercole, & Pickering, 2000).

As words are read, the child must simultaneously access the meaning of the language in order to comprehend what is read, with the temporal lobe responsible for nouns and the frontal lobe responsible for verbs (see Hale & Fiorello, 2004; Perani et al., 1999). Simultaneous with this basic skills instruction is language development, including vocabulary, semantics, and syntax, which must continue to support comprehension (Snowling & Stackhouse, 2006; Wiig, 2008). Other structures involved include Broca's area for articulation, the dorsolateral prefrontal-subcortical circuit for working memory, memory encoding and retrieval, the cingulate circuit for processing speed, corpus callosum for interhemispheric communication, and the cerebellum for timing and automaticity, important for rapid access of lexical-semantic knowledge (Eden et al., 1996; Fine et al., 2007; Fiorello et al., 2006; Nicholson & Fawcett, 2001; Simos et al., 2005; Stein, 2001). In addition, the magnocellular, occulomotor circuits, and cerebellum may be impaired in some children with reading disability, leading to visual tracking and sequential processing problems (Fawcett & Nicholson, 2001; Fiorello et al., 2006; Ram-Tsur, Faust, & Zivotofsky, 2006; Stein, 2001). Therefore, reading instruction across the early grades must target not just basic skills, but develop a wide range of processes to foster phonemic awareness, phonics, fluency, vocabulary, and comprehension (National Reading Panel, 2000). Hemispheric involvement follows an inverse u-shaped pattern, with right hemisphere processes important in beginning reading and then again in late childhood and adolescence when increased text complexity, meaning ambiguity, and inferential comprehension become more relevant (Bryan & Hale, 2001; Goldberg, 2001; Hale & Fiorello, 2004).

As a result, it is clear that neuropsychological evaluation can be useful for identifying the cause of *dyslexia* (i.e., reading disability), and developing targeted interventions. Group studies are limited because meta-analysis results and subtype studies suggest there are multiple SLD subtypes with different patterns of assets and deficits (Kavale & Nye, 1986; Fiorello et al., 2006). This could explain why reading disability group studies are limited, because subtypes are collapsed into a single group with different patterns of performance (e.g., Semrud-Clikeman & Pliszka, 2005). In the Fiorello et al. study, different cognitive patterns and achievement outcomes were evident, suggesting assessment-intervention relationships could be facilitated when subtypes are examined (Licht, 1994; Zadina, Corey, & Casbergue, 2006). Phonological, orthographic, fluency/comprehension, and global reading SLD subtypes were found in Fiorello et al., consistent with the literature (Bakker, Van Strien, Licht, & Smit-Glaude, 2007; King, Giess, & Lombardino, 2007; Masutto, Bravar, & Fabbro, 1994; Morris et al., 1998; Richman & Wood, 2002; Torppa et al., 2007; Zadina et al., 2006). An interesting finding was that the Arithmetic-Coding-Information-Digit Span (ACID) profile (Prifitera & Dersh, 1993; Vargo, Grossner, & Spafford, 1995) was evident for all reading SLD subtypes, even though concerns over its utility have been noted (Watkins, Kush, & Glutting, 1997). Recent commonality analyses suggest that left hemisphere-crystallized and concordant-convergent thought, and executive working memory and processing speed factors, were the strongest predictors of reading competency and disability (Hale, Fiorello, Miller, et al., 2008), with results consistent with CHC research (e.g., Evans, Floyd, McGrew, & Leforgee, 2002). The frontal-left hemisphere interaction in reading competency and disability may account for the high rates of reading disability-attention/deficit hyperactivity disorder (ADHD) comorbidity (e.g., Willcutt, Pennington, Olson, Chhabildas, & Hulslander, 2005).

NEUROPSYCHOLOGICAL PROCESSES RELEVANT FOR MATH ACHIEVEMENT

Basic number sense and quantitative knowledge develops naturally quite early in development (Gelman & Gellistel, 1978), but mathematical skill requires mastery of a symbolic system similar to reading, and integration of multiple frontal and right hemisphere systems for problem solving and calculation (Hale, Fiorello, Dumont, et al., 2008). Unfortunately, substantially less empirical work has been done on the neuropsychological processes involved in math skill and disability, but this evidence is emerging (e.g., Geary, Hamson, & Hoard, 2000; Hale, Fiorello, Miller, et al., 2008; Hale, Fiorello, Dumont, et al., 2008; Mazzocco, 2001; Swanson & Jerman, 2006). Math SLD is often comorbid with reading and written language SLD, with similar cognitive/neuropsychological explanations for the cormorbidity (Ardila, Concha, & Rosselli, 2000; Helland, 2007), yet some children with math SLD have characteristics of *nonverbal* SLD, presumably due to right hemisphere dysfunction (Palombo, 2006; Rourke, 2000; Stein & Krishnan, 2007). Although it has been suggested that all math disability is due to right hemisphere dysfunction, previous studies have found auditory-verbal-crystallized abilities and executive functions to be most predictive of mathematics achievement and disability (Hale, Fiorello, Bertin, & Sherman, 2003), with right hemisphere processes most important for solving word problems (Hain et al., 2009; Hale, Fiorello, Dumont, et al., 2008; Hale, Fiorello, Miller, et al., 2008). Neuropsychological research confirms that frontal, left, and right hemisphere systems are necessary for math computation and reasoning skills (e.g., Geary, 2004; Hale et al., 2003; Hale, Fiorello, Miller et al., 2008; Hale, Fiorello, Dumont, et al., 2008; Mazzocco, 2001; Palombo, 2006; Proctor, Floyd, & Shaver, 2005; Rourke, 2000), suggesting that dysfunction in one or more brain regions (Benbow, Lubinski, & Hyde 1997) and both left- and right-hemisphere damage (Cirino, Morris, & Morris, 2007 ; Grafman, Passafiume, & Faglioni, & Boller, 1982), can lead to math SLD.

As is the case with reading disabilities, there is no one cause for math disability, and different predictor relationships are found for typical children and children with math disability. Hale et al. (2001) showed crystallized, working memory, fluid reasoning, and processing speed were strong predictors of math calculation skills. Hale et al. (2003) found similar relationships for math calculation and math word problems, with the former requiring more left hemisphere-crystallized functions, and the latter more right hemisphere-fluid reasoning functions. An interesting finding was that the auditory-verbal Digit Span subtest predicted the visual-motor *Numerical Operations* (NO) subtest, and the visual-motor Block Design subtest predicted the auditory-verbal *Math Reasoning* (MR) subtest. Although counterintuitive to the old verbal-nonverbal hemispheric dichotomy, these results suggest the *neuropsychological processes* involved in Digit Span (sequential processing for step-by-step calculations) and Block Design (analysis and synthesis) are more important than either input or output demands in the prediction of math competence (Hale et al., 2003; Hale, Fiorello, Dumont, et al., 2008; Hale, Fiorello, Miller, et al., 2008).

In recent studies on math competency and disability (Hale, Fiorello, Dumont, et al., 2008; Hale, Fiorello, Miller, et al., 2008), we found that novel problem solving and visual-spatial relationships, most likely due to right hemisphere functions (e.g., Palombo, 2006; Proctor, Floyd, & Shaver, 2005; Rourke, 2000), were important in the prediction of math competency and disability, consistent with the interrelationship of quantitative and fluid reasoning (Flanagan, Ortiz, Alfonso, & Dynda, 2006). Left hemisphere-crystallized-concordant-convergent functions consistently predict math competency (Floyd, Evans, & McGrew, 2003; Hale et al., 2001, 2003, 2007; Hale, Fiorello, Dumont, et al., 2008; Hale, Fiorello, Miller, et al., 2008), likely reflecting prior knowledge of math concepts and language facility for word problems. As has been found elsewhere (e.g., Floyd et al., 2003; Hale et al., 2003), working memory demands were more important in predicting MR than NO performance, suggesting executive demands for problem solving are necessary for this task. An interesting and consistent finding in these studies is that processing speed is a strong predictor for children with math disability, perhaps reflecting difficulty in white matter/hemispheric integration or the laborious nature of math computation because of limited math fact automaticity (Hale, Fiorello, Dumont, et al., 2008; Hale, Fiorello, Miller et al., 2008).

Not surprisingly, our SLD subtype studies have shown that there are several reasons why children have math difficulty. In Hale, Fiorello, and Miller, (2008), we found five subtypes of math SLD, fluid/quantitative reasoning, mild executive/working memory, right hemisphere (NVLD), consistent with the notion of a right hemisphere predominance for math function and dysfunction (Rourke, 2000), attesting to the interrelationship of right hemisphere, frontal executive, and math competency (Hale, Fiorello, Dumont, et al., 2008; Stein & Krishnan, 2007), as has been suggested in ADHD (Hale, Fiorello, & Brown, 2005) and right–hemisphere SLD (Greenham, Stelmack, & van der Vlugt, 2003). In our study of psychopathology and SLD subtypes (Hain, Hale, & Kendorski, 2009), we again found differences among subtypes with apparent right frontal and right posterior dysfunction. Interestingly, it was the right frontal subtype who experienced significant psychopathology in this study. However, we also found a numeric/quantitative and dycalculia/Gerstmann syndrome subtypes, which are likely due to left hemisphere dysfunction (see Helland, 2007; Light & DeFries, 1995; Shalev & Gross-Tsur, 2001). These results again attest to the value of a CHT approach to evaluating children with math difficulties. Children with math SLD may have deficits in numeric concepts, computational knowledge, working memory, long-term memory storage and/or retrieval, problem solving, and/or visual-spatial processing problems (Geary, Hamson, & Hoard, 2000; Hale & Fiorello, 2004; Hale et al., 2003; Mazzocco, 2005), and different subtypes may require different interventions to overcome their disability and achieve math competency (Hale, Fiorello, Dumont, et al., 2008; Hale, Fiorello, Miller, et al., 2008).

COGNITIVE/NEUROPSYCHOLOGICAL PROCESSES AND INTERVENTION

The focus of many psychologists and neuropsychologists has been accurate identification of disorders, and this will continue to be an important skill to have, especially for children who do not respond to interventions (Berninger, 2006; Hale et al., 2006; Hale, Fiorello, Dumont, et al.,2008; Kavale, Holdnack, & Mostert, 2005; Semrud-Clikeman, 2005; Willis & Dumont, 2006). However, the real value in neuropsychological assessment is in developing effective interventions that have demonstrated ecological and treatment validity, which is the second major goal of the CHT model described earlier (Hale & Fiorello, 2004). We would like to claim that accurate identification leads to successful interventions in all cases, but in reality, interventions require continued problem-solving, single subject data collection, and recycling interventions until the child responds (Fiorello et al., 2009). Many claim that cognitive and neuropsychological data do not inform intervention (Reschly, 2005), and use this old argument to admonish practitioners to avoid administering standardized cognitive and/or neuropsychological tests, but this outdated belief is no longer valid given the plethora of cognitive/ neuropsychological intervention research that has emerged in recent years (Hale, Fiorello, Miller, et al., 2008).

In this chapter we explore these findings for reading, as this has been the focus of many cognitive/neuropsychological intervention researchers (for math and written expression interventions, see Berninger & Richards, 2002; Geary & Hoard, 2005; Hale & Fiorello,

2004; Naglieri & Pickering, 2003). Interventions that target auditory processing, including pitch discrimination, slowed phonological discrimination, and phoneme–grapheme conversion can improve phonological awareness, single word and pseudoword reading, and spelling (Berninger & Richards, 2002; Santos, Joly-Pottuz, Moreno, Habib, & Besson, 2007; Tallal, 2004). Teaching the alphabetic principle, or mapping phonemes onto graphemes, is one of the most successful approaches for improving single word reading deficits (Berninger et al., 2003; Wise, Sevcik, Morris, Lovett, & Wolf, 2007), but for many children with reading SLD, language interventions such as vocabulary, verbal memory, and verbal reasoning are also helpful (Bryant, Goodwin, Bryant, & Higgins, 2003; Wiig, 2008).

Although a majority of children with reading SLD have phonological problems (Morris et al., 1998), some have orthographic problems with executive and visual-spatial deficits instead of auditory processing deficits, and show better response when interventions target those weaknesses (Bowers & Wolf, 1993; Eckert et al., 2003; Gustafson, Ferreira, & Ronnberg, 2007). Interventions addressing phonological, orthographic, and morphological components can improve both reading comprehension and language processing, with normalization of brain function found with interventions that are targeted for the deficits experienced by the child (Aylward et al., 2003; Berninger et al., 2006; Corina et al., 2001; Simos et al., 2007). In our recent reading SLD subtype study (Fiorello et al., 2006), we present a case with orthographic/visual sequencing problems that responded to a visual tracking intervention following nonresponse to a phonics intervention. But for other children who demonstrate auditory/linguistic deficits and do not respond to standard phonological, orthographic, and fluency training, a strength-based approach might prove more valuable, drawing upon the intact right hemisphere processes (e.g., Smit-Glaude, van Strien, Licht, & Bakker, 2005).

As noted earlier, reading fluency is critical for comprehension of text (Wolf & Katzir-Cohen, 2001). Difficulties may result from insufficient automatization of basic reading skills, with intensive basic skills instruction and repeated readings often offered to improve reading fluency (O'Connor, White, & Swanson, 2007). Although word reading skill development and repeated readings may be sufficient interventions for some children with fluency problems, executive metacognitive strategies have proven effective for others (Konrad, Fowler, Walker, Test, &

Wood, 2007, Montague, 2007), including individualized interventions such as goal setting, question generation, and performance feedback (Morgan & Sideridis, 2006; Therrien, Wickstrom, & Jones, 2006). Some intervention programs combine a variety of approaches, such as the RAVE-O program, which targets retrieval, automaticity, vocabulary development, and orthography (Wolf, Miller, & Donnelly, 2000). Clearly, given that there are multiple causes for subtypes of reading disability (Fiorello et al., 2006; Torppa et al., 2007), comprehensive neuropsychological evaluation is necessary for children who do not succeed following preventative RTI interventions (Hale, Fiorello, Miller, et al., 2008).

BEST PRACTICES FOR NEUROPSYCHOLOGISTS PRACTICING IN SCHOOLS

As is the case for identification, cognitive and neuropsychological evaluation can be useful for both assessment and intervention purposes, as has been suggested in our CHT model (Hale & Fiorello, 2004). No longer relegated to assessment of individuals with brain-damage, neuropsychologists can conduct comprehensive CHT evaluations for high-incidence disorders such as ADHD or SLD, because these disorders are also suggestive of brain dysfunction and require targeted interventions as a result (Hale, Fiorello, Miller, et al., 2008; Hale et al., 2009). These assessment and intervention practices can be accomplished in a school setting by those trained in school neuropsychology (Miller & Hale, 2008), or by those conducting Independent Educational Evaluations, such as pediatric neuropsychologists. In addition to the biological basis of most academic disorders discussed here, there is a growing body of evidence that most, if not all, psychopathologies have a brain–behavior basis, with different frontal-subcortical circuits and neurotransmitter interactions resulting in the socioemotional disorders commonly seen in children (e.g., Hale & Fiorello, 2004; Hale et al., 2009; Lichter & Cummings, 2001)

Learning and behavior disability subtype studies and comparisons of typical children and children with disabilities are needed to clarify the findings presented here, and how brain systems interact to produce the pattern seen during testing and intervention. This is especially relevant when children are unresponsive to our best attempts at preventing disability in an RTI model (Hale et al., 2006), because empirical evidence confirms that different children have different causes for their learning and psychosocial problems, and most childhood disorders are in part related to brain functioning (Fiorello et al., 2008; Hale & Fiorello, 2004; Hale et al., 2009.

It is the well-trained neuropsychologist who can carefully examine brain–behavior–environment interactions to develop a comprehensive picture of a child's level and pattern of performance, and this information is critical for developing specific, targeted interventions designed to meet individual learner needs. As most educators have little knowledge of brain–behavior relationships (Hale, Fiorello. Miller, et al., 2008; Hale et al., 2009), neuropsychologists can consult with educators and school psychologists to facilitate understanding of individual learner differences in the classroom. Accurate diagnosis is likely following thorough comprehensive evaluations conducted by neuropsychologists practicing in schools, but the real utility of such approaches is in showing the ecological and treatment validity of their findings (Hale, Fiorello, Miller, et al., 2008). Once both accurate assessment and intervention practices are consistently achieved in the fields of school and pediatric neuropsychology, and RTI practices ensure that low achievers or those who have received inadequate instruction also respond, we can be confident that indeed no child with academic or behavioral difficulty will be left behind in an educational system designed to serve all children with and without disability.

REFERENCES

Alarcon, M., Pennington, B. F., Filipek, P. A., & DeFries, J. C. (2000). Etiology of neuroanatomical correlates of reading disability. *Developmental Neuropsychology, 17,* 339–360.

Ardila, A., Concha, M., & Rosselli, M. (2000). Angular gyrus syndrome revisited: Acalculia, finger agnosia, right-left disorientation and semantic aphasia. *Aphasiology, 14,* 743–754.

Aylward, E. H, Richards, T. L, Berninger, V. W, Nagy, W. E., Field, K. M., Grimme, A. C., et al. (2003). Instructional treatment associated with changes in brain activation in children with dyslexia. *Neurology, 61,* 212–219.

Bakker, D. J., Van Strien, J. W., Licht, R., & Smit-Glaude, S. W. D. (2007). Cognitive brain potentials in kindergarten children with subtyped risks of reading retardation. *Annals of Dyslexia, 57,* 99–111.

Barnett, D. W., Daly, E. J., Jones, K. M., & Lentz, F. E. (2004). Response to intervention: Empirically based special service decisions from single-case designs of increasing and decreasing intensity. *Journal of Special Education, 38,* 66–79.

Baron, I. S. (2005). Test review: Wechsler Intelligence Scale for Children-fourth edition (WISC-IV). *Child Neuropsychology, 11*, 471 –475.

Barth, A. E., Stuebing, K. K., Anthony, J. L., Denton, C. A., Mathes, P. G., Fletcher, J. M., & Francis, D. J. (2008). Agreement among response to intervention criteria for identifying responder status. *Learning and Individiual Differences, 18*, 296–307.

Benbow, C. P., Lubinski, D., & Hyde, J. S. (1997). Mathematics: Is biology the cause of gender differences in performance? In M. R. Walsh (Ed.), *Women, men, & gender: Ongoing debates* (pp. 271–287). New Haven, CT: Yale University Press.

Berninger, V. W. (2006). Research-supported ideas for implementing reauthorized IDEA with intelligent professional psychological services. *Psychology in the Schools, 43*, 781–796.

Berninger, V. W., Abbott, R. D., Brooksher, R., Lemos, Z., Ogier, S., Zook, D., et al. (2000). A connectionist approach to making the predictability of English orthography explicit to at-risk beginning readers: Evidence for alternative, effective strategies. *Developmental Neuropsychology, 17*, 241–271.

Berninger, V. W., Abbott, R. D., Jones, J., Wolf, B. J., Gould, L., Anderson-Youngstrom, M., et al. (2006). Early development of language by hand: Composing, reading, listening, and speaking connections. *Developmental Neuropsychology, 29*, 61–92.

Berninger. V., & Richards, T. L. (2002). *Brain literacy for educators and psychologists*. Boston: Academic Press.

Berninger, V. W., Vermeulen, K., Abbott, R. D., McCutchen, D., Cotton, S., Cude, S., Dorn, S., & Sharon, T. (2003). Comparison of three approaches to supplementary reading instruction for low-achieving second-grade readers. *Language, Speech, and Hearing Services in Schools, 34*, 101–116.

Bowers, P. G. (2001). Exploration of the basis for rapid naming's relationship to reading. In M. Wolf (Ed.), *Dyslexia, fluency, and the brain* (pp. 41–64). Timonium, MD: York Press.

Bowers, P. G., & Wolf, M. (1993). Theoretical links among naming speed, precise timing mechanisms, and orthographic skill in dyslexia. *Reading and Writing, 5*, 69–85.

Breier, J. I., Simos, P. G., Fletcher, J. M., Castillo, E. M., Zhang, W., & Papanicolaou, A. C. (2003). Abnormal activation of temporoparietal language areas during phonetic analysis in dyslexia. *Neuropsychology, 17*, 610–621.

Brown-Chidsey, R., & Steege, M. W., (2005). *Response to intervention: Principles and strategies for effective practice*. New York: Guilford Press.

Bryan, K. L., & Hale, J. B. (2001). Differential effects of left and right hemisphere accidents on language competency. *Journal of the International Neuropsychological Society, 7*, 655–664.

Bryant, D. P., Goodwin, M., Bryant, B. R., & Higgins, K. (2003). Vocabulary instruction for students with learning disabilities: A review of research. *Learning Disability Quarterly, 26*, 117–128.

Castellanos, F. X., Lee, P. P., Sharp, W., Jeffries, N. O., Greenstein, D. K., Clasen, L. S., et al. (2002). Developmental trajectories of brain volume abnormalities in children and adolescents with attention-deficit/hyperactivity disorder. *Journal of the American Medical Association, 288*, 1740–1748.

Chenault, B., Thomson, J., Abbott, R. D., & Berninger, V. W. (2006). Effects of prior training on child dyslexics' response to composition instruction. *Developmental Neuropsychology, 29*, 243–260.

Cirino, P. T., Morris, M. K., & Morris, R. D. (2007). Semantic, executive, and visuospatial abilities in mathematical reasoning in referred college students. *Assessment, 14,* 94–104.

Coch, D., Dawson, G., & Fischer, K. W. (2007). *Human behavior, learning, and the developing brain.* New York: Guilford Press.

Corina, D. P., Richards, T. L., Serafini, S., Richards, A. L., Steury, K., Abbott, R. D., et al. (2001). fMRI auditory language differences between dyslexic and able reading children. *Neuroreport: For Rapid Communication of Neuroscience Research, 12,* 1195–1201.

D'Amato, RC, Fletcher-Janzen, E., and Reynolds, C. R. (Eds.). (2005). *The handbook of school neuropsychology,* New York: John Wiley.

Denckla, M. B. (2007). Executive function: Binding together the definitions of attention-deficit/hyperactivity disorder and learning disabilities. In L. Meltzer (Ed.), *Executive function in education: From theory to practice* (pp. 5–18). New York: Guilford Press.

Deno, S. L. (2002). Problem solving as "best practice." In A. Thomas & J. Grimes (Eds.), *Best practices in school psychology IV* (pp. 37–56). Bethesda, MD: National Association of School Psychologists.

Dombrowski, S. C., Kamphaus, R. W., & Reynolds, C. R. (2004). After the demise of the discrepancy: Proposed learning disabilities diagnostic criteria. *Professional Psychology: Research and Practice, 35,* 364–372.

Eckert, M. A., Leonard, C. M., Richards, T. L., Aylward, E. H., Thomson, J., & Berninger, V. W. (2003). Anatomical correlates of dyslexia: Frontal and cerebellar findings. *Brain, 126,* 482–494.

Eden, G. F., VanMeter, J. W., Rumsey, J. W., Maison, J., & Zeffiro, T. A. (1996). Functional MRI reveals differences in visual motion processing in individuals with dyslexia. *Nature, 382,* 66–69.

Evans, J. J., Floyd, R. G., McGrew, K. S., & Leforgee, M. H. (2002). The relations between measures of Cattell-Horn-Carroll (CHC) cognitive abilities and reading achievement during childhood and adolescence. *School Psychology Review, 31,* 364–372.

Fawcett, A. J., & Nicholson, R. I. (2001). Speed and temporal processing in dyslexia. In M. Wolf (Ed.), *Dyslexia, fluency, and the brain* (pp. 277–306). Timonium, MD: York Press.

Federal Register. (2006). 34 C.F.R. Parts 300 and 301 Final Regulations. Washington, DC: Author.

Fiez, J. A., & Petersen, S. E. (1998). Neuroimaging studies of word reading. *Proceedings of the National Academy of Sciences USA, 95,* 914–921.

Filipek, P. A. (1999). Neuroimaging in the developmental disorders. The state of the science. *Journal of Child Psychology and Psychiatry, 40,* 113–128.

Fine, J. G., Semrud-Clikeman, M., Keith, T. Z., Stapleton, L. M., & Hynd, G. W. (2007). Reading and the corpus callosum: An MRI family study of volume and area. *Neuropsychology, 21,* 235–241.

Fiorello, C. A., Hale, J. B., Decker, S. L., & Coleman, S. (2009). Neuropsychology in school psychology. In E. Garcia-Vazquez, T. D. Crespi, & C. A. Riccio (Eds.), *Handbook of education, training and supervision of school psychologists in school and community, volume 1* (pp. 213–232). New York, NY: Taylor & Francis.

Fiorello, C. A., Hale, J. B., Holdnack, J. A., Kavanagh, J. A., Terrell, J., & Long, L. (2007). Interpreting intelligence test results for children with disabilities: Is global intelligence relevant? *Applied Neuropsychology, 14,* 2–12.

Fiorello, C. A., Hale, J. B., McGrath, M., Ryan, K., & Quinn, S. (2001). IQ interpretation for children with flat and variable test profiles. *Learning and Individual Differences, 13,* 115–125.

Fiorello, C. A., Hale, J. B., & Snyder, L. E. (2006). Cognitive hypothesis testing and response to intervention for children with reading disabilities. *Psychology in the Schools, 43,* 835–854.

Fiorello, C. A., Hale, J. B., Snyder, L. E., Forrest, E., & Teodori, A. (2008). Validating individual differences through examination of converging psychometric and neuropsychological models of cognitive functioning. In S. K. Thurman & C. A. Fiorello (Eds.), *Applied cognitive research in K-3 classrooms.* New York: Routledge.

Fitch, R. H., & Tallal, P. (2003). Neural mechanisms of language-based learning impairments: Insights from human populations and animal models. *Behavioral and Cognitive Neuroscience Reviews, 2,* 155–178.

Flanagan, D. P., Ortiz, S. O., Alfonso, V. C., & Dynda, A. M. (2006). Integration of response to intervention and norm-referenced tests in learning disability identification: Learning from the Tower of Babel. *Psychology in the Schools, 43,* 807–825.

Fletcher, J. M., Coulter, A. W., Reschly, D. J., & Vaughn, S. (2004). Alternative approaches to the definition and identification of learning disabilities: Some questions and answers. *Annals of Dyslexia, 54,* 304–331.

Fletcher, J. M., Denton, C., & Francis, D. J. (2005). Validity of alternative approaches for the identification of learning disabilities: Operationalizing unexpected underachievement. *Journal of Learning Disabilities, 38,* 545–552.

Fletcher, J. M., Shaywitz, S. E., Shankweiler, D. P., Katz, L., Liberman, I. Y., Stuebing, K. K., et al. (1994). Cognitive profiles of reading disability: Comparisons of discrepancy and low achievement definitions. *Journal of Educational Psychology, 85,* 1–18.

Fletcher-Janzen, E., & Reynolds, C. R. (2008). *Neuropsychological perspectives on learning disabilities in the era of RTI: Recommendations for diagnosis and intervention.* Hoboken, NJ: John Wiley.

Flowers, D. L., Jones, K., Noble, K., VanMeter, J., Zeffiro, T. A., Wood, F. B., et al. (2004). Attention to single letters activates the left extrastriate cortex. *NeuroImage, 21,* 829–839.

Floyd, R. G., Evans, J. J., & McGrew, K. S. (2003). Relations between measures of Cattell-Horn-Carroll (CHC) cognitive abilities and mathematics achievement across the school-age years. *Psychology in the Schools, 40,* 155–171.

Francis, D. J., Shaywitz, S. E., Stuebing, K. K., Shaywitz, B. A., & Fletcher, J. M. (1996). Developmental delay versus deficit models of reading disability: A longitudinal, individual growth curve analysis. *Journal of Educational Psychology, 88,* 3–17.

Fuchs, D., & Deshler, D. D. (2007). What we need to know about responsiveness to intervention (and shouldn't be afraid to ask). *Learning Disabilities Research & Practice, 22,* 129–136.

Fuchs, D., Deshler, D. D., & Reschly, D. J. (2004). National research center on learning disabilities: Multimethod studies of identification and classification issues. *Learning Disability Quarterly, 27,* 189–195.

Fuchs, D., Fuchs, L. S., & Compton, D. L. (2004). Identifying reading disabilities by responsiveness to instruction: Specifying measures and criteria. *Learning Disability Quarterly, 27,* 216–227.

Fuchs, D., Fuchs, L. S., Mathes, P. G., Lipsey, M. W., & Roberts, P. H. (2001). *Is learning disabilities just a fancy term for low achievement: A meta-analysis of reading differences between low achievers with and without a label.* Paper presented at Learning Disabilities Summit: Building a Foundation for the Future. Washington, DC: ED/ OSERS.

Gathercole, S. E., & Pickering, S. J. (2000). Assessment of working memory in six- and seven-year-old children. *Journal of Educational Psychology, 92,* 377–390.

Geary, D. C. (2004). Mathematics and learning disabilities. *Journal of Learning Disabilities, 37,* 4–15.

Geary, D. C., Hamson, C. O., & Hoard, M. K. (2000). Numerical and arithmetical cognition: A longitudinal study of process deficits in children with learning disabilities . *Journal of Experimental Child Psychology, 77,* 236–263.

Geary, D. C., & Hoard, M. K. (2005). Learning disabilities in arithmetic and mathematics: Theoretical and empirical perspectives. In J. I. D. Campbell (Ed.), *Handbook of mathematical cognition* (pp. 253–267). New York: Psychology Press.

Gelman, R., & Gallistel, C. R. (1978). *The child's understanding of number.* Cambridge, MA: Harvard University Press.

Gerber, M. M. (2005). Teachers are still the test: Limitations of response to instruction strategies for identifying children with learning disabilities. *Journal of Learning Disabilities, 38,* 516–523.

Goldberg, E. (2001). *The executive brain: Frontal lobes and the civilized mind.* New York: Oxford University Press.

Grafman, J., Passafiume, D., Faglioni, P., & Boller, F. (1982). Calculation disturbances in adults with focal hemispheric damage. *Cortex, 18,* 37–50.

Greenham, S. L., Stelmack, R. M., & van der Vlugt, H. (2003). Learning disability subtypes and the role of attention during the naming of pictures and words: An event-related potential analysis. *Developmental Neuropsychology, 23,* 339–358.

Gresham, F. M., Reschly, D. J., Tilly, D. W., & Fletcher, J., Burns, M., Crist, T., et al. (2005). Comprehensive evaluation of learning disabilities: A response to intervention perspective. *School Psychologist, 59*(1), 26–29.

Gustafson, S., Ferreira, J., & Ronnberg, J. (2007). Phonological or orthographic training for children with phonological or orthographic deficits. *Dyslexia: An International Journal of Research and Practice, 13,* 211–228.

Hain, L. A., Hale, J. B., & Kendorski, J. G. (2009). Comorbidity of psychopathology in cognitive and academic SLD subtypes. In S. G. Feifer & G. Rattan (Eds.), *Emotional disorders: A neuropsychological, psychopharmacological, and educational perspective.* Middletown, MD: School Neuropsych Press.

Hale, J. B. (2006). Implementing IDEA with a three-tier model that includes response to intervention and cognitive assessment methods. *School Psychology Forum: Research and Practice, 1,* 16–27.

Hale, J. B., & Fiorello, C. A. (2004). *School neuropsychology: A practitioner's handbook.* New York: Guilford Press.

Hale, J. B., Fiorello, C. A., Bertin, M., & Sherman, R. (2003). Predicting math competency through neuropsychological interpretation of WISC-III variance components. *Journal of Psychoeducational Assessment, 21,* 358–380.

Hale, J. B., Fiorello, C. A., & Brown, L. (2005). Determining medication treatment effects using teacher ratings and classroom observations of children with ADHD: Does neuropsychological impairment matter? *Educational and Child Psychology, 22,* 39–61.

Hale, J. B., Fiorello, C. A., Dumont, R., Willis, J. O., Rackley, C., & Elliott, C. (2008). Differential Ability Scales–Second Edition (neuro)psychological predictors of math performance for typical children and children with math disabilities. *Psychology in the Schools, 45,* 838–858.

Hale, J. B., Fiorello, C. A., Kavanagh, J. A., Hoeppner, J. B., & Gaither, R. A. (2001). WISC-III predictors of academic achievement for children with learning disabilities: Are global and factor scores comparable? *School Psychology Quarterly, 16,* 31–55.

Hale, J. B., Fiorello, C. A., Kavanagh, J. A., Holdnack, J. A., & Aloe, A. M. (2007). Is the demise of IQ interpretation justified? A response to special issue authors. *Applied Neuropsychology, 14,* 37–51.

Hale, J. B., Fiorello, C. A., Miller, J. A., Wenrich, K., Teodori, A. M., & Henzel, J. (2008). WISC-IV assessment and intervention strategies for children with specific learning disabilities. In A. Prifitera, D. H. Saklofske, & L. G. Weiss (Eds.), *WISC-IV clinical assessment and intervention* (2nd ed., pp. 109–171). New York: Elsevier.

Hale, J. B., Flanagan, D. P., & Naglieri, J. A. (2008). Alternative research-based methods for IDEA (2004) identification of children with specific learning disabilities. *Communiqué, 36*(8), 14–17.

Hale, J. B., Kaufman, A., Naglieri, J. A., & Kavale, K. A. (2006). Implementation of IDEA: Integrating response to intervention and cognitive assessment methods. *Psychology in the Schools, 43,* 753–770.

Hale, J. B., Reddy, L. A., Wilcox, G., McLaughlin, A., Hain, L., Stern, A., Henzel, J., & Eusebio, E. (2009). Assessment and intervention for children with ADHD and other frontal-striatal circuit disorders. In D. C. Miller (Ed.), *Best practices in school neuropsychology: Guidelines for effective practice, assessment and evidence-based interventions* (pp. 225–279). Hoboken, NJ: John Wiley.

Helland, T. (2007). Dyslexia at a behavioural and a cognitive level. *Dyslexia: An International Journal of Research and Practice, 13,* 25–41.

Horwitz, B., Rumsey, J. M., & Donohue, B. C. (1998). Functional connectivity of the angular gyrus in normal reading and dyslexia. *Proceedings of the National Academy of Sciences U S A., 95,* 8939–44.

Individuals With Disabilities Education Improvement Act of 2004 (IDEA), Pub. L. No. 108–446, 118 Stat. 2647 (2004). [Amending 20 U.S.C. §§ 1400 et seq.].

Joseph, J. E., Noble, K., & Eden, G. F. (2001). The neurobiological basis of reading. *Journal of Learning Disabilities, 34,* 566–579.

Kavale, K. A., & Flanagan, D. P. (2007). Ability-achievement discrepancy, response to intervention, and assessment of cognitive abilities/processes in specific learning disability identification: Toward a contemporary operational definition. In S. R. Jimerson, M. K. Burns, & A. M. VanDerHeyden (Eds.), *Handbook of response to intervention: The science and practice of assessment and intervention* (pp. 130–147). New York: Springer Publishing Company.

Kavale, K. A., & Forness, S. R. (2000). What definitions of learning disability say and don't say: A critical analysis. *Journal of Learning Disabilities, 33,* 239–256.

Kavale, K. A., Holdnack, J. A., & Mostert, M. P. (2005). Responsiveness to intervention and the identification of specific learning disability: A critique and alternative proposal. *Learning Disability Quarterly, 28,* 2–16.

Kavale, K. A., Fuchs, D., & Scruggs, T. E. (1994). Setting the record straight on learning disabilities and low achievement. *Learning Disabilities Research & Practice, 9,* 70–77.

Kavale, K. A., Kaufman, A. S., Naglieri, J. A., & Hale, J. B. (2005). Changing procedures for identifying learning disabilities: The danger of poorly supported ideas. *School Psychologist, 43*(7), 753–770.

Kavale, K. A., & Nye, C. (1986). Parameters of learning disabilities in achievement, linguistic, neuropsychological, and social/behavioral domains. *Journal of Special Education, 19,* 443–458.

King, W. M., Giess, S. A., & Lombardino, L. J. (2007). Subtyping of children with developmental dyslexia via bootstrap aggregated clustering and the gap statistic: Comparison with the double-deficit hypothesis. *International Journal of Language & Communication Disorders, 42,* 77–95.

Konrad, M., Fowler, C. H., Walker, A. R., Test, D. W., & Wood, W. M. (2007). Effects of self-determination interventions on the academic skills for students with learning disabilities. *Learning Disability Quarterly, 30,* 89–113.

Kovaleski, J.F. (2002). Best practices in operating pre-referral intervention teams in Pennsylvania. In A. Thomas & J. Grimes (Eds.), *Best practices in school psychology IV* (pp. 645–655). Bethesda, MD: NASP.

Koziol, L. F., & Budding, D. E. (2009). *Subcortical structures and cognition: Implications for neuropsychological assessment.* New York: Springer Publishing Co.

Licht, R. (1994). Differences in word recognition between P- and L-type reading disability. In R. Licht & G. Spyer (Eds.), *The balance model of dyslexia: Theoretical and clinical progress* (pp. 41–55). Assen, Netherlands: Van Gorcum.

Lichter, D. G., & Cummings, J. L. (Eds.). (2001). *Frontal-subcortical circuits in psychiatric and neurological disorders.* New York: Guilford Press.

Light, G. J., & DeFries, J. C. (1995). Comborbidity of reading and mathematics disabilities: Genetic and environmental etiologies. *Journal of Learning Disabilities, 28,* 96–106.

Lovett, M. W., Steinbach, K. A., & Frijters, J. C. (2000). Remediating the core deficits of developmental reading disability: A double-deficit hypothesis. *Journal of Learning Disabilities, 33,* 334–358.

Luria, A. R. (1973). *The working brain.* New York: Basic Books.

Machek, G. R., & Nelson, J. M. (2007). How should reading disabilities be operationalized? A survey of practicing school psychologists. *Learning Disabilities Research & Practice, 22,* 147–157.

Manis, F. R., & Freedman, L. (2001). The relationship of naming speed to multiple reading measures in disabled and normal readers. In M. Wolf (Ed.), *Dysflexia, fluency, and the brain* (pp. 65–92). Timonium, MD: York Press.

Marston, D. (2005). Tiers of intervention in responsiveness to intervention: Prevention outcomes and learning disabilities identification patterns. *Journal of Learning Disabilities, 38,* 539–544.

Masutto, C., Bravar, L., & Fabbro, F. (1994). Diagnosis and rehabilitation in childhood dyslexia: A neuropsychological approach. *Archivio di Psicologia, Neurologia e Psichiatria, 54,* 249–262.

Mather, N., & Gregg, N. (2006). Specific learning disabilities: Clarifying, not eliminating, a construct. *Professional Psychology: Research and Practice, 37,* 99–106.

Mayes, S. D., & Calhoun, S. L. (2006). WISC-IV and WISC-III profiles in children with ADHD. *Journal of Attention Disorders, 9,* 486–493.

Mazzocco, M. M. M. (2001). Math learning disability and math LD subtypes: Evidence from studies of Turner syndrome, fragile X syndrome, and neurofibromatosis type 1. *Journal of Learning Disabilities, 34,* 520–533.

Mazzocco, M. M. M. (2005). Challenges in identifying target skills for math disability screening and intervention. *Journal of Learning Disabilities, 38,* 318–323.

McDermott, P. A., Fantuzzo, J. W., & Glutting, J. J. (1990). Just say no to subtest analysis: A critique on Wechsler theory and practice. *Journal of Psychoeducational Assessment, 8,* 290–302.

McGrew, K. S., & Wendling, B. J. (in press). CHC cognitive-achievement relations: What we have learned from the past 20 years of research. *Psychology in the Schools.*

Miller, D. C. (2007). *Essentials of school neuropsychological assessment.* Hoboken, NJ: John Wiley.

Miller, D. C. (Ed.) (2009). *Best practices in school neuropsychology. Guidelines for effective practice, assessment, and evidence-based intervention.* Hoboken, NJ: John Wiley.

Miller, D. C., & Hale, J. B. (2008). Neuropsychological applications of the WISC-IV and WISC-IV Integrated. In A. Prifitera, D. H. Saklofske, & L. G. Weiss (Eds.), *WISC-IV clinical assessment and intervention* (2nd ed., pp. 445–495). New York: Elsevier Science.

Miller, J. A., Getz, G., & Leffard, S. A. (2006, February). *Neuropsychology and the diagnosis of learning disabilities under IDEA 2004.* Poster presented at the 34th annual meeting of the International Neuropsychological Society, Boston, MA.

Montague, M. (2007). Self regulation and mathematics instruction. *Learning Disabilities Research & Practice, 22,* 75–83.

Morgan, P. L., & Sideridis, G. D. (2006). Contrasting the effectiveness of fluency interventions for students with or at-risk for learning disabilities: A multilevel random coefficient modeling meta-analysis. *Learning Disabilities Research & Practice, 24,* 191–210.

Morris, R. D., Shaywitz, S. E., Shankweiler, D. P., Katz, L., Stuebing, K. K., Fletcher, J. M., et al. (1998). Subtypes of reading disability: Variability around a phonological core. *Journal of Educational Psychology, 90,* 347–373.

Naglieri, J. A., & Johnson, D. (2000). Effectiveness of a cognitive strategy intervention in improving arithmetic computation based on PASS theory. *Journal of Learning Disabilities, 33,* 591–597.

Naglieri, J. A., & Pickering, E. B. (2003). *Helping children learn. Intervention handouts for use in school and at home.* Baltimore, MD: Brookes.

National Reading Panel. (2000). *Teaching children to read: An evidence-based assessment of the scientific research literature on reading and its implications for reading instruction.* Retrieved March 15, 2006, from http://www. nationalreadingpanel.org/Publica tions/publications.htm

Nicholson, R. I., & Fawcett, A. J. (2001). Dyslexia, learning, and the cerebellum. In M. Wolf (Ed.), *Dyslexia, fluency, and the brain* (pp. 159–188). Timonium, MD: York Press.

O'Connor, R.E., Harty, K.R., & Fulmer, D. (2005). Tiers of intervention in kindergarten through third grade. *Journal of Learning Disabilities, 38,* 532–538.

O'Connor, R. E., White, A., & Swanson, H. L. (2007). Repeated reading versus continuous reading on reading fluency and comprehension. *Exceptional Children, 74,* 31–47.

Ofiesh, N. (2006). Response to intervention and identification of specific learning disabilities: Why we need comprehensive evaluations as part of the process. *Psychology in the Schools, 43,* 883–888.

Palombo, J. (2006). *Nonverbal learning disabilities: A clinical perspective.* New York: W. W. Norton.

Perani, D., Cappa, S. F., Schnur, T., Tettamanti, M., Collina., S., Rosa, M. M., & Fazio, F. (1999). The neural correlates of noun and verb processing. A PET study. *Brain, 122,* 2337–2344.

Prifitera, A., & Dersh, J. (1993). Base rates of WISC-III diagnostic subtest patterns among normal, learning disabled, and ADHD samples. *Journal of Psychoeducational Assesssment (WISC-III Monograph),* 43–55.

Proctor, B. E., Floyd, R. G., & Shaver, R. B. (2005). Cattell-Horn-Carroll broad cognitive ability profiles of low math achievers. *Psychology in the Schools, 42,* 1–12.

Pugh, K. R., Mencl, W. E., Shaywitz, B. A., Shaywitz, S. E., Fulbright, R. K., Constable, R. T., et al. (2000). The angular gyrus in developmental dyslexia: Task-specific differences in functional connectivity within posterior regions. *Psychological Science 11,* 51–56.

Ramus, F. (2004). The neural basis of reading acquisition. In M.S. Gazzaniga (Ed.), The cognitive neurosciences (3rd ed., pp. 815–824). Cambridge, MA: MIT Press.

Ram-Tsur, R., Faust, M., & Zivotofsky, A. Z. (2006). Sequential processing deficits of reading disabled persons is independent of inter-stimulus interval. *Vision Research, 46,* 3949–3960.

Reddy, L. A., & Hale, J. B. (2007). Inattentiveness. In A. R. Eisen (Ed.), *Clinical handbook of childhood behavior problems: Case formulation and step-by-step treatment programs* (pp. 156–211). New York: Guilford Press.

Reschly, D. J. (2005). Learning disabilities identification: Primary intervention, secondary intervention, and then what? *Journal of Learning Disabilities, 38,* 510–515.

Reschly, D. J., & Hosp, J. L. (2004). State SLD policies and practices. *Learning Disability Quarterly, 27,* 197–213.

Reynolds, C. R., & Shaywitz, S. E. (2009). Response to intervention: Remediation, perhaps, diagnosis, no. *Child Development Perspectives, 3,* 44–47.

Richards, T. L., Aylward, E. H., Field, K. M., Grimme, A. C., Raskind, W., Richards, A. L., et al., (2006). Converging evidence for triple word form theory in children with dyslexia. *Developmental Neuropsychology, 30,* 547–589.

Richman, L. C., & Wood, K. M. (2002). Learning disability subtypes: Classification of high functioning hyperlexia. *Brain and Language, 82,* 10–21.

Rourke, B. P. (2000). Neuropsychological and psychosocial subtyping: A review of investigations within the University of Windsor Laboratory. *Canadian Psychology, 41,* 34–51.

Santos, A., Joly-Pottuz, B., Moreno, S., Habib, M., & Besson, M. (2007). Behavioural and event-related potentials evidence for pitch discrimination deficits in dyslexic children: Improvement after intensive phonic intervention. *Neuropsychologia, 45,* 1080–1090.

Schrank, F. A., Miller, J. A., Caterino, L., & Desrochers, J. (2006). American Academy of School Psychology survey on the independent educational evaluation for a specific learning disability: Results and discussion. *Psychology in the Schools, 43,* 771–780.

Scruggs, T. E., & Mastropieri, M. A. (2002). On babies and bathwater: Addressing the problems of identification of learning disabilities. *Learning Disability Quarterly, 25,* 155–168.

Semrud-Clikeman, M. (2005). Neuropsychological aspects for evaluating learning disabilities. *Journal of Learning Disabilities, 38,* 563–568.

Semrud-Clikeman, M., Guy, K. A., & Griffin, J. D. (2000). Rapid automatized naming in children with reading disabilities and attention deficit hyperactivity disorder. *Brain and Language 74,* 70–83.

Semrud-Clikeman, M., & Pliszka, S. R. (2005). Neuroimaging and psychopharmacology. *School Psychology Quarterly, 20,* 172–186.

Shalev, R. S., & Gross-Tsur, V. (2001). Developmental dyscalculia. *Pediatric Neurology, 24,* 337–342.

Shaywitz, S. E., & Shaywitz, B. E. (2005). Dyslexia (specific reading disability). *Biological Psychiatry, 57,* 1301–1309.

Shaywitz, S. E., Shaywitz, B. A., Fulbright, R., Skudlarski, P., Mencl, W. E., Constable, R. T., et al. (2003). Neural systems for compensation and persistence: Young adult outcome of childhood reading disability. *Biological Psychiatry 54,* 25–33.

Shinn, M. R. (2002). Best practices in using curriculum-based measurement in a problem-solving model. In A. Thomas & J. Grimes (Eds.), *Best practices in school psychology IV* (pp. 671–697). Washington, DC: National Association of School Psychologists.

Simos, P. G., Fletcher, J. M., Bergman, E., Breier, J. I., Foorman, B. R., Castillo, E. M., et al. (2002). Dyslexia-specific brain activation profile becomes normal following successful remedial training. *Neurology, 58,* 1–10

Simos, P. G., Fletcher, J. M., Sarkari, S., Billingsley, R. L., Denton, C., & Papanicolaou, A. C. (2007). Altering the brain circuits for reading through intervention: A magnetic source imaging study. *Neuropsychology, 21,* 485–496.

Simos, P. G., Fletcher, J. M., Sarkari, S., Billingsley, R. L., Francis, D. J., Castillo, E. M., et al. (2005). Early reading development of neurophysiological processes involved in normal reading and reading disability: A magnetic source imaging study. *Neuropsychology, 19,* 787–798.

Smit-Glaude, S. W. D., van Strien, J. W., Licht, R., & Bakker, D. J. (2005). Neuropsychological intervention in kindergarten children with subtyped risks of reading retardation. *Annals of Dyslexia, 55,* 217–245.

Snowling, M., & Stackhouse, J. (2006). *Dyslexia, speech and language: A practitioner's handbook.* Hoboken, NJ: Wiley.

Stanovich, K. E. (1994). Are discrepancy-based definitions of dyslexia empirically defensible? In K. P. van den Bos, L. S. Siegel, D. J. Bakker, & D. L. Share (Eds.), *Current directions in dyslexia research* (pp. 15–30). Lisse, Netherlands: Swets & Zeitlinger.

Stanovich, K. E., & Siegel, L. S. (1994). Phenotypic performance profile of children with reading disabilities: A regression-based test of the phonological-core variable-difference model. *Journal of Educational Psychology, 86,* 24–53.

Speece, D. L. (2005). Hitting the moving target known as reading development: Some thoughts on screening children for secondary interventions. *Journal of Learning Disabilities, 38,* 487–493.

Stein, J. A., & Krishnan, K. (2007). Nonverbal learning disabilities and executive function: The challenges of effective assessment and teaching. In L. Meltzer (Ed.), *Executive function in education: From theory to practice* (pp. 106–132). New York: Guilford Press.

Stein, J. F. (2001). The neurobiology of reading difficulties. In M. Wolf (ed.), *Dyslexia, fluency, and the brain* (pp. 3–22). Timonium, MD: York Press.

Sunseth, K., & Bowers, P. G. (2002). Rapid naming and phonemic awareness: Contributions to reading, spelling, and orthographic knowledge. *Scientific Studies of Reading, 6,* 401–429.

Swanson, H. L., & Jerman, O. (2006). Math disabilities: A selective meta-analysis of the literature. *Review of Educational Research, 76,* 249–274.

Tallal, P. (2004). Improving language and literacy is a matter of time. *Nature Reviews Neuroscience, 5,* 721–728.

Therrien, W. J., Wickstrom, K., & Jones, K. (2006). Effect of a combined repeated reading and question generation intervention on reading achievement. *Learning Disabilities Research & Practice, 21,* 89–97.

Thomson, J. B., Chenault, B., Abbott, R. D., Raskind, W. H., Richards, T., Aylward, E., et al. (2005). Converging evidence for attentional influences on the orthographic word form in child dyslexics. *Journal of Neurolinguistics, 18,* 93–126.

Tilly, W. D., Reschly, D.J., & Grimes, J. (1999). Disability determination in problem-solving systems: Conceptual foundations and critical components. In D. Reschly, W. D. Tilly, & J. Grimes (Eds.), *Special education in transition: Functional assessment and noncategorical programming* (pp. 285–321). Longmont, CO: Sopris West.

Torgesen, J. K. (2000). Individual differences in response to early interventions in reading: The lingering problem of treatment resisters. *Learning Disabilities Research and Practice, 15,* 55–64.

Torgesen, J. K., Rashotte, C. A., & Alexander, A. W. (2001). Principles of fluency instruction in reading: Relationships with established empirical outcomes. In M. Wolf (Ed.), *Dyslexia, fluency, and the brain* (pp. 333–355). Timonium, MD: York Press.

Torppa, M., Tolvanen, A., Poikkeus, A., Eklund, K., Lerkkanen, M. K., Leskinen, E., et al. (2007). Reading development subtypes and their early characteristics. *Annals of Dyslexia, 57,* 3–52.

VanDerHeyden, A. M., Witt, J. C., & Gilbertson, D. (2007). A multi-year evaluation of the effects of a Response to Intervention model on identification of children for special education. *Journal of School Psychology. 45,* 225–256.

Vargo, F. E., Grosser, G., & Spafford, C. S. (1995). Digit Span and other WISC-R scores in the diagnosis of dyslexia in children. *Perceptual and Motor Skills, 80,* 1219–1229.

Vaughn, S., Linan-Thompson, S., & Hickman, P. (2003). Response to instruction as a means of identifying students with learning/reading disabilities. *Exceptional Children, 69,* 391–409.

Vellutino, F. R., Scanlon, D. M., Sipay, E. R., Small, S. G., Pratt, A., Chen, R., et al. (1996). Cognitive profiles of difficult-to-remediate and readily remediated poor readers: Early intervention as a vehicle for distinguishing between cognitive and experiential deficits as basic causes of specific reading disability. *Journal of Educational Psychology, 88,* 601–638.

Watkins, M. W., Glutting, J. J., & Lei, P. W. (2007). Validity of the full-scale IQ when there is significant variability among WISC-III and WISC-IV factor scores. *Applied Neuropsychology, 14,* 13–20.

Watkins, M. W., Kush, J. C., & Glutting, J. J. (1997). Discriminant and predictive validity of the WISC-III ACID profile among children with learning disabilities. *Psychology in the Schools, 34,* 309–319.

Wiig, E. H. (2008). Language disabilities. In A. Prifitera, D. H. Saklofske, & L. G. Weiss, (Eds.), *WISC-IV clinical assessment and intervention* (pp. 173–193). San Diego, CA: Elsevier.

Willcutt, E. G., Pennington, B. F., Olson, R. K., Chhabildas, N., & Hulslander, J. (2005). Neuropsychological analyses of comorbidity between reading disability and attention deficit hyperactivity disorder: In search of the common deficit. *Developmental Neuropsychology, 27,* 35–78.

Willis, J. O., & Dumont, R. (2006). And never the twain shall meet: Can response to intervention and cognitive assessment be reconciled? *Psychology in the Schools, 43,* 901–908.

Wise, J. C., Sevcik, R. A., Morris, R. D., Lovett, M. W., & Wolf, M. (2007). The growth of phonological awareness by children with reading disabilities: A result of semantic knowledge or knowledge of grapheme-phoneme correspondences? *Scientific Studies of Reading, 11,* 151–164.

Wodrich, D. L., Spencer, M. L., & Daley, K. B. (2006). Combining RTI and psychoeducational assessment: What we must assume to do otherwise. *Psychology in the Schools, 43,* 797–806.

Wolf, M. (2007). *Proust and squid. The story and science of the reading brain.* New York: Harper Collins.

Wolf, M., & Bowers, P. (1999). The "Double-Deficit Hypothesis" for the developmental dyslexias. *Journal of Educational Psychology, 91,* 1–24.

Wolf, M., & Katzir-Cohen, T. (2001). Reading fluency and its intervention. *Scientific Studies of Reading, 5,* 211-239.

Wolf, M., Miller, L., & Donnelly, K. (2000). Retrieval, automaticity, vocabulary elaboration, orthography (RAVE-O): A comprehensive fluency-based reading intervention program. *Journal of Learning Disabilities, 33,* 375–386.

Yeates, K. O., Ris, M. D., & Taylor, H. G. (1999). *Pediatric neuropsychology: Research, theory, and practice.* New York: Guilford Press.

Ysseldyke, J. E., & Marston, D. (2000). Origins of categorical special education services in schools and a rationale for changing them. In D. Reschly & D. Tilly (Eds.), *Functional and noncategorical special education* (pp. 137–146). Longmont, CO: Sopris West.

Zadina, J. N., Corey, D. M., & Casbergue, R. M. (2006). Lobar asymmetries in subtypes of dyslexic and control subjects. *Journal of Child Neurology, 21,* 922–931.

11 Neuropsychology and Special Education Law

MELODY NICHOLS DILK

OVERVIEW OF NEUROPSYCHOLOGICAL EVALUATION[1]

A good clinical neuropsychological evaluation gathers information and data from a variety of sources such as home, school, medical records, and test results, and uses the data to understand the child's unique neurodevelopmental and neurocognitive characteristics and functioning. The neuropsychologist conducts an intraindividual analysis of the child that integrates and synthesizes information reflecting emotional, regulatory, motor, sensory, cognitive, social, and academic functioning (Bernstein, 2000). The neuropsychologist then uses the understanding of the child's neuropsychological status and functioning to provide guidance to the child, parents, and other important adults (such as teachers, service providers, and physicians) to facilitate the child's success, competence, satisfaction, and independence in his or her natural environment (Baron, 2000).

Clinical neuropsychological evaluations typically have two main focuses: neurodiagnostic, targeting the nature and extent of brain dysfunction, and neurofunctional or neurobehavioral, targeting how the strengths and limitations of the individual's neural processes affect the person's day-to-day functioning. Inpatient evaluations typically occur soon after a known neurologically related event (such as a head injury or acute exposure to a neurotoxin) and primarily tend to emphasize neurodiagnostics. Outpatient evaluations occur because of a comparatively broader array of referral issues, often with no known or medically documented cause. In addition to those referred because of a medically documented neural impairment, persons with suspected learning disabilities, attention deficit disorder, developmental disorders, speech and language disruptions, and Asperger's, among others, seek outpatient neuropsychological evaluations.

Most, if not all, children seen by child neuropsychologists in outpatient settings have issues affecting learning or behavioral–social–emotional functioning in their educational environment. For many children experiencing academic issues, a standard psychoeducational evaluation provides sufficient information to guide intervention or remediation. Some children, however, who have complex medical, academic, or psychosocial issues or who have not responded as expected to interventions at school or at home need to have a more detailed examination of neurocognitive processes to understand and address educationally related issues (Rourke, Fisk, & Strang, 1986).

The neuropsychologist's expertise regarding how a child's unique neuropsychological characteristics affects and interacts with aspects of the child's living and learning environments can render the neuropsychologist a valuable resource. Neuropsychologists can provide scientifically oriented, research-based information to teachers, school personnel, multidisciplinary evaluation teams, and individualized educational planning (IEP) teams endeavoring to facilitate the child's success, competence, satisfaction, and independence in the educational setting.

Neuropsychologists have an important responsibility in providing guidance and direction to parents and teachers regarding appropriate interventions, accommodations, and modifications that will improve the child's functioning and success at school (Baron, 2004). Essential and critical to the neuropsychologist's ability to provide effective guidance and direction is a solid knowledge and understanding of laws materially influencing educational and related services within the child's educational environment.

All too often, key persons in a child's life, such as neuropsychologists, school psychologists, school personnel, parents, and advocates have inaccurate or limited knowledge or understanding of special education and special education laws critical to the child's academic success.

Such lack of accurate knowledge unnecessarily compounds obstacles resulting from the child's area of disability. Limited or inaccurate knowledge of the law significantly reduces the neuropsychologist's usefulness to those most directly responsible for the child's health, education, and well-being.

Laws pertaining to special education contain no provisions particular to neuropsychology or neuropsychological services. However, neuropsychologists working with children and adolescents who attend school necessarily must assume additional responsibilities *because* of special education law. For children with disabilities, the law provides the framework that shapes and defines their educational environments. Just as knowledge of special education law enables schools to better educate, and parents to better advocate for children with disabilities, understanding relevant sections of special education laws enables neuropsychologists to provide services from which patients can derive real, useful, and practical benefit in their primary environments, namely, home and school.

OVERVIEW OF RELEVANT SPECIAL EDUCATION LAW

Relative to neuropsychology and special education law, two sets of federal laws currently have the most significant importance: Section 504 of the Rehabilitation Act of 1973 (Section 504) (incorporated into the Americans with Disabilities Act (ADA) in 1990) and the Individuals with Disabilities Improvement Act of 2004 (IDEIA). Both Section 504 and IDEIA guarantee children with disabilities the right to a free appropriate public education (34 CFR 104.33 & 34 CFR 300.101, respectively). IDEIA and corresponding regulations have more detailed procedures, definitions, and requirements than Section 504 (U.S. Department of Education, 2007a) and, as such, will receive the bulk of focus in this chapter with reference and incorporation of Section 504 as appropriate.

Federal law now known as the Individuals with Disabilities Education Act (IDEA) originated in 1975 as Public Law 94-142 known as the Education for All Handicapped Children Act (1975). Before enactment of that legislation millions of children and adolescents with disabilities were entirely excluded from the public school system and from education with nondisabled peers. Those children received no educational or vocational instruction. The small percentage of children with disabilities enrolled in public schools received, at best, minimal educational services in segregated settings (IDEA, 1997; U.S. Department of Education, 2007b). In 1975, for the first time in the United States, Public Law 94-142 guaranteed children with disabilities a free and appropriate public education in the least restrictive setting appropriate.

During the 30-plus years since enactment, Public Law 94-142 (renamed IDEA in 1990), has seen significant evolution toward improving access to effective educational opportunities for children with disabilities in the least restrictive settings with as much interaction and integration with nondisabled peers as possible (U.S. Department of Education, 2007). Though the educational situation of children with disabilities had progressed, Congress enacted the Individuals with Disabilities Improvement Act of 2004 (IDEIA) (20 USC 1400) to address implementation problems caused by "low expectations, and an insufficient focus on applying replicable research on proven methods of teaching and learning for children with disabilities" (20 USC 1400 §600(c)(4)).

The federal government entices states to adopt federal laws and standards by making access to federal monies contingent on adoption of and compliance with the federal law. When a state accepts the federal monies attached to a federal law the state agrees to implement the provisions of the federal law. Federal law establishes the *minimum* levels of protections and entitlements. States can have provisions in laws that establish higher levels of protections and entitlements to residents of the state. In such cases, those more stringent provisions in the state law preempt analogous federal law provisions. Federal law preempts any state laws that afford lower levels of protections or that directly contradict federal law. If the federal law contains provisions that state laws do not include or address, the states are required to implement the federal law provisions as of the date of enactment of the federal law.

Because of the administrative and implementation complexities of many statutes, federal and state legislatures often include provisions that give executive branch agencies, such as the Department of Education, authority to interpret and enforce statutes and devise rules or regulations to facilitate implementation. At the federal level, the law enacted by U.S. Congress is the United States Code (as in 20 USC 1400). The regulations promulgated to guide implementation are the Code of Federal Regulations (as in 34 CFR—regulations pertaining to education). The rules and regulations are subordinate to the enacted code.

The federal law under IDEIA and associated regulations set the minimum standards and rules with which states must comply. As such, the remainder of this chapter will reference the relevant parts of the federal law. However, readers should familiarize themselves with their own state special education laws because, as indicated above, some states have standards and rules that protect the rights of children with disabilities and their parents at a more stringent level than the minimum required by IDEIA.[2]

When dealing with statutes and regulations, it is important to realize that words and terms used in the law do not always have the same usage or meaning as when used in other contexts. Sometimes, lawmakers include sections that define certain words to specify what the words mean as used in the particular statute. For example, in common language, the word *disability* broadly means "being disabled...inability to pursue an occupation because of a physical or mental impairment (Merriam-Webster, 2008). However, for the purposes of the Rehabilitation Act of 1973, Congress defined the word *disability* as follows:

> ..."disability" means...a physical or mental impairment that constitutes or results in a substantial impediment to employment; or...a physical or mental impairment that substantially limits one or more major life activities. (29 USC 16 § 705(9))

Under IDEIA, Congress used a much more specific and detailed meaning for a *child with a disability* as follows:

> (A)...The term "child with a disability" means a child—(i) with mental retardation, hearing impairments (including deafness), speech or language impairments, visual impairments (including blindness), serious emotional disturbance (referred to in this chapter as "emotional disturbance"), orthopedic impairments, autism, traumatic brain injury, other health impairments, or specific learning disabilities; and (ii) who, by reason thereof, needs special education and related services.
>
> (B)...The term "child with a disability" for a child aged 3 through 9...may, at the discretion of the State and the local educational agency, include a child—(i) experiencing developmental delays, as defined by the State and as measured by appropriate diagnostic instruments and procedures, in 1 or more of the following areas: physical development; cognitive development; communication development; social or emotional development; or adaptive development; and (ii) who, by reason thereof, needs special education and related services. (20 USC 33 § 1401(3))

As addressed later herein, the Code of Federal Regulations adds specificity to the definition of disability by defining each sub-area of disability.

Statutes and regulations do not include definitions of all the key terms or phrases. If not defined in the statute or regulations, the interpretation of the term relative to that law is usually based on the dictionary or common meaning of the term. Problems occur when substantial variation exists in the use of the term. For example, the 1997 version of IDEA defined learning disability as a disorder in which a severe discrepancy exists between a child's ability and achievement. IDEA did not, however, define severe discrepancy.

As an effort to gain consistency in criteria used to determine whether a severe discrepancy existed, many states and school corporations created recommendations and guidelines schools could use when making eligibility determinations. In many, if not most cases, the guidelines defined severe discrepancy by a simple mathematical equation subtracting achievement scores from composite scores on intelligence tests (usually the Full Scale IQ). If the discrepancy was greater than a certain number, the student would be deemed to have a severe discrepancy and likely eligible for special education services. Some guidelines included provisions allowing consideration of other factors that supported the presence of an ability–achievement discrepancy in situations where the IQ–achievement discrepancy did not meet the cutoffs. Unfortunately, in those cases the other factors were frequently dismissed and the overly simplistic IQ–achievement discrepancy formula ruled and eligibility was denied. In many cases, the IQ–achievement discrepancy became the *only* factor used to determine eligibility.

The state or local education agencies intend guidelines or policies to promote consistency in eligibility determinations. Unfortunately, many people very mistakenly confuse guidelines and policy with *law*, when, in fact, they are actually just basic guidelines. Though IDEA explicitly prohibited the use of a single measure to determine eligibility, the ease, simplicity, and black-and-white nature of the IQ–achievement discrepancy formula contributed to its widespread use as a sole factor in eligibility determinations. Many professionals and lay people still wrongly believe the discrepancy formula is legally required to determine eligibility.

IDEA never required or intended the use of a discrepancy calculation used by many schools to determine eligibility for special education services. To the contrary, the requirement of a multidisciplinary team to determine eligibility emphasizes the importance of drawing different types of data from a variety of sources, including, among others, parents, teachers, and specialists.

Congress addressed the widespread problems stemming from the use of over-simplified discrepancy score cutoffs when determining eligibility for special education services in the 2004 IDEIA. The IDEIA added a section specific to evaluation and eligibility of children with specific learning disabilities that prohibits local education agencies from being required to consider whether a severe discrepancy exists:

> a local educational agency shall not be required to take into consideration whether a child has a severe discrepancy between achievement and intellectual ability in oral expression, listening comprehension, written expression, basic reading skill, reading comprehension, mathematical calculation, or mathematical reasoning....In determining whether a child has a specific learning disability, a local educational agency may use a process that determines if the child responds to scientific, research-based intervention as a part of the evaluation procedures. 20 USC §§ 614(b)(6)(A) & (B)

IDEIA does not prohibit the school from including the question of severe discrepancy as part of eligibility determination. Some states, such as Indiana, expressly prohibit schools from using a severe discrepancy method to determine eligibility for children with specific learning disabilities (Ind. Auth. Code, Title 511 Art. 7 §40-5(g)(2)(A)(ii) (2008)).

Knowing the differences among common terms and statutory and regulatory definitions of terms and phrases such as *disability, traumatic brain injury, learning disability, evaluation*, among others, enhances communication among providers, parents, and school personnel. Understanding and addressing similarities and differences among usage of similar terms can facilitate dialogue and avoid timely and costly disputes.

Neuropsychological Evaluation in the Context of Special Education Law

Clinical Diagnosis versus Eligibility Classification

Evaluations in the special education context have two primary purposes: To assist in determining whether the child has a disability as defined by the law and to assist in the child's educational planning (34 CFR

300.304(b)). The Code of Federal Regulations defines a child with a disability as one who has been evaluated (using CFR specified procedures) and found to have at least 1 of 13 defined areas of disability under which a child may be found eligible for special education services (34 CFR 300.8(c)). In general, the classifications represent broad categories within which may fall various diagnostic categories used in the *Diagnostic and Statistical Manual of Mental Disorders (DSM-IV*; American Psychiatric Association, 1994).

Frequently, disputes arise between schools and parents about the child's classification. Often, the difficulties have to do with confusion of areas of classification with a diagnostic term or a commonly used term for a condition. For example, many professionals, lay persons, and articles use the term dyslexia to refer to a particular subtype of reading disorders. Diagnostically, a *DSM-IV* diagnosis of Reading Disorder includes conditions such as those commonly called dyslexia. The IDEIA disability classification of Specific Learning Disability includes, among others, conditions diagnosed as Reading Disorders, conditions commonly referred to as dyslexia, mathematics disorders, and disorders of written expression.

For educational planning purposes, the term used to describe a condition or the disability classification has little relevance.

> The IDEA concerns itself not with labels, but with whether a student is receiving a free appropriate public education. A disabled child's individual education plan must be tailored to the unique needs of that particular child....The IDEA charges the school with developing an appropriate education, not with coming up with a proper label with which to describe [the student's] multiple disabilities. (*Heather S. v. Wisconsin*, 1997)

A disability classification area serves only to determine whether a child meets eligibility to receive special education and related services in any area. If a child meets the criteria of any area, the educational plan has to address the child's needs affecting educational progress in whatever area necessary. For example, a child who has a reading disorder and a speech disorder meets eligibility criteria under the classification of specific learning disability, but does not meet the criteria for the classification of speech and language impairment. If, in addition to the reading issues, the child's speech disorder adversely affects the child's educational progress, the education plan must provide for appropriate speech services even though the child does not meet eligibility criteria to be classified as having a speech and language impairment as well as a specific learning disability. Inclusion of a *DSM* diagnosis or a common usage term such as dyslexia or dysgraphia in the child's individual educational plan (IEP) serves no actual educational purpose.

A neuropsychologist can defuse potential disputes over terminology by making reference in the diagnostic section of the report to commonly used terms associated with the child's *DSM-IV* diagnosis and refer to the IDEIA disability classification area that might be consistent with the child's diagnosis. For example:

> Casey's history and test results support and confirm the following *DSM-IV* diagnoses: Reading Disorder (315.00); Mathematics Disorder (315.1); Disorder of Written Expression (315.2); Attention Deficit / Hyperactivity Disorder, combined type (314.01). The nature and type of reading and writing disorders reflect subtypes of language arts disorders commonly referred to as dyslexia. For the purposes of Special Education classifications, if a Case Conference Committee determines Casey meets the eligibility criteria established by state law, Reading Disorder, Mathematics Disorder and Disorder of Written Expression would fall within the Specific Learning Disability classification area and Attention Deficit / Hyperactivity Disorder, combined type would fall within the Other Health Impaired classification.

The law expressly prohibits the use of "any single measure or assessment as the sole criterion for determining whether a child is a child with a disability and for determining an appropriate educational program for the child" (34 CFR §300.304(b)(2)). Although a good neuropsychological evaluation incorporates data from a variety of sources and addresses emotional, regulatory, motor, sensory, cognitive, social, and academic functioning, the neuropsychological evaluation as a whole constitutes a single assessment or source of information. The IEP Team is a multidisciplinary team that includes the child's parents, teachers, and school administrators. By law, the IEP Team has the authority and responsibility to use the findings from the neuropsychological evaluation along with information from other sources such as the school psychologist evaluation, parent and classroom observations, local or statewide test scores, and observations by related service providers when making eligibility and educational planning decisions regarding the child (34 CFR 300.305(a); 34 CFR 300.306(c)).

When discussing a diagnosis or making recommendations pertaining to classification considerations, the neuropsychologist must take care to avoid usurping or undermining the statutory authority given the multidisciplinary evaluation team or IEP team or Section 504 team. The following shows a way of making a recommendation to the IEP team in a way that emphasizes incorporation of other sources of data when reviewing the neuropsychological evaluation

Case Example

Sam's parents need to review these results with his Case Conference Committee. As with all children participating in special education services, the Case Conference Committee should review the current evaluation results in conjunction with other test results and current and historical information from other sources. The Case Conference Committee combines all the data and information to address Sam's need for effective educational interventions and accommodations that facilitate ongoing skill development, accurate assessment, and consistent implementation of his IEP within his instructional environment. For reasons detailed above, Sam needs more instructional time than his peers and he needs specialized direct instruction to further learning of fundamental reading, writing, and math. Sam's particular array of difficulties indicates he requires educational interventions that include multi-modal, applied instruction in phonemic analysis of letters, numbers, and symbols, and orthographic representation of language.

A neuropsychologist involved with the child may serve directly as a part of the group of professionals or, more frequently, the multidisciplinary evaluation team or IEP team considers the neuropsychologist's findings and recommendations from a written report. Either way, the neuropsychologist essentially serves as an unbiased consultant regarding matters of the child's neurodevelopment and neuropsychological characteristics and implications for the educational setting.

IDEIA requires matters of eligibility and determination of educational need to be determined by a group of qualified professionals in collaboration with the child's parents (34 CFR 300.306[a, b]).[3] The law intends for a multidisciplinary team, not one or two individuals, to make decisions regarding placement and educational planning for children with disabilities. The team represents a collaboration of experts with different areas of expertise about the child and the child's response to education. Although neuropsychologists can often provide valuable knowledge, insights, and observations regarding the child's educational environment, the neuropsychologist remains only one expert among many involved with the child.

Factors to Consider When Conducting Evaluations and Making Recommendations

Test Selection and Reporting. Neuropsychologists should have extensive knowledge and training in analysis and in the evaluation of complex brain–behavior relationships and the application of findings to real-life activities and situations (Baron, 2004). When selecting tests and procedures for use in an outpatient evaluation of a child or adolescent that will be used directly or indirectly for educational purposes, neuropsychologists need to use test batteries and procedures that reflect characteristics of the disability area(s) in question and report findings and recommendations with clear, plain language. In an outpatient setting, evaluation reports focused on presumed neuroanatomical correlates and filled with medical terms or psycho-medical jargon provide little useful information to those who have the most daily contact and interaction with the child, namely, the parents and teachers.

The definitions of all classification areas of disability include the provision that the condition must adversely affect the child's educational performance (see Table 11.1). Outpatient neuropsychological evaluation of school-age children and adolescents should routinely address the child's academic functioning and describe how the child's unique neuropsychological strengths and limitations affect specific aspects of functioning in the educational environment. Outpatient neuropsychological evaluations should avoid using psychometrically weak instruments such as the NEPSY (Korkman, Kirk, & Kemp, 1997), which has been criticized for the conceptual as well as statistical limitations of the subtests and neuropsychological domains it purports to assess (Baron, 2004). In their review of the NEPSY, Strauss, Sherman, and Spreen (2006) state:

> Given weak subtest specificity for some subtests but lack of evidence for five separate Core domains, it is difficult to determine how exactly NEPSY performance should be interpreted in a clinical context. (p. 216)

Table 11.1

DEFINITIONS OF DISABILITY AREAS UNDER 34 CFR §300.8(c) AND ASSOCIATED *DSM-IV* DIAGNOSES

AREA OF DISABILITY	CFR DEFINITION	POTENTIALLY ASSOCIATED *DSM-IV* DIAGNOSES
Autism	Developmental disability significantly affecting verbal and nonverbal communication and social interaction, generally evident before age 3, that adversely affects a child's educational performance. Other characteristics often associated with autism are engagement in repetitive activities and stereotyped movements, resistance to environmental change or change in daily routines, and unusual responses to sensory experiences. Does not apply if a child's educational performance is adversely affected primarily because the child has an emotional disturbance. A child who manifests the characteristics of autism after age 3 could be identified as having autism if the above criteria are satisfied.	299.00 Autistic disorder 299.80 Pervasive developmental disorder, NOS
Deaf-blindness	Concomitant hearing and visual impairments, the combination of which causes such severe communication and other developmental and educational needs that they cannot be accommodated in special education programs solely for children with deafness or children with blindness.	
Deafness	A hearing impairment that is so severe that the child is impaired in processing linguistic information through hearing, with or without amplification that adversely affects a child's educational performance.	

Table 11.1 *(continued)*

AREA OF DISABILITY	CFR DEFINITION	POTENTIALLY ASSOCIATED *DSM-IV* DIAGNOSES
Emotional disturbance	A condition exhibiting one or more of the following characteristics over a long period of time and to a marked degree that adversely affects a child's educational performance: (A) An inability to learn that cannot be explained by intellectual, sensory, or health factors. (B) An inability to build or maintain satisfactory interpersonal relationships with peers and teachers. (C) Inappropriate types of behavior or feelings under normal circumstances. (D) A general pervasive mood of unhappiness or depression. (E) A tendency to develop physical symptoms or fears associated with personal or school problems. Emotional disturbance includes schizophrenia. The term does not apply to children who are socially maladjusted, unless it is determined that they have an emotional disturbance as defined by the above criteria.	312.81 Conduct disorder, childhood onset type 312.82 Conduct disorder, adolescent onset type 312.89 Conduct disorder, unspecified onset 313.81 Oppositional defiant disorder 312.90 Disruptive behavior disorder, NOS 317.52 Pica 309.21 Separation anxiety disorder 313.23 Selective mutism 313.89 Reactive attachment disorder 295.xx Schizophrenia, schizophreniform, schizoaffective disorders 298.90 Psychotic disorder NOS 296.xx Mood disorders & bipolar disorders 300.40 Dysthymic disorder 311.00 Depressive disorder NOS 301.13 Cyclothymic disorder 300.xx Anxiety-related disorders 300.30 Obsessive-compulsive disorder 309.81 Posttraumatic stress disorder 308.30 Acute stress disorder 300.xx Somatoform disorders 307.xx Eating disorders 309.xx Adjustment disorders
Hearing impairment	An impairment in hearing, whether permanent or fluctuating, that adversely affects a child's educational performance but that is not included under the definition of deafness in this section.	

(continued)

Table 11.1 *(continued)*

AREA OF DISABILITY	CFR DEFINITION	POTENTIALLY ASSOCIATED *DSM-IV* DIAGNOSES
Mental retardation	Significantly subaverage general intellectual functioning, existing concurrently with deficits in adaptive behavior and manifested during the developmental period, that adversely affects a child's educational performance.	317.00 Mild mental retardation 318.00 Moderate retardation 318.10 Severe mental retardation 318.20 Profound mental retardation
Multiple disabilities	Concomitant impairments (such as mental retardation-blindness or mental retardation-orthopedic impairment), the combination of which causes such severe educational needs that they cannot be accommodated in special education programs solely for one of the impairments. Multiple disabilities does not include deaf-blindness.	
Orthopedic impairment	A severe orthopedic impairment that adversely affects a child's educational performance. The term includes impairments caused by a congenital anomaly, impairments caused by disease (e.g., poliomyelitis, bone tuberculosis), and impairments from other causes (e.g., cerebral palsy, amputations, and fractures or burns that cause contractures).	

Table 11.1 *(continued)*

AREA OF DISABILITY	CFR DEFINITION	POTENTIALLY ASSOCIATED *DSM-IV* DIAGNOSES
Other health impairment	Having limited strength, vitality, or alertness, including a heightened alertness to environmental stimuli, that results in limited alertness with respect to the educational environment, that is due to chronic or acute health problems such as asthma, attention deficit disorder or attention deficit hyperactivity disorder, diabetes, epilepsy, a heart condition, hemophilia, lead poisoning, leukemia, nephritis, rheumatic fever, sickle cell anemia, and Tourette's syndrome; and adversely affects a child's educational performance.	315.40 Developmental coordination disorder 299.80 Rett's disorder 299.10 Childhood disintegrative disorder 299.80 Asperger's disorder 314.01 Attention-deficit/ hyperactivity disorder, combined type or hyperactive type 314.00 Attention-deficit/ hyperactivity disorder, Inattentive type 314.90 Attention-deficit/ hyperactivity disorder, NOS 307.23 Tourette's disorder 307.22 Chronic motor or vocal tic dsorder 787.60 Encopresis 307.70 Encopresis 307.60 Enuresis 307.30 Stereotypic movement Disorder 294.90 Cognitive disorder, NOS 307.8x Pain disorder 309.xx Adjustment disorders
Specific learning disability	A disorder in one or more of the basic psychological processes involved in understanding or in using language, spoken or written, that may manifest itself in the imperfect ability to listen, think, speak, read, write, spell, or to do mathematical calculations, including conditions such as perceptual disabilities, brain injury, minimal brain dysfunction, dyslexia, and developmental aphasia. Disorders not included: learning problems that are primarily the result of visual, hearing, or motor disabilities, of	315.00 Reading disorder 315.10 Mathematics disorder 315.20 Disorder of written expression 315.90 Learning disorder, NOS 315.31 Expressive language dsorder 315.32 Mixed receptive-expressive language dsorder

(continued)

Table 11.1 *(continued)*

AREA OF DISABILITY	CFR DEFINITION	POTENTIALLY ASSOCIATED *DSM-IV* DIAGNOSES
	mental retardation, of emotional disturbance, or of environmental, cultural, or economic disadvantage.	
Speech or language impairment	A communication disorder, such as stuttering, impaired articulation, a language impairment, or a voice impairment, that adversely affects a child's educational performance.	315.31 Expressive Language Disorder 315.32 Mixed receptive-expressive language disorder 315.39 Phonological disorder 317.00 Stuttering 307.90 Communication disorder, NOS
Traumatic brain injury	An acquired injury to the brain caused by an external physical force, resulting in total or partial functional disability or psychosocial impairment, or both, that adversely affects a child's educational performance. Traumatic brain injury applies to open or closed head injuries resulting in impairments in one or more areas, such as cognition; language; memory; attention; reasoning; abstract thinking; judgment; problem-solving; sensory, perceptual, and motor abilities; psychosocial behavior; physical functions; information processing; and speech. Traumatic brain injury does not apply to congenital or degenerative brain injuries or to brain injuries induced by birth trauma.	
Visual impairment including blindness	An impairment in vision that, even with correction, adversely affects a child's educational performance. The term includes both partial sight and blindness.	

Neuropsychologists need to use psychometrically and scientifically sound measures of neurocognitive functions consistent with instruments used within the school setting (e.g., the *Wechsler Intelligence Scale for Children* for measuring cognitive abilities; Wechsler, 2003). In addition to neurocognitive measures, the evaluation should include strong measures of core academic areas (e.g., current versions of the *Woodcock-Johnson Tests of Educational Achievement*; Woodcock, McGrew & Mather, 2001; or *Wechsler Individual Achievement Test*; Psychological Corporation, 2002). If the child already has current data from standardized individual academic achievement measures, the neuropsychologist needs to supplement the achievement testing as necessary, and integrate those data with the neurocognitive and other neuropsychological measures. Routinely addressing the educational and learning environments, which constitute major components of the child's real-life experience, enables the neuropsychologist to provide the child's multidisciplinary evaluation team or IEP team important information useful for determining eligibility and for educational planning.

By describing in the evaluation report how the child's unique neuropsychological functioning explains aspects of the child's history, the neuropsychologist can facilitate the multidisciplinary or IEP team's understanding about why the child had problems learning or functioning in school. That understanding, in turn facilitates the team's ability to determine why a particular intervention or placement did or did not enable a child to progress as expected and make data-driven adjustments to the child's educational plan based on accepted measures of neurocognitive functions and academic achievement.

Exhibit 11.1 provides two examples of applying neuropsychological findings to the child's real-life educational experience.

Making Recommendations. The law requires schools to identify the child's educational needs and devise educational plans reasonably calculated to enable the child to make academic progress. (*Board of Education of the Hendrick Hudson Central School District v. Rowley*, 1982). The IEP team must specify annual goals and objectives in the IEP (34 CFR §300.320). The law does not mandate the school to identify or explain methods employed to achieve the goals. Both Congress and the courts recognize that determination of methods to effectuate an educational plan is best left to those trained in teaching methods. Schools have

Exhibit 11.1

EXAMPLES OF NEUROPSYCHOLOGICAL FINDINGS APPLIED TO A CHILD'S EDUCATIONAL EXPERIENCE

PATIENT NAME: James (not his real name)
AGE AT EVALUATION: 8 years, 4 months
GRADE PLACEMENT: 1st grade, 3rd month

Synopsis of Neuropsychological Findings. James' results show significantly impaired neuropsychological development in a number of areas critical to learning and daily functioning. Although James has some specific cognitive areas that have developed better than others, he generally shows limitations in development in most core cognitive domains. James' difficulty learning early academic skills stems from underdeveloped intellectual abilities. Quite likely, much of the behavioral disruptions at school occurred because James' cognitive and adaptive development had not progressed to the level he needed to meet the academic and social demands of the classroom environments.

James has a perseverative response tendency, which is a frequent characteristic of children with broad delay of working memory and general cognitive functions. Such tendency contributes to problems in early learning. For James, the perseverative response tendency interferes with his performance within a specific task and with transitions from one task to another. For example, if attempting to learn the spelling of a certain word such as "blue" James may spell the word as "abu" or "bcu". Previously overlearned information (such as, in this example, the beginning of the alphabet) proactively interferes with recall of subsequent information.

When attempting to execute a response in a new-learning situation, the new information triggers recall of associated previously learned information. For children with typical cognitive development, such associated recall facilitates understanding of the new information and enables assimilation of new with old learning. Children with cognitive development similar to James have not developed the mental regulatory and inhibitory mechanisms typical of most children their age. Thus, the children cannot keep the recalled associated information in the background while they work with the new learning task. Parts of the previously learned information invade and mix with the new information as if it is part of the new task, when it is not. As such, the new information becomes garbled and nonsensical, resulting in similarly garbled and confusing responses.

To address the problems caused by unusual proactive interference in the educational environment, James needs to have more repetitions and applications when learning new information. To prevent the previously learned information from garbling the new information, he needs close observation and immediate corrective feedback to increase and facilitate accurate practice of the new material.

Very limited development of neural regulatory and inhibitory mechanisms adds yet another disruption to the learning process. James has significant difficulty inhibiting spontaneous thoughts and actions. Even within a highly structured environment with few visual or auditory distracters, James needs frequent, direct, specific, and firm redirection to enable him to complete tasks. In visually interesting or active environments, he has poor ability to stop impulsive verbalizations or behaviors. Settings with many interesting things to touch or look at place James at risk for significant emotional and behavioral deterioration. In such settings, adults would typically attempt to redirect James or make repeated requests to stop responding to the attractive things that elicited an impulsive response and, instead do something that has less or little interest to him.

Exhibit 11.1 *(continued)*

EXAMPLES OF NEUROPSYCHOLOGICAL FINDINGS APPLIED TO A CHILD'S EDUCATIONAL EXPERIENCE

Because James has underdeveloped mechanisms needed to inhibit impulsive actions, he responds to adults' attempts to redirect his behavior at a level similar to much younger children. The frontal area of the brain, which tends to manage most inhibitory and regulatory processes, develops more gradually than other areas of the brain in most children. That is one reason why toddlers need more repetition of directions and physical prompts than older children need.

For James, development of frontal regulatory areas in the brain is progressing more slowly than typical. However, adults naturally expect James to respond to redirection at a level consistent with his age peers. The incongruity between adult expectations and James' skill development places him at odds with his environment, resulting in increased stress and demands that exceed James' coping resources. When his coping mechanisms reach capacity, behaviors and emotions begin to deteriorate.

James' instructional setting needs to have a strong, consistent structure. Teachers need to be aware James has substantial difficulty inhibiting spontaneous reactions and behaviors in visually or physically active environments. As such, he would likely perform better in a small classroom that does not have a lot of wall hangings or visually noisy decorations or potential auditory distractions.

In combination, underdeveloped intellectual skills, perseverative responses associated with proactive interference, and poorly developed regulatory mechanisms explain why James has had such significant difficulty learning early reading, writing, and math skills. Although James has had 2 years of kindergarten and $1^1/_2$ years of first grade, he cannot consistently write all the letters of the alphabet. When asked to write the alphabet, James showed no obvious signs of avoidance or resistance and produced the following:

After he completed the letters he could recall at that time, James stated he knew how to write numbers, and produced the following;

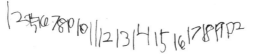

The difficulty James has forming letters and numbers stems from poor development of muscles and coordinated motor movement in James' hands and arms. James has very limited manual dexterity compared with his age peers and the muscles in his hands and arms are unusually weak.

As indicated previously, when teaching fundamental components of reading and writing, the teacher needs to have direct one-to-one interaction with James. The teacher or assistant needs to provide consistent redirection and supportive, but firm structure. The teacher or assistant needs to supervise James closely enough to provide sufficient immediate corrective feedback to decrease interference of previously learned information and to increase correct practice of core academic skills.

(continued)

Exhibit 11.1 *(continued)*

EXAMPLES OF NEUROPSYCHOLOGICAL FINDINGS APPLIED TO A CHILD'S EDUCATIONAL EXPERIENCE

PATIENT NAME: Josh (not his real name)
AGE AT EVALUATION: 7 years, 10 months
EDUCATION: 1st grade, 9th month

Synopsis of Neuropsychological Findings. Evaluation results show Josh has significantly underdeveloped neural mechanisms needed to perceive, discriminate, and interpret visual information accurately. Josh also has bilateral upper extremity hypotonia that impairs fine motor strength and dexterity. Josh's history and previous test results show deficits in visual perception, discrimination, and interpretation and deficits in fine motor functioning are long-standing, thus, indicative of a lag in neurodevelopment. As such, current findings do *not* reflect transient or situation-specific deficits. The markedly underdeveloped visual-perceptual interpretive processes undoubtedly explain the extreme difficulty Josh has had learning fundamental reading, writing, and written math skills.

Results also show Josh has impaired ability to analyze and process sequential language containing conditions, qualifiers, and limiters. Despite intact auditory perception and good contextual auditory memory, the underdeveloped sequential receptive language function substantially interferes with Josh's ability to track and process certain auditory information accurately. This disorder interferes with his ability to follow multistep auditory directions consistently. Well-meaning teachers and other adults often perceive the problems following multistep directions and other behaviors associated with inaccurate auditory processing and mistakenly attribute the difficulties to oppositional behavior or problems with attention and concentration. Although those disorders result in some similar behaviors, the underlying causes and etiologies are quite different as are the intervention implications.

Accurate visual perception and rapid visual and verbal associative processes provide the means by which children learn that certain specific information represents or connects to certain other specific information. Underdeveloped discriminative, perceptual, or associative processes interfere with learning the associations necessary for reading, writing, and math.

When developing reading decoding skills for a word such as "cat," children first must learn to recognize the separate letters of the word and make associations between the visual representations of the individual letters and their sounds. When confronted in text with the sequence of letters "cat" (assuming they have not learned the word by sight) they must accurately discriminate the visual symbols representing each letter and retrieve the verbal form of each letter from long-term memory. Then, they must retrieve from long-term memory the sound associated with each individual letter; in this case /k/ for "c", /ā/ for "a" and /t/ for "t". The retrieval of each sound for each letter must proceed quickly enough to make it possible for children to merge each sound with the next sound so that, ultimately, they stop working with each separate sound, and instead produce the final product ...."cat" when prompted by the letter sequence.

Exhibit 11.1 *(continued)*

EXAMPLES OF NEUROPSYCHOLOGICAL FINDINGS APPLIED TO A CHILD'S EDUCATIONAL EXPERIENCE

If perception or discrimination of the visual information is inaccurate, the child will not have a link to a correct associated sound, letter, or word. If the visual and auditory associated memories are not retrieved quickly enough the word will continue to consist of separate sound units rather than a final whole word. With more complicated words such as "rate," children have to retrieve not only the separate sound-symbol associations, but also the "long vowel, silent 'e'" rule quickly enough to arrive at the correct memory trace of the whole word.

Records and current results show Josh has had very significant difficulty learning early fundamental reading and writing skills. By early kindergarten, most children can recognize and write all the upper and lower case letters of the alphabet and match all consonant sounds to corresponding letters. By mid-kindergarten, children should be able to spell high frequency words such as "man" and "cat" correctly. They should be able to count by ones, fives, and tens to 100.

Currently, Josh cannot correctly write his first name consistently. He can recite the alphabet, but he cannot write all the letters of the alphabet in order without omissions. He recognizes letters and words at a level exceeding only 1% of his age peers. Josh cannot write simple meaningfully connected words or phrases (such as black cat or big dog). Josh can write numbers, but the number he writes does not consistently match the number he states or intends to write.

Underdeveloped visual perceptual and visual discrimination functions have interfered with Josh's achievement in writing. Josh's difficulty in accurately perceiving and interpreting letters and numbers impairs his ability to create orthographic reproductions of letters, numbers, and other graphic information others have typed or written. The impaired functions also limit Josh's ability to discriminate and interpret letters, numbers, and figures he writes. As such, he does not have a strong set of visual perceptual tools needed to notice, for example, when a number or letter he writes does not match the number or letter he thought about in his mind or stated, or when he forms a letter or number incorrectly.

Josh's orthographic and writing progress has been further limited by upper extremity bilateral hypotonia. Josh's grip-strength is significantly weaker in both his dominant and nondominant hand than typical for children his age. He also has poorly coordinated fine motor dexterity in both hands. Josh's grip strength and fine-motor manual dexterity is more than two standard deviations lower bilaterally than typical for children his age. Limited manual strength and dexterity increases muscle fatigue and interferes with the fine motor functioning needed to make fluid, controlled movements with a pencil, pen, or other marker to create letters, numbers, and drawings.

Josh likely has substantial difficulty copying written material, even if the copy source is placed directly above the paper where he is supposed to write. He may benefit from use of adaptive writing instruments such as a writing frame to facilitate ease of grasp while tracing letters and words. He likely needs much repeated practice with verbalization about what he writes to facilitate associative memory development ....

discretion to determine which methods to use when implementing an IEP, as long as the methods address the student's individual needs in order for the child to progress in the curriculum (*Board of Education v. Rowley*, 1982).

Neuropsychologists often make recommendations that a child should participate in a specific program that uses a particular methodology. When making such recommendations, neuropsychologists should carefully describe the characteristics of the methodology or program and explain aspects of the child's neuropsychological findings that make the methodology or program conducive to the child's educational planning. By so doing, the reference to a specific method or program serves more appropriately as an example of a method or program that has characteristics useful to the child's needs. The IEP team may choose to use the referenced method or to incorporate the program method characteristics relevant to the child in another way.

If a neuropsychologist recommends that an educational intervention uses a specific methodology or particular program, the neuropsychologist needs to explain thoroughly the rationale for the recommendation. The neuropsychologist must maintain scientific objectivity and avoid becoming an advocate. As stated previously, the school has discretion and authority to determine which methods to use to implement the child's IEP. The IEP team determines the appropriate program or educational placement. If a child has an appropriate IEP in place and the child's parents want to pursue an intervention using a particular methodology or a program independent of the child's IEP, the parent may do so and pay for the services privately.

Significant controversy and problems arise when a neuropsychologist or other provider essentially begins to advocate for a specific intervention or program to be included as part of the child's IEP. In such cases, the dispute centers around the question of whether the school must use the specified methodology or program in order to provide the child a free appropriate public education in compliance with federal and state laws. Although some circumstances can support the need for a particular methodology or program placement, such is not the case in many, if not most, instances.

If a neuropsychologist or other provider recommends that the school needs to include a specific methodology or program in a child's IEP, the neuropsychologist needs to have solid, concrete, clear, and specific scientifically based justifications. Furthermore, if a neuropsychologist or other provider renders an opinion that a child has not received an appropriate education, current and historical evaluation data must clearly support that opinion. The U.S. Supreme Court in Rowley (1982) made it clear that schools have to devise and implement an individualized educational plan reasonably calculated to convey an educational benefit to the child. Programs or methods may exist from which a child may benefit more than they would through the educational plan within the public school. However, the standard set for a free appropriate public education requires an individualized plan from which the child could reasonably benefit. That standard holds even if the child might benefit more from a different program within or external to the school.

Laws Pertaining to Postsecondary Programs

IDEIA provisions apply to children and young persons ages 3 through 21 through the twelfth grade. Once a young person either completes the twelfth grade or reaches the age of 22, he or she no longer falls under the protections and provisions of IDEIA. However, the provisions of the Americans with Disabilities Act (ADA) apply to individuals with disabilities (as defined by the statute) regardless of the age. As indicated earlier in this chapter, ADA does not have the level of detailed substantive provisions relative to education compared with IDEIA. However, the ADA continues to provide important procedural protections to persons with disabilities pursuing postsecondary education.[4]

At the postsecondary level, the law does not require educational institutions to provide educational interventions. For persons with disabilities (as defined by the act), federal, state, and local entities have to make reasonable accommodations to prevent nonrelevant aspects of the person's disability from interfering with participation in programs for which the person would otherwise be qualified. The ADA states, in pertinent part, as follows:

> [N]o qualified individual with a disability shall, by reason of such disability, be excluded from participation in or be denied the benefits of the services, programs, or activities of a public entity, or be subjected to discrimination by any such entity. (42 U.S.C. § 12132)

To qualify for protection under the ADA, an individual seeking to participate in an activity or program offered by a public entity must prove that he or she is:

1. disabled as defined by ADA,
2. otherwise qualified for the program, and
3. excluded or denied benefits solely because of the disability.

The question of accommodations arises only *after* the person shows he or she is otherwise qualified for a program *and* is disabled under ADA. The ADA defines disability as a "physical or mental impairment that substantially limits one or more of the major life activities of such individual" (42 U.S.C. § 12102[2][A]). Otherwise qualified means one who "meets the essential eligibility requirements...for participation in [a given] program provided by a public entity...with or without reasonable modifications to rules, policies, or practices...." (42 U.S.C. § 12131[2]).

Determining whether a person is otherwise qualified for a program requires a two-step analysis. First, the person must have the requisite cognitive capacity, knowledge base, or skills to perform the essential components of the activity at the requisite level of competency. Second, reasonable modifications must exist that will enable the person to participate in the activity at the requisite level of competency. In other words, the person must show that a reasonable accommodation exists that would effectively remove the obstacles attributable to the disabling condition such that the person could perform the essential components of the activity at the requisite level of competency.

For example, if a person requests an extended time accommodation for a college entrance examination, the person must document the presence of a disability that substantially interferes with the person's ability to take the examination within the standard time limits. Documenting *only* that the person has a disability does not satisfy the ADA requirements. To qualify for an ADA accommodation, the disability *must* substantially limit the person's ability to perform a nonrelevant aspect of the activity at issue. To meet the otherwise qualified component, the person would have to show he or she meets the prerequisites to sit for the exam (e.g., graduation from high school with an academic diploma or completion of a graduate equivalency diploma, [GED]). The person also has to show that on a test involving substantial reading, an extended time accommodation would enable the person to demonstrate more accurately the competencies the test is designed to assess (because the accommodation removes the nonrelevant reading rate obstacle created by the disabling condition).

As another example, a person with a documented spinal cord injury who has limited upper extremity mobility and fine-motor dexterity requests an alternative response accommodation for a computerized licensing examination that typically requires the examinee to enter responses to multiple choice questions using a keyboard. The person would need to show that the disabling condition substantially limits his or her ability to use the standard response format (the computer keyboard). The person would also need to show he or she meets the requirements to sit for the licensing examination to meet the otherwise qualified component. In addition, to support the request for the alternative response accommodation, the person might provide documentation that use of a mouse or track-ball to enter responses reduces extraneous errors (caused by hitting unintended keys on a keyboard), reduces fatigue, or decreases the amount of time needed to enter responses.

Courts have held that educational institutions have a "real obligation" to seek suitable avenues to reasonably accommodate persons with disabilities and to carry out this statutory obligation conscientiously (*Wynne v. Tufts Univ. School of Medicine,* 1991). That notwithstanding, courts have also held that the student must show that a reasonable accommodation exists that does not interfere with the institution's essential eligibility requirements (*Zukle v. Regents of the University of California,* 1999; *Kaltenberger v. Ohio College of Podiatric Medicine,* 1998).

To comply with ADA, agencies and institutions have to meet the procedural requirements of the statute. Because the regulations regarding administration of ADA in educational institutions have much less complexity compared to IDEIA regulations, significant variability in policies and requirements exists across post-educational institutions and administrating bodies for entrance, competency, certification, and licensing examinations. Neuropsychologists performing evaluations or consultation for persons in post-secondary endeavors need to obtain information directly from the post-secondary program or entity (such as educational testing services, law school admissions council, or the professional licensing or certification board). Such entities often have specific procedures and types of tests that need to be included in evaluations and reports documenting the presence of a disabling condition. The entities also often have certain types of accommodations allowed or not allowed and specify the type of information that needs to be included in the written report to support a recommended accommodation.

CONCLUSIONS

Consider the following two cases.[5] Both involve 14- to 15-year-old children in the eighth to ninth grades. Both had significant cognitive and physical impairments secondary to serious illness during infancy causing extensive neurological damage, with markedly compromised right hemispheric functions and at least mildly impaired left functions. Both children had received special education services since preschool and had attended public school through the sixth or seventh grade. Each child had been parentally placed in private educational settings for a year or more. Each child's parents brought claims against the schools asserting the school had failed to provide a free appropriate public education and wanting the schools to pay for the private educational placements. Each child had a neuropsychological evaluation and each neuropsychologist testified at the child's due process hearing. Dr. A was the neuropsychologist for child one ("Charlie") and Dr. B was the neuropsychologist for child two ("Joe").

Case Example: Charlie

Dr. A conducted Charlie's neuropsychological evaluation, reviewed evaluation results from the public school, other private evaluators, and the private educational placement. Dr. A reviewed Charlie's academic and behavioral records and reviewed the educational curricula, speech, occupational, and physical therapy services at the public and private placements. At the hearing, when Dr. A was asked about test results that appeared to conflict with findings from the neuropsychological evaluation, Dr. A identified reasonable explanations for the apparent conflict (such as tests with similar names that measure very different functions or processes, significant emotional events in proximity to an assessment date, differences in effects of medication regimen). Dr. A responded to every question regarding Charlie in a manner that explained and related to Charlie's neuropsychological and neurodevelopmental characteristics.

Dr. A answered questions about services and interventions Charlie received at the public and private schools by identifying how different aspects of the programs appeared to address Charlie's neuropsychological strengths and limitations. Dr. A integrated and unified data from teachers and parents, from assessments at the public and private schools, from the neuropsychological evaluation, and from occupational, physical, and speech therapists and presented evidence-based information centered around how the data reflected the interaction between Charlie's brain–behavior relationships and his responses to his educational environments.

Case Example: Joe

Dr. B conducted Joe's neuropsychological evaluation, reviewed evaluation results from the public school, other private evaluators, and the private educational placement. Dr. B had some familiarity with Joe's academic records, but little knowledge about the components or services within either the public or private educational placements. At the hearing, when Dr. B was asked about test results that appeared to conflict with findings from the neuropsychological evaluation, Dr. B dismissed the incongruent findings and stated the school's psychoeducational evaluation had nothing of value to offer. Dr. B testified that the school could not and would not provide appropriate educational services for Joe, but Dr. B provided no substantive neuropsychological findings or other data to support that conclusion.

Dr. B strongly recommended the private program, which used a specific methodology for Joe. Instead of relating specific aspects of the program to Joe's neuropsychological characteristics, Dr. B made broad statements about the general methodology the program employed. When asked about data that showed Joe had benefitted from services he had at the public school that were not available at the private placement, Dr. B referred to the services and benefit as being of little importance and inconsequential. Dr. B made statements about Joe's abilities and needs that contradicted the neuropsychological evaluation results and responded to questions about the contradictions by reiterating the statements and conclusions. The bulk of Dr. B's testimony focused very narrowly on the neuropsychological evaluation results. Dr. B's testimony largely consisted of broad conclusions about the inadequacies of the public school and the superiority of the private placement with little actual data to support the conclusions.

Both of the preceding cases were extremely emotionally wrenching for the children's parents, who spent tens of thousands of dollars in attorney fees. *If* the parent prevails at the hearing, on administrative appeal, or on judicial appeal, the federal district court *might* order the school to pay the parent's attorney fees in whole or in part. However, if the parents do not prevail, the parents bear the entire cost of their attorney fees and possibly court costs.

The neuropsychologist's value in the special education law context has to do with the ability to maintain objective, scientific inquiry into a child's brain–behavior relationships and analyze the interaction of those relationships within the educational environment. That type of objective analysis, demonstrated so aptly by Dr. A, enables neuropsychologists to look at components of a child's experience in terms of the child's unique neurocognitive and neurodevelopmental functions. The neuropsychologist can then explain how the child's individual characteristics fit or do not fit with characteristics of various programs or methods. By so doing, neuropsychologists such as Dr. A provide the value of neuropsychological research and knowledge to persons involved with special education law.

NOTES

1. Clinical neuropsychological evaluation as used herein does not include forensics evaluations.
2. It is beyond the scope of this chapter to cover the unique characteristics of each state's special education law. State laws particular to special education can be obtained from the state Department of Education. Most of the states have viewable or downloadable versions of the applicable state law available on the Web site for the special education or exceptional learners division of the state Department of Education.
3. Regulations for Section 504 requires placement decisions to be made by "a group of persons" but does not expressly require inclusion of the parent as part of the group (34 CFR §104.34[c]).

4. ADA pertains to all agencies and programs receiving state or federal money. However, this section focuses only on provisions as they relate to post-secondary education entities.
5. The cases discussed are real cases involving two unrelated children and two different neuropsychologists. Synopses of the neuropsychologists' testimony were derived from actual public records of the Due Process Hearings. Because of the sensitivity of the matters involved, the records will not be referenced.

REFERENCES

American Psychiatric Association. (1994). *Diagnostic and statistical manual of mental disorders* (4th ed.). Washington, DC: American Psychiatric Press.

Americans with Disabilities Act of 1990. 42 U.S.C. 12131. (1990).

Americans with Disabilities Act of 1990. 28 C.F.R. Part 35. (1991).

Baron, I. S.(2000). Clinical implications and practical applications of child neuropsychological evaluations. In K. O. Yeates, M. D. Ris, & H. G. Taylor (Eds.), *Pediatric neuropsychology* (pp. 439–456). New York: Guilford Press.

Baron, I. S. (2004). *Neuropsychological evaluation of the child*. New York: Oxford University Press.

Bernstein, J. S. (2000). Developmental neuropsychological assessment. In K. O. Yeates, M. D. Ris, & H. G. Taylor (Eds.), *Pediatric neuropsychology* (pp. 405–438). New York: Guilford Press.

Board of Education of the Hendrick Hudson Central School District v. Rowley, 458 U.S. 176, 102 S. Ct. 3034. U.S. S. Ct. (1982).

Education for All Handicapped Children Act, Pub.L. No. 94-142. (1975).

Heather S. v. Wisconsin, 125 F.3d 1045, 1055, 7th Cir. (1997).

Indiana Authoritative Code, Title 511, Article 7. (2008).

Individuals with Disabilities Education Act. 20 U.S.C. § 1400, et seq. (1997).

Individuals with Disabilities Education Improvement Act. 20 U.S.C. §1400, et seq. (2004).

Individuals with Disabilities Education Improvement Act. 34 C.F.R. Part 300, et seq. (2005).

Kaltenberger v. Ohio College of Podiatric Medicine, 6th Cir. (1998).

Korkman, M., Kirk, U., & Kemp, S. (1997). *NEPSY: A developmental neuropsychological assessment*. San Antonio, TX: Psychological Corporation.

Merriam-Webster Online. (2008). *Disability*. Retrieved September 5, 2008, from http://www.merriam-webster.com/dictionary/disability

The Psychological Corporation. (2002). *Wechsler Individual Achievement Test—second edition*. San Antonio, TX: Author.

Rehabilitation Act of 1973, as amended, 29 USC 16 § 705(9) (1973).

Rehabilitation Act of 1973, as amended. 29 U.S.C. § 794 (Section 504). (1973).

Rehabilitation Act of 1973, as amended. 34 C.F.R. Part 104. (1980).

Rourke, B. P., Fisk, J. L., & Strang, J. D. (1986). *Neuropsychological assessment of children*. New York: Guilford Press.

Strauss, E., Sherman, E. M. S., & Spreen, O. (2006). *A compendium of neuropsychological tests* (3rd ed.) New York: Oxford University Press.

U.S. Department of Education (2007a). *Free appropriate public education for students with disabilities: Requirements under Section 504 of the Rehabilitation Act of 1973.* Washington, DC: U.S. Government Printing Office.

U.S. Department of Education (2007b). *Thirty years of progress in educating children with disabilities through IDEA.* Washington, DC: U.S. Government Printing Office.

Wechsler, D. (2003). *The Wechsler Intelligence Scale for Children* (4th ed.). San Antonio, TX: Psychological Corporation.

Woodcock, R. W., McGrew, K. S., & Mather, N. (2001). *Woodcock-Johnson III Tests of Achievement*. Itasca, IL: Riverside Publishing.

Wynne v. Tufts Univ. School of Medicine, 932 F.2d 19,795, 1st Cir. (1991).

Zukle v. Regents of the University of California, 9th Cir. (1999).

Neuropsychological Testing for Adults

12 Neuropsychological Evaluation of Adults With Psychiatric Disorders

ASHLEY A. GORMAN AND WILFRED G. VAN GORP

This chapter describes the cognitive deficits commonly associated with various psychiatric conditions in adults and discusses how a neuropsychological evaluation integrates the results of cognitive and personality/emotional testing to better inform treatment planning. The scope of this discussion is limited to mature adults and excludes those individuals who exhibit onset of psychiatric symptoms in the context of aging or a dementia process, as psychiatric symptoms in these populations are typically associated with a unique clinical presentation and underlying etiology that is beyond the scope of this chapter.

Neuropsychological testing plays a particularly useful role when treating psychiatric patients, in that it can serve as a window into the true nature of their cognitive abilities and act as an objective marker of both cognitive and emotional symptoms. The limitations of using neuropsychological testing to differentiate between various psychiatric conditions and predicting real world functioning is also explored in this chapter. Finally, in the hopes that referring clinicians can have a realistic understanding of how neuropsychological testing can appropriately be used to meet their specific diagnostic and treatment goals, we will highlight referral questions that neuropsychological test results can help address and those that neuropsychological tests results, in isolation, should not be used to answer.

HOW IS A NEUROPSYCHOLOGICAL EVALUATION USEFUL IN EVALUATING PATIENTS WITH PSYCHIATRIC DISORDERS?

For a neuropsychological evaluation to benefit both the patient and the referring clinician, it is important to understand the types of referral questions that a neuropsychological evaluation can help answer. Historically, referral questions posed to neuropsychologists suggested a false diagnostic distinction between *organic* (i.e., neurological) and *nonorganic* (i.e., psychogenic) brain disease. For example, a common referral question to neuropsychologists historically was whether a patient had *organic* brain disease versus schizophrenia, setting forth a false distinction to the neuropsychologist, as if one condition were related to brain function and the other condition (schizophrenia) were not. We now understand that the answer to this question can be quite simple: Yes and yes: Both are related to brain malfunction as schizophrenia is now universally regarded as a psychiatric manifestation of an underlying brain illness. The fields of neuropsychology and psychiatry have addressed these misguided attempts to artificially compartmentalize psychiatric conditions from their neurological underpinnings. The types of referral questions now posed to neuropsychologists often pertain to differential diagnostic issues in patients with various psychiatric and/or neurological symptoms, such as: Are a patient's memory and attention complaints due to a primary attention disorder, such as attention-deficit/hyperactivity disorder (ADHD), or to a mood disorder, such as major depression? In addition, the referral question may pertain not merely to a diagnostic question, but to issues of functional capacity in a patient's everyday life. This chapter outlines the types of cognitive problems typically found in various psychiatric patients and how these cognitive problems relate to their real-world abilities.

HOW CAN A NEUROPSYCHOLOGICAL EVALUATION HELP GUIDE TREATMENT PLANNING?

A neuropsychological assessment can serve as an invaluable tool in guiding treatment planning for individuals with various types of psychiatric conditions. For example, a depressed patient with severe cognitive slowing and forgetfulness related to their depression may have difficulty following complex, therapeutic recommendations spoken quickly by the clinician and may require simplified, slowly spoken instructions and frequent repetition. A patient with memory problems may have trouble remembering the content of previous psychotherapy sessions, or may have difficulty following complex medication regimens, in which case emphasis on repetition, note taking, and pill boxes/medication assistance may become a focus of treatment. Finally, a patient with executive dysfunction may, on the surface, appear to have the overall cognitive abilities necessary for functioning independently and maintaining successful employment; however, their inability to organize and effectively use their cognitive abilities in a goal-directed way may limit their success in their real-world environment. These patients may frustrate the clinician and appear to be noncompliant with treatment, when in reality they are struggling to cope with compromised executive functioning abilities. A neuropsychological evaluation can help identify these areas of cognitive weakness and hence better inform the clinician and the patient about specific treatment strategies that might uniquely help with the specific case in question.

The neuropsychological evaluation is unique in that it integrates multiple sources of information in order to draw conclusions about a patient's symptoms. In the case of an adult psychiatric patient, the objective cognitive and personality testing is certainly an important aspect of the evaluation, but emphasis is also placed on informant ratings (typically a family member or someone who knows the patient well), behavioral observations during the examination, and a thorough clinical history. With regard to this latter point, the referring clinician and the patient's family are often instrumental in gathering relevant background documentation, such as medical records, educational records, work history, and so on, that are necessary to complete an integrated neuropsychological evaluation. The results of cognitive testing should not be interpreted outside the context of a patient's unique psychosocial environment and the onset and course of his or her particular symptom constellation. The integration of multiple sources of information allows the neuropsychologist to aid not only in the differential diagnostic question at hand, but also to offer real-world predictions and practical recommendations to the patient, his or her family, and the referring health care provider.

In addition to raising the referring clinician's awareness about existing cognitive weaknesses in their patients, a neuropsychological evaluation can also emphasize strengths that may not be readily apparent in the context of a complex symptom presentation. Studies have shown that in a variety of both psychiatric patient populations and nonpsychiatric clinical populations (e.g., HIV, multiple sclerosis, epilepsy), subjective ratings of cognitive impairment are often more closely correlated with depression or other psychiatric etiology than with actual, objective impairment on neuropsychological testing (Maor, Olmer, & Mozes, 2001; Moore, van Gorp, Hinkin, Stern, Swales, & Satz, 1997; Moritz, Ferahli, & Naber, 2004; Sawrie, Martin, & Kuzniecky, 1999; Van Den Bosch, & Rombouts, 1998; van Gorp et al., 1991). For example, a severely anxious patient may complain of distractibility and memory problems in everyday life that significantly interfere with their ability to perform adequately at work. However, results of neuropsychological tests may indicate that under conditions of reduced stress, their attention and memory abilities are actually quite normal, or even above average. It could be that factors such as depression or anxiety prevent the affected individual from accurately monitoring his or her thinking and understanding the true cause of subjective cognitive complaints. Helping a patient appreciate his or her true cognitive potential and the impact that emotional symptoms can have on his or her everyday life is crucial to both psychotherapeutic interventions (e.g., individuals' maladaptive beliefs about their cognitive ability can be countered using objective evidence) and pharmacological interventions (e.g., concerns about cognitive side effects of medication can be explored).

COGNITIVE DEFICITS IN VARIOUS PSYCHIATRIC POPULATIONS

The cognitive manifestations associated with a particular psychiatric disorder may be conceptualized as symptoms associated with the underlying brain condition, in the same way that the noncognitive, emotional or psychiatric manifestations reflect the same underlying illness. For example, reduced performance on tasks of verbal fluency or problem solving may be reflective of the underlying neurological abnormalities in schizophrenia, whereas a presentation of predominantly negative symptoms may reflect the same underlying condition (Weinberger &

Berman, 1986). The nature and severity of cognitive dysfunction in other psychiatric disorders, such as unipolar depression, bipolar disorder, and obsessive-compulsive disorder, are less well understood and may vary across individuals. This chapter reviews the neuropsychological deficits associated with these various psychiatric conditions, as well as those found in schizophrenia.

Neuropsychological Assessment of Unipolar Depression

Although subjective cognitive complaints in depressed patients are sometimes disproportionate to their objective cognitive performance, depression can result in a pattern of cognitive impairment and can play a major role in an individual's day-to-day functioning. In some individuals, particularly the elderly, cognitive complaints can be the chief presenting complaint of depression, as opposed to frank mood complaints such as sadness or anhedonia. These cognitive complaints may include difficulty concentrating, forgetfulness, and disorganization in their everyday life.

Research has demonstrated that depressed patients may demonstrate impairments in learning, attention, motor function, and problem solving (Austin, Mitchell, & Goodwin, 2001; Burt, Zembar, & Niederehe, 1995; Elliott, 1998). Studies of memory functioning in particular have demonstrated that memory impairments tend to be secondary to underlying attention problems and reflect encoding and retrieval problems, rather than a true deficit in learning and consolidating new information (Goodwin, 1997; Massman, Delis, Butters, Dupont, & Gillin, 1992). In other words, depressed patients' conscious or nonconscious preoccupation with their negative mood state often results in inattentiveness to incoming information. Because of inattentiveness, these patients may not adequately encode new information, which later hinders their ability to retrieve this new information efficiently. Although their encoding may be less than optimal under these circumstances, depressed patients are usually able to encode and store new information (i.e., keep memories of new information) and can demonstrate what they remember when given cues or reminders from the environment to trigger their memory recall. Diminished psychomotor processing speed is also a major finding among depressed individuals, such that they complete tasks slower and less efficiently (Hartlage, Alloy, Vazquez, & Dykman, 1993; White, Myerson, & Hale, 1997), and this slowing may also interfere with their ability to process incoming information.

As a result of the observation that depressed patients often demonstrate impairments in retrieval-based memory problems and slowed psychomotor processing, some have suggested that the cognitive impairments in depression may be secondary to motivational issues. Although depressed patients have a tendency to give up easily on difficult tasks, recent studies have consistently demonstrated that individuals with depression, ranging from mild to severe, do not exhibit poor performance on a wide range of objective measures of effort, thus contradicting the theory that cognitive impairment on objective neuropsychological testing is due solely to poor effort or motivation (Goldberg, Back-Madruga, & Boone, 2007).

Many depressed patients presenting with cognitive complaints often ask: "Will my thinking improve when my depression gets better?" In other words, is neurocognitive impairment a *state* or a *trait* phenomenon? Most research has shown that cognitive impairments apparent during acute depressive states are reversible upon remission from depression (Beats, Sahakian, & Levy, 1996; Biringer et al., 2007; Merens, Booij, & Van Der Does, 2008; Williams et al., 2000). Others, however, have challenged that the follow-up intervals used in many of these studies have been too short (< 12 months) or that the patient populations used have been too heterogeneous with regard to age, gender, education level, and medication status (Marcos, Salamero, Gutierrez, Catalan, Gasto, & Lazaro,1994; Paradiso, Lamberty, Garvey, & Robinson, 1997). Although most individuals experience an improvement in subjective memory complaints when depressive symptoms remit, it is important to continue to treat this issue on a case by case basis. Follow-up neuropsychological testing can offer an objective tracking system for depressed patients throughout the course of their recovery and help monitor interval changes in cognitive and emotional functioning.

Although a clear pattern of cognitive deficits has been demonstrated in some depressed patients, many depressed patients show minimal to no neuropsychological impairment on objective testing, even in the context of significant self-reported memory or attention problems. An interesting finding was that studies have consistently shown that the self-report of a depressed patient is often a poor predictor of actual cognitive functioning on objective testing (Austin, Mitchell, & Goodwin, 2001; Moritz, Ferahli, & Naber, 2004; Schofield, Marder, Dooneief, Jacobs, Sano & Stern, 1997).

Although depression can be accompanied by attentional deficits and slowed information processing speed, these deficits are often less severe than an individual's self report. For example, a 52-year-old woman who had been diagnosed with anxiety and depression was referred to our clinic for neuropsychological testing by her psychologist due to worsening cognitive complaints such as memory and concentration problems. She felt that these cognitive problems significantly interfered with her ability to maintain successful employment, such that she had been terminated from two jobs in the past year. Neuropsychological testing showed that her performance on tests of intelligence, attention, memory, language, and executive functioning abilities were all in the average to superior range, with no area of notable weakness. Her self-report ratings of depression and anxiety, as measured by the *Beck Depression Inventory–2nd Edition* (Beck, Steer, & Brown, 1996) and *Beck Anxiety Index* (Beck & Steer, 1993) were both in the severe range. Based on these test results, it was concluded that her cognitive abilities would allow her to continue working at the level she has maintained in the past and that factors other than actual cognitive impairment, such as emotional and interpersonal functioning, were likely contributing to her occupational difficulties. She was encouraged to continue treatment with her psychologist in order to address these ongoing issues, and it was suggested that her psychotherapeutic treatment focus on increasing insight into her true abilities, minimizing catastrophic thinking regarding benign forgetfulness or careless errors, and using relaxation techniques when she experiences concentration difficulties.

Performance on objective cognitive testing is one piece of the puzzle when performing an integrated neuropsychological evaluation. Behavioral observations and results of objective measures of emotional and personality functioning are also critical components of the assessment. It is widely known that the behavioral hallmarks of a depressed patient might include a restricted range of affect, tearful and depressed mood, poor eye contact, and slowed psychomotor speed. However, during the course of a neuropsychological evaluation, additional behavioral manifestations of their depression may also become apparent. First, the depressed patient may become easily overwhelmed by tasks and have a negative perspective on their ability to complete these tasks. As discussed earlier, patients with depression often report a level of cognitive problems that is disproportionate to their actual cognitive abilities. Consistent with this finding, depressed patients may become frustrated with difficult tasks and have a tendency to "give up" easily. They may also perceive their performance to be much worse than it actually is and may make frequent self-deprecating statements. Therefore, the clinician should make efforts to provide positive feedback when appropriate.

In addition to behavioral observations, results of objective testing of emotional functioning can also provide useful information regarding the nature and severity of an individual's symptoms. Widely used instruments include the *Beck Depression Inventory–2nd Edition (BDI-II*; Beck, Steer, & Brown, 1996), Beck Anxiety Inventory (BAI; Beck & Steer, 1993), *Minnesota Multiphasic Personality Inventory–2nd Edition (MMPI-2*; Butcher, Dahlstrom, Graham, Tellegen, & Kaemmer, 1989), and *Personality Assessment Inventory (PAI*; Morey, 2007). The purpose of this chapter is not to provide a detailed discussion of these measures in particular, but rather to discuss, in a general way, how the results of these measures can be used in conjunction with neuropsychological test data to guide treatment. First, a patient's subjective level of distress can be measured with these instruments, and results can serve as a baseline against which to compare relative improvement or decline. Second, a patient's individual symptoms can be better understood through the use of measures which differentiate various subcomponents of a psychiatric diagnosis. In the case of depression, objective testing can yield information on whether a patient tends to differentially report somatic, cognitive, or affective complaints. In addition, measures that include validity scales can help better understand an individual's tendency to over- or underreport his or her symptoms and whether he or she has appropriate insight into the nature and severity of these symptoms.

The ultimate goal of neuropsychological testing in patients with depression is not only to understand the presence and/or severity of cognitive impairment, but to help inform treatment planning. The first factor to consider is whether a patient has objective evidence of cognitive impairment and to what degree this cognitive impairment may impair their ability to participate in treatment. In some situations, cognitive deficits may be so severe as to warrant increased support and supervision in day-to-day life, and treatment recommendations may initially focus on environmental modifications or basic compensatory strategies for cognitive problems. These might include breaking tasks into smaller, time limited sections and performing complex activities in a quiet and nondistracting setting. For example, an individual may have previously been able to pay bills and balance his/her checkbook while simultaneously watching television; however, in his/her current state of depression, that person may require a less distracting setting to complete the same task. Second, the degree of an individual's cognitive impairment should be considered in determining whether they can comply with a medication regimen, as they might be too inattentive or distracted to remember to take their medications.

In the case of a depressed individual who reports significant cognitive problems, but demonstrates normal cognitive performance on testing (sometimes referred to as the "worried well"), treatment planning may focus on insight-oriented techniques to help the individual understand the origins of their cognitive problems. Increased understanding of the individual's true abilities may help foster self-confidence and decrease the demoralization that a depressed person might experience. Increased insight might also help an individual better monitor early signs of depression. Various therapeutic techniques may also be considered depending on an individual's relative cognitive strengths. For example, someone with strong verbal and abstract reasoning skills may benefit more from insight-oriented therapy, whereas someone with a more concrete thinking style may be overwhelmed by this type of therapy and would benefit more from a behavioral approach.

Neuropsychological Assessment of Bipolar Disorder

Bipolar disorder (BD) is a psychiatric condition in which the patient cycles between phases of depression and mania. The cognitive profile of patients with BD differs from that of the depressed patient, and these cognitive deficits may continue to be apparent even during periods of euthymia. Therefore, understanding how cognitive deficits complicate the symptom presentation of a bipolar patient greatly aids in the clinician's ability to formulate treatment plans, promote compliance, and prevent/manage relapse.

In contrast to studies of unipolar depression, which do not show a consistent relationship between depression severity and greater cognitive deficits, research with bipolar patients has found that greater disease severity and chronicity, particularly earlier age of onset and increased exposure to antipsychotic mediation, is associated with greater neuro-psychological impairments (Denicoff et al., 1999; Zubieta, Huguelet, Lajiness O'Neil, & Giordani, 2001). Specifically, cognitive domains typically affected in BD include memory learning and recall (Ali et al., 2000; Coffman, Bornstein, Olson, Schwarzkopf, & Nasrallah, 1990; Quraishi & Frangou, 2002; Wolfe, Granholm, Butters, Saunders, & Janowsky, 1987), sustained attention (Ali et al., 2000; Albus, Hubmann, Wahlheim, Sobizack, Franz, & Mohr, 1996; Quraishi & Frangou), and executive functions (set-shifting, concept formation, planning, and problem solving; Coffman et al.; Murphy et al., 2001; Quraishi & Frangou; Sweeney, Kmiec, & Kupfer, 2000). Some studies have suggested that patients with BD demonstrate declines in nonverbal intelligence, as compared to their verbal intellectual abilities, suggesting a right-hemisphere involvement in this disorder (Bearden, Hoffman, & Cannon, 2001; Borkowska & Rybakowski, 2001). However, other factors such as slowed processing speed and processing of novel information may also contribute to deficits in nonverbal intelligence (Kluger & Goldberg, 1990), and it is probably inaccurate to conclude an underlying right hemisphere abnormality in this population, although more research is needed to clarify this issue.

Attention deficits in BD may be more severe than in unipoloar depression (Brand & Jolles, 1987). Similar to unipolar depression, bipolar depression is associated with difficulty encoding new information, but storing/consolidation of memories over time is intact. During periods of mania, bipolar patients also demonstrate problems with sustained attention, although they are more likely to be impulsive, rather than simply inattentive (Sax, Strakowski, McElroy, Keck, & West, 1995). Memory and executive functions are also impaired during manic episodes, and patients are more likely to be impulsive and make poor-quality decisions during manic episodes.

The presence of cognitive symptoms during periods of euthymia for bipolar patients is less well understood, although Goodwin and Jamison (1990) reported that up to 32% of BD patients exhibit persistent cognitive deficits during euthymic states. Although this area is less well studied than the depression phase of BD, research has shown that persistent cognitive deficits are evident in the areas of verbal memory, sustained attention, and general executive dysfunction. Deficits in intellectual functioning notable during the depressive phase typically resolve during euthymia (Coffman et al., 1990; Donnelly, Murphy, Goodwin, &

Waldman, 1982; Ferrier, Stanton, Kelly, & Scott, 1999; Silverstein, Harrow, & Bryson, 1994; van Gorp, Altshuler, Theberge, Wilke, Dixon, 1998). In general, BD is associated with cognitive deficits similar to those seen in unipolar depression, although these deficits may be more pronounced and may continue to be apparent during euthymic states. In addition, disease severity, such as the duration of illness, number of manic and/or depressive episodes, and number of hospitalizations, predicts the severity of cognitive impairment (Fossati, Harvey, Le Bastard, Ergis, Jouvent, & Allilaire, 2004; Zubieta, et al., 2001).

Behavioral observations during the neuropsychological assessment of BD may also lend greater insight to the patient's current level of functioning. First, if a bipolar patient presents as acutely manic, then neuropsychological testing may be contraindicated because the patient may be too agitated or distractible to tolerate testing. Subjecting a patient in such a state to many hours of testing would be inappropriate because results would not be a stable marker of the patient's abilities and would not yield additional clinical information. However, neuropsychological testing may reveal that a euthymic patient actually demonstrates impulsivity, poor problem solving, and attention problems (particularly as the day progresses) that might not be apparent if you are only able to spend a brief amount of time in the room with the patient. Results of objective emotional and personality testing can also help monitor depressive and/or manic symptoms and can inform the clinician as to the patient's overall level of insight into his or her symptoms.

The most salient question for most psychiatrists and other treatment providers working with patients with BD related to a neuropsychological assessment is: How can neuropsychological testing aid in treatment planning for my patient? To answer this question, it is important to understand how cognitive deficits may interact with certain aspects of treatment, such as medication compliance, psychotherapy, and rehabilitation. First, acknowledging any cognitive deficits that are affecting the patient's ability to understand and comply with their medication regimen will have important implications for relapse prevention, and these patients may require additional support systems to ensure medication adherence. Second, the presence of cognitive deficits during periods of euthymia suggests that the focus of treatment during this time might include not only management of affective symptoms, but also practical guidelines for coping with cognitive symptoms. These guidelines might include cognitive remediation, compensatory strategies, and appropriate environmental modifications. For example, patients with poor executive dysfunction may have difficulty with task completion and may have difficulty maintaining employment. Finally, neuropsychological assessment may reveal that cognitive function is intact, at least during euthymic periods. In fact, there is some research to suggest that there may be a subgroup of BP patients who do not demonstrate executive dysfunction or verbal memory deficits, and those with less cognitive impairment tend to have better overall functioning in their everyday lives (Altshuler, Bearden, Green, van Gorp, & Mintz, 2008). An integrative neuropsychological assessment can identify cognitive strengths and weaknesses, assist in treatment planning, and add insight into long-term functioning and prognosis.

Neuropsychological Assessment of Obsessive-Compulsive Disorder

In addition to classic symptoms of obsessive-compulsive disorder (OCD) as outlined in the *DSM-IV*, the cognitive and physiological abnormalities in OCD have garnered much attention in the past decade of research. These cognitive deficits may have implications in both understanding the etiology of the disorder and in formulating an appropriate treatment plan. Objective neuropsychological testing can be particularly useful in this population, as patients with OCD often have a subjective sense of self-doubt and expectations for perfection, which may cloud their insight into their true abilities. Similar to other psychiatric conditions, OCD has been associated with difficulty encoding new information on memory testing, although they are able to store this new information over time (Savage et al., 2000). Neuropsychologists working with patients who have OCD must be particularly cautious that poor performance on memory or attention testing is not solely due to his or her engagement in obsessive-compulsive thoughts or rituals during testing. If a patient is actively engaging in a mental compulsion during testing, then test results would not be an accurate indicator of his or her true ability, although certainly these results would provide a window into the patient's functional impairments in his or her day-to-day life.

Other common findings in this population include executive dysfunction (i.e., organization, set-shifting, planning, problem solving) and speed of information processing ([review by] Greisberg & McKay, 2003; [review by] Kuelz, Hohagen, & Voderholzer, 2004; Purcell, Maruff, Kyrios, & Pantelis, 1998). This pattern of deficits is consistent with the proposed neuroanatomical underpinnings of this disorder involving the frontal-subcortical circuits (Kang et al., 2003). Patients with OCD often recognize that their obsessions are nonsensical or not reality-based, and yet they are compelled to engage in ritualistic behaviors to cope with these obsessions. This process suggests that a break-down in cognitive functioning may be contributing to this pattern of behavior. In fact, the inability to control engaging in compulsive behavior, despite having an awareness that the obsession underlying the behavior is not reality-based, has been linked to executive dysfunction (Lezak, 1995).

Understanding the meaning of executive dysfunction in these patients may add insight into the maintenance of obsessive-compulsive symptoms. For example, a patient's inability to resist engaging in compulsive behaviors may be related to a cognitive process (namely, executive functions), and not merely a manifestation of his or her anxiety or maladaptive beliefs. Furthermore, the extent to which these cognitive impairments remit following treatment of obsessive-compulsive symptoms is unknown. Therefore, understanding whether cognitive impairment exists may influence the scope or focus of psychotherapeutic interventions. Namely, an individualized treatment that also addresses cognitive inefficiencies, in addition to symptom management, may result in increased ability to manage work, school, and day-to-day activities.

Neuropsychological Assessment of Schizophrenia

Unlike other psychiatric disorders in which only a moderate percentage of patients manifest cognitive deficits in association with their mental illness, perhaps the majority of patients with schizophrenia demonstrate abnormalities on neuropsychological testing (Goldberg, et al., 1990; Keefe, Eesley, & Poe, 2005; Palmer et al., 1997). These cognitive impairments often impact patients' functional capacities, even in the absence of acute psychotic symptoms (Reichenberg & Harvey, 2007). In fact, the nature and severity of neuropsychological deficits in these patients may predict functional outcome (including community living and skill learning) and recovery better than the classical symptoms as defined by the *DSM-IV* (Elvevag & Goldberg, 2000; Green, 1996). Neuropsychological impairment may also be present prior to full onset of the disorder and can therefore be helpful in early diagnosis (David, Malmberg, Brandt, Allebeck, & Lewis, 1997). Cognitive impairments can affect treatment compliance, insight, and interpersonal relationship with others, including the therapist. Therefore, neuropsychological assessment is very relevant and informative in patients with schizophrenia and can help quantify the nature and severity of their cognitive impairment, which can subsequently help the clinician formulate an appropriate treatment plan and help prepare patients and their families to make necessary environmental modifications.

There is a vast literature on the specific neuropsychological deficits in schizophrenia. To summarize, patients with schizophrenia typically show notable and widespread neuropsychological impairment. They demonstrate generalized neuropsychological impairment, affecting intellectual ability (particularly in the nonverbal domain), level of alertness, executive functions, processing speed, immediate and delayed verbal and nonverbal memory, working memory (holding and manipulating information in short-term memory), and, to a lesser degree, visuospatial deficits (Green, 2006; Harvey, Green, Keefe, & Velligan, 2004; Horan et al., 2008). Memory deficits in patients with schizophrenia may be largely mediated by executive deficits (i.e., their inability to effectively organize incoming information). However, unlike other psychiatric populations who have difficulty encoding new memories, patients with schizophrenia have also been shown to have a decay of learned information over time (i.e., they forget what they previously learned), although this aspect of their memory problem is less severe than their difficulty learning (encoding) new information (Cirillo & Seidman, 2003). Overall, cognitive deficits in schizophrenic patients have been shown to be as much as two standard deviations below the mean of healthy controls (Harvey & Keefe, 1997; Heinrichs & Zakzanis, 1998; Saykin, Gur, & Gur, 1991) and are not simply a side effect of antipsychotic medication or other symptoms of the illness, such as negative or positive symptoms (Reichenberg & Harvey, 2007; Harvey et al., 2004).

Because of the severity of cognitive impairment often present in schizophrenic patients, a clinician may be aware of cognitive deficits in their patients based on behavioral observations and family reports alone. Therefore, why might a medical provider or mental health professional refer a patient for neuropsychological testing? First, although the presence of cognitive deficits may be quite apparent, the nature of the cognitive deficits (i.e., which cognitive processes are disturbed and which are preserved) may not be readily observable, and the incremental change in cognitive functioning over time may not be easily quantified by clinical observations. Second, a cognitive decline in a high-functioning individual may not be as apparent to the clinician if this decline does not cause the patient's functioning to diminish below that of the average person. In other words, in the early, prodromal stages of the disease, an individual may have cognitive functions that are in the *average* range, hence allowing them to function adequately; however, this level of cognitive ability may actually represent a decline from the individual's previously high average level of functioning. Neuropsychological testing can estimate premorbid levels of intellectual functioning to serve as a benchmark against which to compare current status. Third, as described above, neuropsychological deficits are often noted in the early stages of the disease before gross functional disturbances are apparent; therefore, neuropsychological testing can assist in early diagnosis. Finally, patients with schizophrenia and their families are often faced with the challenge of making life changes based on the onset of symptoms in young adulthood. For example, the patient's ability to attend school, work, or live independently might be pressing questions. Neuropsychological assessment may help inform these decisions by providing objective data about cognitive abilities.

Understanding the presence and/or severity of cognitive deficits present in persons with schizophrenia can also have an important role in treatment planning, particularly in the context of cognitive/psychiatric rehabilitation. Remediation of neuropsychological deficits in these patients in order to increase functional abilities is a growing area of clinical and research attention. Meta-analyses have suggested that participation in cognitive rehabilitation can enhance attention, learning, and executive functioning (Kurtz, Moberg, Gur, & Gur, 2001), and improvements in learning and attention have been shown to have functional significance in the real world (Brekke, Hoe, & Green, 2009). Neuropsychological assessment can help identify patients who may be good candidates for cognitive rehabilitation. For those patients who might benefit from such an intervention, the integrated neuropsychological evaluation's wealth of information on patterns of cognitive strengths, cognitive weaknesses, emotional state, and learning style serves as a ready platform for cognitive remediation planning.

PATTERNS OF IMPAIRMENT: ATTENTION, PROCESSING SPEED, AND EXECUTIVE DYSFUNCTION

Processing speed, attention, and executive functions are the most common domains typically affected in a variety of mood disorders. Decreased psychomotor speed may reduce an individual's overall efficiency and productivity, and problems with attention may have a resulting impact on all other cognitive functions. Executive dysfunction, in particular, is often emphasized in these populations, although *executive functioning* is a broad, often nebulous term, which does not always have a concrete meaning for the patient or the referring clinician. This term is used with increasing frequency, but remains an elusive concept that is sometimes difficult to disentangle from other cognitive functions. As described earlier, executive functions include mental flexibility, planning, organization, response inhibition, and problem solving. Individuals with executive dysfunction often have the most difficulty in environments that lack clear structure, boundaries, limits, and expectations. Therefore, patients with executive dysfunction, particularly high-functioning individuals, may appear more intact in the neuropsychological testing environment than in real life because the testing environment itself can act as his or her frontal lobes by establishing a clear set of rules and behavioral expectations. As a result of an impaired ability to initiate, plan, or monitor the appropriate sequence of actions, real world functioning may pose greater problems for individuals with executive dysfunction because they cannot effectively employ other cognitive skills, which may be intact. For example, a patient with normal to above-average memory, but impaired executive function, may experience a great deal of difficulty managing work-related duties, not because they cannot understand or remember what is asked of them, but because they cannot effectively plan and initiate the small, incremental steps involved in accomplishing the larger task at hand. Also, this person may have difficulty discerning irrelevant details from the broader picture and as a result may get "lost in the details." Therefore, a patient with executive dysfunction may be very bright from an intellectual standpoint, but may be functioning well below their expected level as a result of problems in the area of executive functions.

NEUROPSYCHOLOGICAL ASSESSMENT
AND VALIDITY OF SELF-REPORTED SYMPTOMS

Cognitive complaints are common across numerous psychiatric populations. In fact, up to 45% of psychiatric inpatients over the age of 60
and 29% of younger psychiatric inpatients report severe memory complaints (Chandler & Gerndt, 1988). Subjective cognitive problems may
be frightening to patients, and they may misperceive their significance
or etiology. However, the nature and severity of emotional symptoms
can be difficult to ascertain by self-report alone, as self-report of symptoms may be influenced by a variety of emotional and motivational
factors. In some cases, a patient's reported symptoms may be influenced
by the level of insight into his or her condition and/or his or her
motivation to be seen in a certain light. Therefore, it can be difficult
to determine the level of psychopathology and make an accurate differential diagnosis in these cases. Neuropsychological testing can help
determine whether a patient's self-reported cognitive symptoms reflect
real cognitive impairment or whether the symptoms reported are falsely
elevated or exaggerated for external or internal motivational reasons.
Specifically, neuropsychological assessment can be helpful in differentiating conversion disorder, somatoform disorders, and malingering from
other mood or neurological disorders through objective cognitive and
emotional testing.

For example, a young woman was once referred to our clinic by
her treating psychiatrist with a history of increasing social isolation,
significant dependency on her parents, odd behaviors, and restricted
affect. The patient reported significant attention and concentration
problems, whereas her parents wondered if the patient's symptoms were
volitional and motivated by external factors (e.g., financial support from
the parents). Differential diagnoses included an affective disorder, an
emerging psychotic process, and/or personality disorder. Results of
our neuropsychological assessment revealed that this patient was not
feigning her cognitive symptoms, such that she passed all objective
tests of effort that were administered to her, and her responses on
objective personality testing did not indicate that she was exaggerating
her symptoms report. Results of testing were also able to rule out a
psychotic process and confirm the presence of true cognitive problems

consistent with a learning disorder that was affecting her ability to relate well to others on an interpersonal level. These results were valuable to the referring psychiatrist in devising a treatment plan, which directly addressed these issues and helped the family better manage the problematic behaviors.

This case example illustrates how a neuropsychological assessment might include objective measures of effort to gauge whether someone is putting forth effort to perform well. These tests are sensitive to suboptimal effort and have been standardized in a variety of clinical populations. Although effort testing is most common in forensic cases in which there is a clear, often financial, motive to perform poorly, effort testing has also been used with increasing frequency in the context of psychiatric populations. Although nonlitigating patients with various mood disorders may not have an easily identifiable motive to perform poorly on testing, these patients often feel hopeless, distressed, and misunderstood, and may feel they need to "prove" their difficulties to the clinician. These processes can be conscious or unconscious. Recent research has shown that, with the exception of psychotic patients, patients with depression and/or various anxiety disorders are able to perform within normal ranges on objective measures of effort, thus validating the use of these measures in these populations. Therefore, neuropsychological testing can offer objective data on whether a patient is exaggerating his or her cognitive problems for emotional reasons. If this is the case, this information can be very helpful for the clinician working with this patient, as the focus of treatment may shift to include increasing insight and understanding unconscious processes. It is also helpful to rule out cognitive impairment when formulating a treatment plan to which the patient can adhere.

Finally, it is important for clinicians working with patients with mood disorders to be aware of the relationship between mood status and self-reported cognitive problems. Most research has shown that self-reported cognitive symptoms are more closely related to mood status than to actual performance on cognitive testing (Antikainen et al., 2001; West, Boatwright, & Schleser, 1984), and subjective cognitive complaints often decline when depression remits (Antikainen et al.). Therefore, neuropsychological testing can be extremely useful for ruling out the presence of cognitive problems in psychiatric patients with cognitive complaints. These results can be very beneficial to the patient, as they can reduce fears that there is "something wrong with my brain."

These results can also provide the basis for psychoeducation, which can normalize the experience of cognitive slippage in everyday life, and also increase the patient's insight regarding symptoms of their mental illness. Knowledge that cognitive symptoms may remit if mood improves may serve as a motivation to engage in treatment.

PRACTICAL APPLICATIONS OF NEUROPSYCHOLOGICAL TESTING

In many psychiatric populations, patients with more severe cognitive problems associated with their mental illness generally have a less favorable outcome with regard to daily functioning and recovery. Therefore, neuropsychological testing during the early, diagnostic phase may help the patient, his or her family, and the treating clinician better understand the nature of a complex constellation of symptoms. In turn, this can help the clinician with appropriate treatment planning.

Anyone working with psychiatric patients can appreciate the heterogeneity of this population. Although research in areas of psychiatric patients and neuropsychological functioning can and should inform treatment, research is typically performed at the group level, whereas clinicians are faced with treating the individual. Therefore, there could be subgroups of patients with a particular disorder who present with a different onset and course of a disorder than the average population, or there could be other unknown variables influencing the patient's particular symptom manifestation. For example, although research might show that some patients with depression exhibit decreased processing speed with relatively preserved memory storage over time, your particular patient might present with a unique pattern of symptoms that do not fit this mold.

Neuropsychological testing can assist in understanding the individual strengths and weaknesses of each patient, which is important when formulating an individualized treatment plan. Initially, the results of neuropsychological testing can be used in psychoeducation with a patient. Unfortunately, the majority of neuropsychologists are not able to meet with their patients for more than one session to discuss the results and implications of the testing. Therefore, the mental health provider who meets with the patient on a more regular basis has the opportunity to integrate findings from a neuropsychological evaluation into ongoing treatment. In cases in which testing fails to reveal evidence of cognitive impairment, despite the patient's self-report of memory problems, psychoeducation can focus on normalizing the subjective experience of cognitive problems in the context of a mood disorder, thus reframing these symptoms for the patient. Although some patients may be comforted to learn that there is nothing "wrong with their brain," others may feel frustrated that their experience of memory or attention problems was not validated by testing. They are then left to feel that their cognitive complaints are "in their head" or not "real." It is important for clinicians to validate for patients that although there is likely no neurological cause for their cognitive symptoms, that these cognitive symptoms are in fact "real" in the sense that they can interfere with daily functioning.

Helping the patient understand the etiology of his or her particular cognitive complaint can increase insight and guide therapeutic interventions. For example, an anxious patient may report that they are not able to remember anything they've read several minutes later. Results of neuropsychological testing might inform the patient that this experience is because of his or her failure to adequately encode information (i.e., get the information into memory), and not as a result of an inability to store (i.e., keep) new memories. Psychoeducation for this patient might focus on increasing understanding that his or her preoccupation with anxious thoughts diminishes his or her ability to focus on material in a book and interferes with adequate encoding, hence leaving the patient feeling as if he or she can't remember anything. Once this patient is able to have insight into this process, therapeutic interventions might include increasing the patient's awareness in the moment that they are feeling anxious, taking steps to reduce the anxiety (e.g., use of relaxation techniques, scheduling regular breaks, or writing anxious thoughts down in a journal), and then resuming the activity. Other patients may dwell on occasional mistakes or forgetfulness, which can trigger self-doubt, rumination, and catastrophic thinking. In these cases, psychoeducation and/or insight-oriented therapy may be considered that focuses on normalizing occasional lapses in attention or memory in everyday life.

LIMITATIONS: WHAT NEUROPSYCHOLOGICAL TESTING ALONE CANNOT DO

The preceding sections of this chapter were designed to convey the usefulness of neuropsychological assessment for a wide variety of clinicians working with adult psychiatric populations. However, neuropsychological testing certainly has limitations, and the conclusions that can be drawn from test results should be carefully tempered by these limitations. In any given individual's neuropsychological profile, patterns of strengths and weaknesses, in and of themselves, do not differentiate between various psychiatric conditions. Research has not yet identified definitive patterns of cognitive functioning that have a strong relationship or that serve as specific markers to distinguish between and among specific psychiatric conditions, such as unipolar depression, bipolar disorder, or obsessive-compulsive disorder. As it currently stands, the research on cognitive deficits in these various patient populations indicates that different psychiatric conditions may result in a similar pattern of cognitive deficits (e.g., attention problems, executive dysfunction, and decreased processing speed). Therefore, test data can help understand whether cognitive deficits are present in a particular patient, but the pattern of deficits, interpreted in isolation, is unlikely to be unique to a specific psychiatric disorder.

Second, poor performance on a single test should not be over-interpreted to mean that the patient has a deficit in that particular domain. Normal individuals often exhibit variability on neuropsychological testing, which is often reflective of relative strengths and weaknesses within the individual rather than a sign of cognitive impairment (Schretlen, Munro, Anthony, & Pearlson, 2003). Additionally, most neuropsychological tests assess higher order, complex cognitive processes that are supported by complex neural networks. For example, as discussed previously, poor performance on a memory test may be due to a variety of factors, such as impaired attention, executive dysfunction, or an inability to store new memories. Therefore, poor performance on a single neuropsychological test could be due to the result of any number of causes, and test results should be interpreted in aggregate by resting clinical interpretation on patterns of impairment made up of many test scores.

Finally, there are limitations in the extent to which performance on neuropsychological testing predicts real world behavior. The purpose of neuropsychological testing has historically been to assist in differential diagnosis in a variety of neurological conditions. In recent years, there has been a shift away from diagnostic questions to questions pertaining to a patient's real-world functioning, such as his or her ability to work, go to school, live independently, drive a car, or participate in rehabilitative therapies. Although the referral questions to neuropsychologists have changed over the years, the neuropsychological tests used in these evaluations have largely remained the same, raising the concern that our current instruments lack the ecological validity to make real-world predictions. As a result, there have been an increasing number of studies examining the relationship between neuropsychological test data and outcome measures related to everyday functioning. A recent literature review revealed that neuropsychological performance can predict return to work and other everyday cognitive skills in a variety of psychiatric and neurological patient populations, although the effect sizes tend to be in the moderate range (Chaytor & Schmitter-Edgecombe, 2003). Neuropsychological testing has shown less of a relationship with everyday tasks that involve a substantial motor component, such as basic activities of daily living (e.g., dressing, grooming, ambulating; Williams, 1988).

Much of the research that has been conducted in the area of ecological validity of neuropsychological tests has been done with neurologically impaired individuals diagnosed with conditions such as dementia or traumatic brain injury. Less is known about the ecological validity of neuropsychological testing in neurologically intact individuals with a specific treatment question, such as whether or not someone's cognitive symptoms of depression will interfere with their ability to participate in group therapy. Therefore, more research is needed to understand the relationship between neuropsychological test data and real-world functioning in various psychiatric populations. Given that neuropsychological testing cannot account for 100% of the variance in everyday life activities, other areas of information are often taken into consideration in a thorough neuropsychological evaluation, including personality and emotional measures, informant ratings, behavioral observations, and background information. Pulling this information together constitutes an integrated neuropsychological evaluation that can best serve to make real-world predictions for the patient and to offer practical recommendations to the referring health care provider.

CONCLUSION

This chapter has illustrated how the results of a neuropsychological evaluation can be applied to adults with various types of psychiatric illness to better understand the cognitive strengths and weaknesses unique to a particular patient. This information can be useful in differentiating certain diagnostic questions as well as in treatment planning. For instance, results may reveal a pattern of cognitive impairments that are impacting a patient's everyday life and his or her ability to participate in psychiatric treatment. In this case, these results may guide the clinician to incorporate environmental modifications or medication adjustments into the patient's treatment plan or lead the clinician to change his or her approach to the psychotherapy. Conversely, a neuropsychological evaluation may reveal intact cognitive functioning, despite a patient's self-report of cognitive problems, and may lead the clinician to emphasize alternative strategies in the patient's treatment, such as insight-oriented approaches or relaxation training. In addition to understanding the utility of a neuropsychological evaluation with psychiatric patients, this chapter has also reviewed the limitations of neuropsychological test results and how these findings should not be used, in isolation, to make differential diagnoses between various psychiatric disorders. We hope that this chapter has been successful in helping clinicians from a variety of disciplines gain a thorough and realistic understanding of how a neuropsychological evaluation integrates the results of cognitive and personality/emotional testing to better inform treatment planning.

REFERENCES

Albus, M., Hubmann, W., Wahlheim, C., Sobizack, N., Franz, U., & Mohr, F. (1996). Contrasts in neuropsychological test profile between patients with first-episode schizophrenia and first-episode affective disorders. *Acta Psychiatrica Scandinavica, 94*, 87–93.

Ali, S. O., Denicoff, K. D., Altshuler, L. L., Hauser, P., Li, X. M., Conrad, A. J., et al. (2000). A preliminary study of the relation of neuropsychological performance in neuroanatomic structures in bipolar disorder. *Neuropsychiatry, Neuropsychology, and Behavioral Neurology, 13*, 20–28.

Altshuler, L. L., Ventura, J., van Gorp, W., Green, M. F., Theberge, D. C., & Mintz, J.. (2004). Neurocognitive function in clinically stable men with Bipolar I Disorder or schizophrenia and normal control subjects. *Biological Psychiatry, 56*, 560–569.

Altshuler, L. L., Bearden, C. E., Green, M. F., van Gorp, W., & Mintz, J. (2008). A relationship between neurocognitive impairment and functional impairment in bipolar disorder: A pilot study. *Psychiatry Research, 157*, 289–293.

Antikainen, R., Hanninen, T., Honkalampi, K., Hintikka, J., Koivumaa-Honkanen, H. Tanskanen, A., et al. (2001). Mood improvement reduces memory complaints in depressed patients. *European Archives of Psychiatry and Clinical Neuroscience, 251*, 6–11.

Austin, M. P., Mitchell, P., & Goodwin, G. M. (2001). Cognitive deficits in depression. *British Journal of Psychiatry, 178*, 200–206.

Bearden, C. E., Hoffman, K. M., & Cannon, T. D. (2001). The neuropsychology and neuroanatomy of bipolar affective disorder: A critical review. *Bipolar Disorder, 3,* 106–150.

Beats, B., Sahakian, B., & Levy, R. (1996). Cognitive performance in tests sensitive to frontal lobe dysfunction in the elderly depressed. *Psychosocial Medicine, 26,* 591–603.

Beck, A. T., & Steer, R. A. (1993). *Beck Anxiety Inventory Manual.* San Antonio, TX: Psychological Corporation Harcourt Brace.

Beck A. T., Steer, R. A., & Brown, G. K. (1996) *Manual for the Beck Depression Inventory* (2nd ed.). San Antonio, TX: Psychological Corporation.

Biringer, E., Mykletun, A., Sundet, K., Kroken, R., Stordal, K. I., & Lund, A. (2007). A longitudinal analysis of neurocognitive function in unipolar depression. *Journal of Clinical and Experimental Neuropsychology, 29*(8), 879-891.

Borkowska, A., & Rybakowski, J. K. (2001). Neuropsychological frontal lobe tests indicate that bipolar depressed patients are more impaired than unipolar. *Bipolar Disorder, 3,* 88–94.

Brand, N., & Jolles, J. (1987). Information processing in depression and anxiety. *Psychological Medicine, 17,* 145–153.

Brekke, J. S., Hoe, M., & Green, M. F. (2009). Neurocognitive change, functional change and service intensity during community-based psychosocial rehabilitation for schizophrenia. *Psychological Medicine, 39,* 1637–1647.

Burt, D. B., Zembar, M. J., & Niederehe, G. (1995). Depression and memory impairment: A meta-analysis of the association, its pattern, and specificity. *Psychological Bulletin, 117* (2), 285–305.

Butcher, J. N., Dahlstrom, W. G., Graham, J. R., Tellegen, A., & Kaemmer, B. (1989). *Manual for administration and scoring: MMPI-2.* Minneapolis, MN: University of Minnesota Press.

Chandler, J. D., & Gerndt, J. (1988). Memory complaints and memory deficits in young and old psychiatric inpatients. *Journal of Geriatric Psychiatry and Neurology, 1*(2), 84–88.

Chaytor, N., & Schmitter-Edgecombe, M. (2003). The ecological validity of neuropsychological tests: A review of the literature on everyday cognitive skills. *Neuropsychological Review, 13*(4), 181–197.

Cirillo, M. A., & Seidman, L. J. (2003). Verbal declarative memory dysfunction in schizophrenia: From clinical assessment to genetics and brain mechanisms. *Neuropsychology Review, 13,* 43–77.

Coffman, J. A., Bornstein, R. A., Olson, S. C., Schwarzkopf, S. B., & Nasrallah, H. A. (1990). Cognitive impairment and cerebral structure by MRI in bipolar disorder. *Biological Psychiatry, 27,* 1188–1196.

David, A. S., Malmberg, A., Brandt, L., Allebeck, P., & Lewis, G. (1997). IQ and risk for schizophrenia: A population-based cohort study. *Psychological Medicine, 27,* 1311–1323.

Denicoff, K. D., Ali, S. O., Mirsky, A. F., Smith-Jackson, E. E., Leverich, G. S., & Duncan, C. C., et al. (1999). Relationship between prior course of illness and neuropsychological functioning in patients with bipolar disorder. *Journal of Affective Disorders, 56,* 67–73.

Donnelly, E. F., Murphy, D. L., Goodwin, F. K., & Waldman, I. N. (1982). Intellectual function in primary affective disorder. *British Journal of Psychiatry, 140,* 633–636.

Elliott, R. (1998). The neuropsychological profile in unipolar depression. *Trends in Cognitive Sciences, 2,* 447–453.

Elvevag, B., & Goldberg, T. E. (2000). Cognitive impairment in schizophrenia is the core of the disorder. *Critical Reviews in Neurobiology, 14,* 1–21.

Ferrier, I. N., Stanton, B. R., Kelly, T. P., & Scott, J. (1999). Neuropsychological function in euthymic patients with bipolar disorder. *British Journal of Psychiatry, 175,* 246–251.

Fossati, P., Harvey, P. O., Le Bastard, G., Ergis, A. M., Jouvent, R., & Allilaire, J. F. (2004). Verbal memory performance of patients with a first depressive episode and patients with unipolar and bipolar recurrent depression. *Journal of Psychiatric Research, 38*(2), 137–144.

Goldberg, H. E., Back-Madruga, C., & Boone, K. B. (2007). The impact of psychiatric disorders on cognitive symptom validity test scores. In K. B. Boone (Ed.), *Assessment of feigned cognitive impairment: A neuropsychological perspective* (pp. 281–309). New York: Guilford Press.

Goldberg, T. E., Ragland, J. D., Torrey, E. F., Gold, J. M., Bigelow, L. B., & Weinberger, D. R. (1990). Neuropsychological assessment of monozygotic twins discordant for schizophrenia. *Archives of General Psychiatry, 47,* 1066–1072.

Goodwin, F. (1997). Neuropsychological and neuroimaging evidence for the involvement of the frontal lobes in depression. *Journal of Psychopharmacology, 11*(2),115–122.

Goodwin, F., & Jamison, K. (1990). *Manic-depressive illness.* New York: Oxford University Press.

Green, M. F. (1996). What are the functional consequences of neurocognitive deficits in schizophrenia? *American Journal of Psychiatry, 153,* 321–330.

Green, M. F. (2006). Cognitive impairment and functional outcome in schizophrenia and bipolar disorder. *Journal of Clinical Psychiatry, 67*(4), 3–8.

Greisburg, S., & McKay, D. (2003). Neuropsychology of obsessive-compulsive disorder: A review and treatment implications. *Clinical Psychology Review, 23*(1), 95–117.

Hartlage, S., Alloy, L. B., Vazquez, C., & Dykman, B. (1993). Automatic and effortful processing in depression. *Psychological Bulletin, 113,* 247–278.

Harvey, P. D., Green, M. F., Keefe, R. S. E., & Velligan, D. I. (2004). Cognitive functioning in schizophrenia: A consensus statement on its role in the definition and evaluation of effective treatments for the illness. *Journal of Clinical Psychiatry, 65*(3), 361–372.

Harvey, P. D., & Keefe, R. S. E. (1997). Cognitive impairment in schizophrenia and implications of atypical neuroleptic treatment. *CNS Spectrum, 2*(1), 1–11.

Heinrichs, R. W., & Zakzanis, K. K. (1998). Neurocognitve deficit in schizophrenia: A quantitative review of the evidence. *Neuropsychology, 12,* 426–444.

Horan, W. P., Braff, K., Nuechterlein, C., Sugar, K., Cadenhead, M., Calkins, D. et al. (2008). Verbal working memory impairments in individuals with schizophrenia and their first-degree relatives: Findings from the consortium on the genetics of schizophrenia. *Schizophrenia Research, 103,* 218–228.

Kang, D. H., Kwon, J. S., Kim, J. J., Youn, T., Park, H. J., Kim, M. S., et al. (2003). Brain glucose metabolic changes associated with neuropsychological improvements after 4 months of treatment in patients with obsessive-compulsive disorder. *Acta Psychiatria Scandinavia, 107,* 291–297.

Keefe, R. S., Eesley, C. E., & Poe, M. P. (2005). Defining a cognitive function decrement in schizophrenia. *Biological Psychiatry, 57,* 688–691.

Kluger, A., & Goldberg, E. (1990). IQ patterns in affective disorder, lateralized and diffuse brain damage. *Journal of Clinical and Experimental Neuropsychology, 12*(2), 182–194.

Kuelz, A. K., Hohagen, F., & Voderholzer, U. (2004). Neuropsychological performance in obsessive-compulsive disorder: A critical review. *Biological Psychology, 65,* 185–236.

Kurtz, M. M., Moberg, P. J., Gur, R. C., & Gur, R. E. (2001). Approaches to cognitive remediation of neuropsychological deficits in Schizophrenia: A review and meta-analysis. *Neuropsychology Review, 11*(4), 197–210.

Lezak, M. D. (1995). *Neuropsychological assessment* (3rd ed.). New York: Oxford University Press.

Maor, Y., Olmer, L., & Mozes, B. (2001). The relation between objective and subjective impairment in cognitive function among multiple sclerosis patients—The role of depression. *Multiple Sclerosis, 7,* 131–135.

Marcos, T., Salamero, M., Gutierrez, F., Catalan, R., Gasto, C., & Lazaro, L. (1994). Cognitive dysfunction in recovered melancholic patients. *Journal of Affective Disorders, 32*(2), 133–137.

Massman, P. J., Delis, D. C., Butters, N., Dupont, R. M., & Gillin, J. C. (1992). The subcortical dysfunction hypothesis of memory deficits in depression: Neuropsychological validation in a subgroup of patients. *Journal of Clinical and Experimental Neuropsychology, 14,* 687–706.

Merens, W., Booij, L., & Van Der Does, W. (2008). Residual cognitive impairments in remitted depressed patients. *Depression and Anxiety, 25,* E27–E36.

Moore, L. H., van Gorp, W. G., Hinkin, C., Stern, M. J., Swales, T., & Satz, P. (1997). Subjective complaints versus actual cognitive deficits in predominantly symptomatic HIV-1 seropositive individuals. *Journal of Neuropsychiatry and Clinical Neurosciences, 9,* 37–44.

Morey, L. C. (2007). *Personality Assessment Inventory professional manual.* Lutz, FL: Psychological Assessment Resources.

Moritz, S., Ferahli, S., & Naber, D. (2004). Memory and attention performance in psychiatric patients: Lack of correspondence between clinician-rated and patient-rated functioning with neuropsychological test results. *Journal of the International Neuropsychological Society, 10*(4), 623–633.

Murphy, F. C., Rubinsztein, J. S., Michael, A., Rogers, R. D., Robbins, T. W., Paykel, E. S., et al. (2001). Decision-making cognition in mania and depression. *Psychological Medicine, 31,* 679–693.

Palmer, B. W., Heaton, R. K., Paulsen, J. S., Kuck, J., Braff, D., Harris, M., et al. (1997). Is it possible to be schizophrenic yet neuropsychologically normal? *Neuropsychology, 11,* 437–446.

Paradiso, S., Lamberty, G. J., Garvey, M. J., & Robinson, R. G. (1997). Cognitive impairment in the euthymic phase of chronic unipolar depression. *Journal of Nervous and Mental Disease, 185*(12), 748–754.

Purcell, R., Maruff, P., Kyrios, M., & Pantelis, C. (1998). Neuropsychological deficits in obsessive-compulsive disorder. *Archives of General Psychiatry, 55*, 415–423.

Quraishi, S., & Frangou, S. (2002). Neuropsychology of bipolar disorder: A review. *Journal of Affective Disorders, 72*(3), 209–226

Reichenberg, A., & Harvey, P. D. (2007). Neuropsychological impairments in schizophrenia: Integration of performance-based and brain imaging findings. *Psychological Bulletin, 133*(5), 833–858.

Sawrie, S. M., Martin, R. C., & Kuzniecky, R. (1999). Subjective versus objective memory change after temporal lobe epilepsy surgery. *Neurology, 53*, 1511.

Savage, C. R., Deckersbach, T., Wilhelm, S., Rauch, S. L., Baer, L., Reid, T., et al. (2000). Strategic processing and episodic memory impairment in obsessive compulsive disorder. *Neuropsychology, 14*(1), 141–151.

Sax, K. W., Strakowski, S. M., McElroy, S. L., Keck, Jr. P. E., & West, S. A. (1995). Attention and formal thought disorder in mixed and pure mania. *Biological Psychiatry, 37*, 420–423.

Sax, K. W., Strakowski, S. M., Zimmerman, M. E., DelBello, M. P., Keck, P. E., & Hawkins, J. M. (1999). Frontosubcortical neuroanatomy and the continuous performance test in mania. *American Journal of Psychiatry, 156*, 139–141.

Saykin, A. J., Gur, R. C., & Gur, R. E. (1991). Neuropsychological function in schizophrenia: Selective impairment in memory and learning. *Archives of General Psychiatry, 48*, 618–624.

Schofield, P. W., Marder, K., Dooneief, G., Jacobs, D. M., Sano, M., and Stern, Y. (1997). Association of subjective memory complaints with subsequent cognitive decline in community-dwelling elderly individuals with baseline cognitive impairment. *American Journal of Psychiatry, 154*, 609–615.

Schretlen, D., Munro, C., Anthony, J. C., & Pearlson, G. D. (2003). Examining the range of normal intraindividual variability in neuropsychological test performance. *Journal of the International Neuropsychological Society, 9*, 864–870.

Silverstein, M. L., Harrow, M., & Bryson, G. J. (1994). Neuropsychological prognosis and clinical recovery. *Psychiatry Research, 52*, 265–272.

Sweeney, J. A., Kmiec, J. A., & Kupfer, D. J. (2000). Neuropsychologic impairments in bipolar and unipolar mood disorders on the CANTAB neurocognitive battery. *Biological Psychiatry, 48*, 674–685.

Van den Bosch, R. J., & Rombouts, R. (1998). Causal mechanisms of subjective cognitive dysfunction in Schizophrenic and Depressed patients. *Journal of Nervous & Mental Disease, 186*(6), 364–368.

van Gorp, W. G., Altshuler, L., Theberge, D. C., Wilke, J., & Dixon, W. (1998). Cognitive impairment in euthymic bipolar patients with and without prior alcohol dependence. A preliminary study. *Archives of Psychiatry, 133*, 429–435.

van Gorp, W. G., Satz, P., Hinkin, C., Selnes, O., Miller, E. N., McArthur, J., Cohen, B., et al. (1991). Metacognition in HIV-1 seropositive asymptomatic individuals: Self-ratings versus objective neuropsychological performance. *Journal of Clinical and Experimental Neuropsychology, 13*, 812–819.

Weinberger, D. R., & Berman, K. F. (1986). Physiologic dysfunction of dorsolateral prefrontal cortex in Schizophrenia. *Archives of General Psychiatry, 43*(2), 114–124.

West, R. L., Boatwright, L. K., & Schleser, R. (1984). The link between memory performance, self-assessment, and affective status. *Experimental Aging Research, 10*(4), 197–200.

White, D. A., Myerson, J., & Hale, S. (1997). How cognitive is psychomotor slowing in depression? Evidence from a meta-analysis. *Aging, Neuropsychology, and Cognition, 4*(3), 166–174.

Williams, J. M. (1988). Everyday cognition and the ecological validity of intellectual and neuropsychological tests. In J. M. Williams & C. J. Long (Eds.), *Cognitive approaches to neuropsychology* (pp. 123–141). New York: Plenum.

Williams, R., Hagerty, B., Cimpric, B., Therrien, B., Bay, E., & Hiroake, O. (2000). Changes in directed attention and short-term memory in depression. *Journal of Psychiatric Research, 34,* 227–238.

Wolfe, J., Granholm, E., Butters, N., Saunders, E., & Janowsky, D. (1987). Verbal memory deficits associated with major affective disorders: A comparison of unipolar and bipolar patients. *Journal of Affective Disorders, 13,* 83–92.

Zubieta, J. K., Huguelet, P., Lajiness O'Neil, R., & Giordani, B. J. (2001). Cognitive function in euthymic Bipolar I Disorder. *Psychiatry Research, 102*(1), 9–20.

13 Neuropsychology and Adult Psychiatry

MOLLY COLVIN PUTNAM AND MARK A. BLAIS

Clinical neuropsychology is an applied science dedicated to studying the relationship between brain activity and behavior. As a clinical discipline, it is relatively new, emerging in the latter half of the 20th century with the rebirth of interest in understanding the biological sources of psychic processes. Many early neuropsychologists worked with brain-injured veterans returning from war, and developed tools to describe the impact of their injuries on behavior and rehabilitation (Lezak, Howieson, & Loring, 2004). At that time, neuropsychologists were among the first to clinically describe how different patterns of behavioral dysfunction resulted from damage to different brain areas. Such work contributed to a growing awareness in the brain sciences that cognitive functions emerged from the activity of specific localized networks in the brain. With this knowledge, neuropsychologists began to develop increasingly specific tests to tap different areas of brain function, in order to relate abnormal behavior to underlying brain pathology. In interpreting test results, the modern neuropsychologist draws from knowledge of how genetic, developmental, and psychosocial influences can also influence behavior, in order to generate a comprehensive perspective of an individual's behavior.

Conceptually, modern clinical neuropsychology exists at the inter-section of neurology and psychiatry. This is fortunate, as over the past few decades, the paths of these two medical specialties have begun to intersect with increasing frequency, reflecting a growing consensus that all human behavior, psychological or physical, is driven by biological activity. This emerging perspective has produced a pronounced shift in the field of psychiatry, which once focused exclusively on understanding psychic processes with little regard to their biological sources. Today, identifying the role of brain activity in psychiatric illness is now at the forefront of psychiatric training, research, and, to an increasing extent, practice. Consistent with this shift in emphases, psychiatry has come to appreciate that many common conditions such as unipolar depression and anxiety disorders, as well as more severe disorders (bipolar illness and psychotic conditions) are often accompanied by cognitive impair-ment (Gualtieri & Morgan, 2008). It is increasingly recognized that the presence of cognitive impairment can complicate treatment, slow progress, and increase the functional impairment experienced by psychi-atric patients. The tradition of separating mental disorders into func-tional and organic etiologies has greatly diminished and psychiatrists routinely assess cognitive functioning when evaluating patients. Unfor-tunately, these assessments typically rely upon brief cognitive screening tests such as the Mini-Mental Status Examination (MMSE; Folstein, Folstein, & McHugh, 1975). These screening tests are generally inade-quate for identifying mild but meaningful cognitive impairment. In addition, they yield a single total score, which is less informative than a profile of scores covering multiple cognitive domains. Despite the growing recognition of the important role of cognitive functioning in psychiatry, psychiatrists have been somewhat slow to incorporate more detailed neuropsychological assessments into routine practice. The inte-gration of neuropsychological assessment into clinical care will allow psychiatrists to develop treatment strategies that are consistent with their patients' unique cognitive strengths and weaknesses (Keefe, 1995). We hope this chapter will help advance the integration process.

A standard neuropsychological evaluation for adult psychiatric pa-tients includes an assessment of cognitive, emotional, and behavioral functioning. Neuropsychologists may employ a fixed-battery or flexible approach, meaning that they may always administer the same tests for all diagnostic questions, or they may select instruments in order to test particular hypotheses raised either by the referral question or ongoing behavioral observations. Regardless of evaluation approach, the primary domains of cognitive function are always assessed. These include intellectual functions, attention and executive functions, learning and memory, language functions, visuospatial functions, and motor functions. Academic functions (e.g., reading, writing, arithmetic) may also be evaluated depending upon the question to be answered. Performances within each of these domains are typically evaluated within the context of the patient's overall intellectual abilities and emotional functioning. The latter is assessed during the clinical interview and also through the administration of self-report and/or projective measures of emotional, personality, and behavioral functions. Once the test data are collected (interpretation phase), the neuropsychologist looks for patterns of strengths and weaknesses across cognitive domains in order to identify brain systems that may be involved. Differential diagnosis involves consideration of possible etiologies that can cause dysfunction within particular brain systems and critically integrates the patient's developmental and clinical history.

In treating patients with psychiatric illness, neuropsychological assessments can be useful in both the inpatient and outpatient settings. In the inpatient setting, a brief neuropsychological assessment can address targeted questions often related to memory (immediate new learning and delayed recall) and executive function (planning, shifting cognitive set, and behavioral inhibition). Such information can aid differential diagnosis (depression versus dementia), help establish functional capacity (ability to decline treatment or leave the hospital against medical advice, or AMA) and also to assist with discharge planning (post-hospital level of care needs). In the outpatient setting, a more comprehensive neuropsychological assessment can establish a patient's baseline level of cognitive functioning. This can be particularly useful in treatment planning, as recent research has demonstrated that cognitive difficulties may persist in many major psychiatric illnesses, even after the acute psychiatric symptoms have abated. The presence of chronic cognitive deficits will continue to negatively impact a patient's everyday functioning. A baseline profile of neuropsychological abilities can be very useful for monitoring a patient's cognitive status over time.

In the sections that follow, we describe common referral questions that an adult psychiatrist or other physician may pose to a neuropsychologist. The included topics are not intended to provide a comprehensive review of the neuropsychological profiles of different psychiatric presentations. Rather, it is our hope that these brief discussions of typical findings, in the context of case examples that are composites drawn from our own practices, will illustrate the utility of neuropsychological evaluations in addressing a variety of clinical issues, from case conceptualization to treatment.

ATTENTION-DEFICIT/HYPERACTIVITY DISORDER

Adult psychiatrists often evaluate and treat patients who present with complaints of inattention and/or hyperactivity. As attention-deficit/hyperactivity disorder (ADHD) has become increasingly recognized as a psychiatric disorder affecting children and adolescents, adult patients may often ask whether they also suffer from ADHD. By definition, ADHD is a neurodevelopmental disorder, as it manifests in childhood and adolescence and likely reflects atypical patterns in brain maturation (e.g., Kieling, Goncalves, Tannock, & Castellanos, 2008). The *Diagnostic and Statistical Manual of Mental Disorders* (DSM-IV; American Psychiatric Association, 1994) diagnostic criteria require significant symptoms of inattention and/or hyperactivity in early childhood, although recent research has raised questions regarding the validity or importance of the early childhood criteria in diagnosing ADHD in adults (Faraone et al., 2006). Regardless, nearly $1/2$ to $2/3$ of adolescents with ADHD will continue to exhibit symptoms in adulthood; overall, approximately 4% of the adult population may be diagnosed with ADHD (Resnick, 2005). Thus, if the clinical history supports such symptoms in childhood or early adolescence, particularly in the context of a strong family history of ADHD, then a neuropsychological evaluation can be helpful in assisting with differential diagnosis and identifying any ongoing impact of the disorder on cognitive functioning.

Successful identification and treatment of ADHD in adults can have dramatic effects on psychosocial functioning. Children and adolescents with ADHD often feel as though "something" is preventing them from meeting their true potential and can be frustrated by their own inconsistent behavior. If their symptoms are left untreated, they are at increased risk of low academic achievement and developing secondary psychological disorders characterized by conduct problems, substance use, affective dysregulation and anxiety (Jensen et al., 2001). Thus, the adult patient with undiagnosed ADHD may initially present with symptoms related to these secondary psychological disorders. Adult patients with ADHD may also present with psychiatric symptoms related to chronic psychosocial stress. Within the families of adult ADHD patients, there are generally higher levels of discord between the patient and his/her spouse, as well as his/her children (e.g., Minde et al., 2003). They often have difficulty managing the demands of daily life, which can be associated with a long history of employment problems, underachievement, and procrastination. In addition ADHD has a high comorbidity with specific learning disabilities, the presence of which may complicate treatment and decrease life success (Semrud-Clikeman et al., 1992). Neuropsychological assessment can help clarify the potential contribution of these associated difficulties.

Case Example

Patient J. N. is a 45-year-old man who was just seen by his primary care physician for his annual physical exam. During this evaluation, he reported that he has experienced increased levels of stress since receiving a big promotion several months ago. He specifically reported that he is having difficulty concentrating and occasionally forgets details related to the several projects he is managing. Upon further questioning, he acknowledged that "details have never been my strength" and that, as a result, his wife has always kept track of managing most aspects of their household's routine activities. In school, he typically made grades of Bs and Cs, and, in retrospect, thinks that his grades would have been higher if he hadn't always procrastinated and kept better track of his assignments. Based on this history and given that the patient is otherwise healthy, the primary care physician wonders whether he may meet diagnostic criteria for ADHD and refers him for a neuropsychological evaluation.

The neuropsychologist, Dr. M., begins the evaluation with a comprehensive clinical interview that focuses on establishing whether significant symptoms of inattention and hyperactivity were present in childhood and/or adolescence, and whether these symptoms had a significant impact on aspects of his psychosocial functioning (e.g., school achievement, relationships with parents and peers, conduct within the community). During the interview, Dr. M. also asks about a history of substance use and/or psychiatric symptoms, particularly related to depression and anxiety, which can mimic or exacerbate longstanding difficulties with attention. During the evaluation, Dr. M. administers tests to assess global intellectual functioning and cognitive functioning in all major domains, but particularly focuses on the domain of attention and executive functions. Dr. M. also asks Patient J. N. to complete a number of self-report questionnaires designed to assess a number of aspects of emotional and behavioral functioning. The results of the evaluation indicate that Patient J. N.'s overall level of intellectual functioning lies in the high average range, with even development of his verbal and nonverbal skills. In this context, relative individual weaknesses (i.e., scores falling approximately one standard deviation below his measured IQ) were noted in aspects of attention and executive functions, including his ability to independently sustain attention, divide his attention between multiple tasks, hold information temporarily in mind (working memory), complete tasks efficiently (processing speed), and organize complex novel information. During testing, he was also noted to perform best after taking short breaks, to begin tasks before being instructed to do so, and to make inattentive errors. Responses to self-report questionnaires did not indicate significant symptoms of depression, anxiety, or another major psychiatric illness. Given these findings, as well as a childhood history of inattention and hyperactivity that significantly impacted his educational performance, he was diagnosed with attention-deficit/hyperactivity disorder, combined type. These results were conveyed to the primary care physician, who prescribed psychopharmacological treatment. Several months later, Patient J. N. noted a significant reduction in his overall stress level and remarked that his relationship with his wife had "never been better."

This case illustrates that, although childhood onset and evidence of educational impairment are required for making the *DSM-IV* diagnosis, these symptoms can manifest in later childhood and persist into adulthood (Faraone et al., 2006), and that adult symptoms can impair function and do respond to treatment.

NEURODEVELOPMENTAL AND LEARNING DISORDERS

In addition to ADHD, other neurodevelopmental conditions and learning disorders may influence the presentation of an adult psychiatric patient. Many of these are more thoroughly reviewed in chapter 6, but are important to mention here, as the lasting presence of a neurodevelopmental condition in an adult patient may significantly impact treatment and prognosis. In such cases, a careful and developmentally oriented diagnostic interview in conjunction with a comprehensive neuropsychological evaluation is often critical in assisting with differential diagnosis.

One of the most common developmental questions to face the adult psychiatrist is whether a patient meets diagnostic criteria for an intellectual disability (i.e., mental retardation), as the rates of comorbidity for psychiatric illness and intellectual disability are relatively high. A recent population-based epidemiological study found that nearly 2% of psychiatric patients were also intellectually disabled and that the lifetime prevalence of psychiatric illness in the intellectually disabled population is approximately 40%. Rates of comorbidity were particularly high in individuals diagnosed with schizophrenia (4–5% of intellectually disabled individuals had co-occurring schizophrenia) (Morgan, Leonard, Bourke, & Jablensky, 2008). Generally, the presence of an intellectual disability will significantly impact factors related to treatment planning (e.g., whether individual psychotherapy is appropriate, need for assistance in managing medications). Thus, when borderline intellectual functioning is suspected, a comprehensive neuropsychological evaluation is indicated in order to assist with differential diagnosis.

Similarly, over the past several years, it has become increasingly apparent that children diagnosed with autism-spectrum disorders are at increased risk of comorbid psychiatric disorders. The severity of these comorbid psychiatric conditions is high; studies have found that nearly one-fourth of children diagnosed with an autism-spectrum disorder had been psychiatrically hospitalized (Mandell, Walrath, Manteuffel, Sgro, & Pinto-Martin, 2005) and that the rates of hospitalization increased with age (Mandell, 2007). Although it remains unclear whether the increasing rates of autism-spectrum disorder diagnoses actually reflect increased prevalence rates, it is clear that in the coming decades (Newschaffer et al., 2007), adult psychiatrists will work with patients who exhibit cognitive and behavioral symptoms of autism-spectrum disorders in addition to psychiatric symptoms. Again, in such cases, an accurate diagnosis is likely to greatly assist with treatment planning, particularly as a neuropsychological evaluation can delineate cognitive strengths that may be assets in successful management of the patient's psychiatric symptoms.

Finally, children with specific learning disabilities impacting academic achievement are at increased risk for developing psychiatric disorders that may present in adulthood. For example, children with a history of reading difficulties are at increased risk of later developing conduct and oppositional disorders or antisocial personality disorder (Beitchman, Wilson, Johnson, et al., 2001; Carroll, Maughan, Goodman, & Meltzer, 2005). Specific learning disabilities impacting reading and mathematics have also been associated with subsequent substance use disorders (Beitchman, Wilson, Douglas, Young, & Adlaf, 2001; Goldston et al., 2007). Reading difficulties have also been associated with increased rates of anxiety and depression (Carroll, Maughan, Goodman, & Meltzer, 2005; Goldston et al., 2007). Thus, one might suspect that adults presenting with features of antisocial personality disorder, substance use, and/or anxiety and depression may have developmental histories that include specific learning disabilities, particularly if there is a history of educational and occupational underachievement. Understanding the nature of these disabilities may be critically important in reducing the risk of long-term psychiatric difficulties.

Case Example

Sixty-year-old patient T. J. was brought to the emergency department by his elderly mother after he fell down a flight of stairs. Upon examination, he was disoriented to the place and performed poorly on questions assessing cognitive function that were included in a mental status screen. A neuroimaging study was negative. There were also no significant findings upon neurological exam. Laboratory findings failed to detect any evidence of substance use or metabolic disturbances. He was hospitalized for treatment of a leg injury related to the fall. A follow-up neurological exam was also unremarkable, and psychiatry was consulted. This evaluation failed to reveal any evidence of psychosis or symptoms of another psychiatric disorder. His mental status remained stable. In speaking with his mother, the psychiatrist established that Patient T. J. had always lived with her and had stopped attending school in the 4th grade because it was "harder for him than most kids." He had never held a job outside of the home and spent his days watching television and feeding pigeons in a local park. Given this information, the psychiatrist requested a neuropsychological evaluation to determine whether he might meet diagnostic criteria for mental retardation, as such a diagnosis might help him obtain additional services upon discharge.

The neuropsychologist, Dr. S., obtained the patient's consent to speak with his mother about his life. During this clinical interview, Dr. S. focused on

Patient T. J.'s developmental history to establish whether he had exhibited delays in most, if not all, aspects of functioning. Dr. S. also asked additional questions about his academic functioning, to determine whether he had experienced difficulties in all domains, and about his ability to independently execute activities of daily living. Upon testing, Patient T. J.'s global intellectual functioning fell within the impaired range (IQ score of < 70). Performances on additional measures of cognitive and academic functioning were commensurate with aptitude-based expectations. His mother completed a questionnaire assessing patient T. J.'s adaptive skills, which were also uniformly below age-based expectations. Based on the results of this evaluation, patient T. J. was diagnosed with mental retardation. A social worker assigned to his case began the process of exploring his eligibility for state services and helping his mother to establish legal guardianship.

SCHIZOPHRENIA SPECTRUM ILLNESSES

For patients who are presenting with a first episode of psychosis, a neuropsychological assessment can be useful in predicting long-term functional outcome. Relative declines in certain aspects of cognitive functioning can be seen the first episode of psychosis. In particular, difficulties with verbal learning, motor speed, and aspects of executive functions, including working memory and impulsivity, have been reported (Friis et al., 2002). This pattern may represent an exacerbation of weaknesses that are evident during the prodromal phase of the illness (Munro et al., 2002), during which a mild decline in global intellectual functioning can also be observed (Woodberry, Giuliano, & Seidman, 2008). Regardless of the etiology, the degree of cognitive impairment during the first episode of psychosis is one factor in determining long-term functional outcome. In general, higher estimates of global intellectual functioning at the time of the first episode have been associated with a better functional prognosis (Carlsson, Nyman, Ganse, & Cullberg, 2005). Thus, in the context of additional factors, including family support and response to medication, a neuropsychological evaluation can be useful in predicting the extent of a patient's ability to later independently manage activities of daily living.

Neuropsychological assessment of patients presenting with longer courses of illness can also be useful in assisting with multiple factors related to treatment planning. First, in cases where the patient's capacity to consent is not easily determined, a targeted neuropsychological evaluation examining aspects of executive functions, including abstract reasoning and problem solving, can be helpful. Second, although treatment with medication may have significant effects on certain aspects of cognitive functioning, a number of studies have suggested that cognitive deficits associated with schizophrenia are relatively stable over time (e.g., Grawe & Levander, 2001). Thus, assessment of a patient's cognitive profile can provide insight into a patient's ability to manage the demands of everyday life, in addition to potentially providing insight into the impact of psychopharmacological treatment. As seen in the context of first episode psychosis, patients with chronic schizophrenia who present with greater compromise of cognitive functions, particularly those related to processing speed, executive functions, attention, and memory, generally suffer from a poorer quality of life.

Case Example

Ms. T. was a 19-year-old female who initially began psychiatric treatment at age 16, after experiencing episodes of marked anxiety and depressive symptomatology. At age 18, she developed delusions and her psychotic symptoms persisted for 3 months, resulting in a diagnosis of schizophreniform disorder. Six months later, she attempted suicide by overdose and underwent an inpatient psychiatric hospitalization. Since that time, she has continued to exhibit some negative symptoms, but her condition has been stable. Her psychiatrist requested a neuropsychological evaluation to characterize her cognitive, emotional, and behavioral functioning so as to inform treatment planning and recommendations.

The neuropsychological evaluation incorporated measures of cognitive and emotional functioning. The results of cognitive testing indicated low average intellectual abilities, and in this context, Ms. T. demonstrated difficulty with aspects of executive functions. She struggled on tasks placing increased demands on divided attention and/or shifting rapidly between task demands, and also on a conceptual-reasoning task requiring her to independently integrate feedback in order to make inferences. Her processing speed was also quite slow. These findings indicated that Ms. T. would likely need more time than most adolescents her age to fully integrate and act upon new information, and that she would be vulnerable to decision-making errors when task demands increased or when she might need to make inferences based on presented material. On self-report questionnaires and projective tests designed to assess aspects of emotional and behavioral functioning, Ms. T.'s response indicated that she is at considerable risk for depression, interpersonal difficulties, and poor decision-making. Although she expressed an interest in establishing close relationships with others, her profile suggested that she may have difficulty accurately interpreting the actions and intentions of others and was quite vulnerable to low self-esteem and social isolation. Furthermore, in stressful situations, particularly those involving high emotional intensity, her responses suggested that she was likely to become easily overwhelmed, placing her at greater risk for decision-making errors.

Thus, Ms. T.'s neuropsychological profile indicated a number of areas of clinical concern and targets for intervention to buffer her risk of developing a chronic severe mental illness. Ms. T.'s psychiatrist referred her for regular individual psychotherapy with a clinical psychologist, and this treatment focused on improving coping and stress management skills, improving tolerance of intense affective experiences, reducing anxiety in social situations and improving social skills, and learning strategies to promote effective reality-testing. Ms. T. reduced her course load at a local community college in order to minimize cognitive and psychosocial stress. Ms. T.'s psychiatrist and psychologist worked closely together to monitor her response to medication and the family's needs. Thus, the neuropsychological evaluation results were able to inform the development of a comprehensive treatment plan designed with Ms. T.'s areas of strengths and weaknesses in mind.

BIPOLAR AFFECTIVE DISORDER

In the acute stage of bipolar disorder, there is similarity between the neuropsychological profiles of patients diagnosed with bipolar disorder and patients diagnosed with schizophrenia. During both manic and depressive episodes, compromised executive functions, including abstract reasoning, behavioral inhibition, and planning, are often observed, in addition to difficulties with sustained attention and verbal memory (for review, see Quraishi & Frangou, 2002). Thus, in an inpatient setting, a neuropsychological evaluation may assist in decisions related to capacity and discharge planning. During euthymic periods, patients diagnosed with bipolar disorder generally do not exhibit the same degree of compromised cognitive function as can be seen during the acute phases of the illness. Yet there is a growing body of evidence to suggest that cognitive weaknesses may persist during the euthymic phase (Malhi et al., 2007; Savitz, Solms, & Ramesar, 2005), and that such symptoms may be related to the extent of functional impairment and overall quality of life (e.g., Martinez-Aran et al., 2007). Thus, neuropsychological assessment during the euthymic phase can also be useful in assisting with treatment planning.

Case Example

Mr. D. was a 47-year-old man who first experienced a hypomanic episode, characterized by elevated mood, increased activity, and increased mental acuity when he was in college. Several years later, while attending law school, he suffered from an episode of severe depression. He dropped out of school and over the course of the next several years, experienced multiple depressive and hypomanic episodes. He was eventually diagnosed with bipolar II disorder. He had been followed by his outpatient psychiatrist for many years, and his symptoms had been reasonably well controlled with medication. However, over the past few months, he has felt that he is "not as sharp" as usual. At work, his productivity had declined and he had been reprimanded for making errors. Yet he consistently described his current mood as euthymic and had been taking his prescribed mood stabilizing medication as directed. His psychiatrist referred him for a neuropsychological evaluation to determine his current level of cognitive and behavioral functioning, in order to assist with differential diagnosis.

The neuropsychological evaluation revealed that Mr. D.'s overall intellectual abilities fell in the high average to superior range, and that his verbal skills were slightly stronger than his nonverbal skills. In this context, he exhibited relative weaknesses in aspects of executive functions, including his ability to mentally manipulate novel information for brief periods of time (working memory), independently sustain his attention for longer periods of time, and shift quickly between different task demands. On learning and memory tasks his ability to quickly learn information presented in an unstructured or unfamiliar format was restricted and after a delay period, his free recall of previously learned material was more reliable than recognition. This pattern of results suggested mild dysfunction within frontostriatal brain systems, an interconnected network involved in many higher-order cognitive functions, including learning and abstract reasoning. When the findings were reviewed with Mr. D., he felt that his subjective reports of increased cognitive difficulties had been validated, thereby improving his relationship with his treating psychiatrist. His psychiatrist also elected to slightly alter his medication regimen, to determine whether such a change might alleviate some of his cognitive difficulties.

SUBSTANCE ABUSE AND DEPENDENCE

Substance-abuse disorders, particularly those involving alcohol, are commonly encountered either as primary or comorbid conditions in psychiatric settings. Substance-abuse disorders represent a heterogeneous group of conditions, all of which can involve cognitive impairment, but given the prominence of alcohol abuse in psychiatric patients, we will focus primarily on this condition. The majority of individuals with an alcohol disorder have at least one comorbid psychiatric condition, with anxiety, mood, and personality disorders being the most common. Although alcohol is a known neurotoxin, lifestyle factors associated with excessive drinking also contribute to the risk for cognitive impairment as heavy drinkers are at risk for traumatic brain injury (TBI). Age is also associated with impairment; older drinkers (35 years and older) are at higher risk for impairment (Allen, Frantom, Forrest, & Strauss, 2006).

The neuroanatomical changes observed in subjects with chronic alcohol abuse involve both white and gray matter abnormalities, with cerebral atrophy a common finding in imaging studies (for review, see Oscar-Berman & Marinkovic, 2007). Excessive alcohol consumption affects specific cognitive domains, including complex visual-spatial abilities, executive functions, and psychomotor speed. Memory deficits, particularly deficits in visual memory, may also be present, but serious memory problems have not been consistently reported for subjects without alcohol dementia or Wernicke-Korsakoff's syndrome. Over-learned skills, particularly language abilities often remain intact (for review, see Hannay, Howieson, Loring, Fischer, & Lezak, 2004). Unfortunately when language abilities are intact, clinicians often miss the presence of cognitive impairment and overestimate the patient's functional capacity.

The Cessation of Alcohol Use and Cognitive Impairment

Cognitive deficits are most prominent during the first few weeks (1 to 3) following the cessation of drinking. During this initial period of abstinence patients may exhibit deficits in all cognitive domains. However, marked and rapid improvement in functioning is generally observed especially for younger patients (those under age 35). During this initial period brief low burden screening tests may help document and track these cognitive changes, but more comprehensive neuropsychological assessment is usually contraindicated. During short-term abstinence the impact of age (or duration of alcohol abuse) becomes apparent. Younger patients may show a complete return of *normal* functioning as soon as 5 to 6 weeks after cessation of alcohol use. Older patients (≥ 40 years of age) and those who have consumed more alcohol typically, also show improvement but may continue to demonstrate relative deficits in executive function (poor problem solving, perseveration, and difficulties independently sustaining an established response pattern), decreased motor speed, and inefficient new learning. The extent to which impairments continue to improve with prolonged sustained abstinence is unclear. Although some deficits (attention and psychomotor speed) may show continued improvement with sustained abstinence, deficits associated with frontal lobe functions may be more persistent particularly for older individuals (Allen et al., 2006). In some cases severe alcohol dependence can also lead to chronic disabling and life threatening neurological disorders such as Wernicke-Korsakoff's syndrome and alcohol dementia.

Case Example

Mr. V. was a 53-year-old college-educated successful freelance writer who consulted Dr. M. because of increased irritation and frustration primarily related to work. "I think I'm getting depressed again," he said during the initial evaluation. However, although Mr. V. had episodes of depression in the past, a clinical interview failed to detect significant symptoms of depression currently, but did reveal a long-standing pattern of heavy social drinking. Mr. V. regularly consumed 5 or more drinks a day during the week, and on weekends he would often drink a fifth of whiskey "plus a few beers." He began drinking in his late teens when he worked as a copy boy at a city newspaper. He was proud of his drinking and felt it connected him to past literary greats like Hemingway. He denied that his drinking ever caused him any occupational or social difficulties.

The frustration and irritability that motivated his seeking care appeared related to difficulties he was having completing his current writing project. He presently was working under a tight deadline to produce a paperback novel loosely based on historical events. Although he had successfully undertaken such projects in the past, currently he was having significant difficulty organizing and integrating the research material for the project. He was behind schedule and was receiving pressure from his editor to complete the project. A head imaging study ordered by his primary care physician (PCP) was unremarkable and a neuropsychological evaluation was obtained.

Mr. V.'s neuropsychological profile was revealing. His full-scale IQ was 111 (high average range) and consistent with his educational achievement. However, his verbal IQ was 125 (superior range), while his nonverbal / performance IQ was 97 (average range). In the absence of a known neurodevelopmental condition, this 28-point difference favoring his verbal skills suggests a possible decline in nonverbal functioning in adulthood (e.g., pattern analysis, ability to apply visuospatial skills to everyday problems, etc.). Furthermore, his performances on the timed IQ subtests were among his worst. His passive attention was intact, but he performed poorly on tests that placed increased burden on working memory and processing speed. On memory tests his memory for aurally presented material (i.e., verbal memory, both immediate and delayed) was generally consistent with his measured full-scale IQ, whereas his memory for visually presented material (i.e., visual memory, both immediate and delayed) was significantly weaker with relative deficits for both new learning and delayed recall. His performance on a test of complex visual spatial ability was also weak. On tests thought to measure executive functions, abstract reasoning, planning, set shifting (i.e., ability to respond flexibly to changes in task demands), and behavioral inhibition he performed consistently well below his measured IQ with scores ranging from 75 (borderline range) to 92 (average range). Self-report measures of psychopathology failed to identify significant depression or anxiety. The overall pattern of finding was highly consistent with that expected from prolonged heavy alcohol consumption: reduced processing speed, visual memory deficits, and a significant decline in executive function in the presence of generally preserved language abilities. Although many of his cognitive deficits were mild or relative, his decline in executive ability was substantial and was likely causing his current functional difficulties. When these findings were reviewed jointly with the patient, Mr. V. agreed to enter treatment for his alcohol use.

DEMENTIA VERSUS DEPRESSION

One of the most common reasons physicians may refer patients for a neuropsychological evaluation is for the differentiation of depression from dementia. In the context of a routine psychiatric evaluation, the clinical presentation of elderly adults suffering from the early stages of a neurodegenerative illness is often indistinguishable from that of elderly adults suffering from depression. Primary complaints are likely to relate to cognitive decline, particularly impacting attention, concentration, and memory. Confusing matters further, patients who are in the early stages of a neurodegenerative process may sometimes also present with comborbid depressive and anxious symptomatology.

In such cases, a neuropsychological evaluation can be quite useful in clarifying the nature of the patient's cognitive difficulties and determining whether the overall pattern of performance is indicative of neurodegenerative illness. Memory impairment arising from depression is typically characterized by relative difficulties with learning new material and with strategic retrieval of previously learned material. In contrast, memory impairment indicative of a neurodegenerative illness impacting medial temporal lobe function (e.g., dementia of the Alzheimer's type) is typically associated with rapid forgetting of newly learned material. Furthermore, in cases of neurodegenerative illness that have progressed beyond the stage of mild cognitive impairment (MCI), relative weaknesses will be observed in additional domains of cognitive functioning, including language, visuospatial, and executive functions. Thus, the overall pattern of neuropsychological test scores can distinguish between depression and dementia, and in cases of dementia, may provide insight into the nature of the neurodegenerative process. Thus, for elderly adults presenting with subjective or observed symptoms of cognitive decline, a neuropsychological evaluation is strongly recommended.

Case Example

Mrs. G. was a 75-year-old woman who was referred for a neuropsychological evaluation after reporting increased memory difficulties to her primary care physician). At the time of the evaluation, she reported that over the previous year, she had experienced an increase in the frequency of lapses in attention and memory. She described frequently walking into rooms and not remembering why she was there, relying more on written lists to keep track of daily tasks, increased difficulty with multitasking, and mild word-finding difficulties. She reported no difficulties executing activities of daily living (ADLs) and remained active in several local community activities. However, she did report increased feelings of loneliness and sleep difficulties following the death of her husband 3 years prior. Her medical history was remarkable for hypertension, well controlled by medication. A recent neurological evaluation was unremarkable.

The neuropsychological evaluation revealed that she was a bright woman, with intellectual abilities falling in the high average to superior range. In this context, she demonstrated mild difficulty learning new information, particularly when it was presented in a relatively unstructured format. Critically, her long-term storage of the material that she did learn was intact. Furthermore, her performances across multiple cognitive domains, including language, visuo-spatial, and executive functions, were intact. On self-report questionnaires assessing symptoms of depression and anxiety, she endorsed mild symptoms of depression, but did not endorse significant symptoms of anxiety.

This neuropsychological profile is most consistent with an exacerbation of age-related cognitive decline due to depression and/or chronic sleep difficulties. Mrs. G.'s reported attentional lapses and memory difficulties reflect mild disruption in brain systems involving the frontal lobes. In the early stages of Alzheimer's disease, one would expect to see cognitive difficulties associated with medial temporal dysfunction (e.g., rapid forgetting of newly learned information) rather than reduced encoding and/or retrieval of newly learned information. These findings prompted a psychiatric referral for a psychopharmacological consultation regarding antidepressants, as well as to identify potential sources of additional psychosocial support in her community. In addition, health education regarding the importance of sleep hygiene was provided and a sleep evaluation was also recommended if her difficulties persisted after these interventions.

CONCLUDING REMARKS

Neuropsychology is a rapidly evolving clinical discipline with significant potential to improve psychiatric care through the comprehensive assessments of cognitive functioning. Unfortunately, the adoption of neuropsychological assessment in routine clinical care has lagged behind that of other diagnostic procedures such as neuroimaging, despite the fact that these procedures often offer less clinical utility (see Renshaw & Rauch, 1999). We hope that the information and case examples provided in this chapter will help psychiatrists become more comfortable and familiar with the benefits of neuropsychological assessment.

REFERENCES

Allen, D., Frantom, L., Forrest T., & Strauss, G. (2006). Neuropsychology of substance use disorders. In P. Snyder, P. Nussbaum, & D. Robins (Eds.), *Clinical neuropsychology: A pocket handbook for assessment* (2nd ed., pp. 649–673).

American Psychiatric Association. (1994). *Diagnostic and statistical manual of mental disorders* (4th ed.) Washington, DC: American Psychiatric Press.

Beitchman, J., Wilson, B., Douglas, L., Young A., & Adlaf, E. (2001). Substance use disorders in young adults with and without LD: Predictive and concurrent relationships. *Journal of Learning Disabilities, 34,* 317–332.

Beitchman, J., Wilson, B., Johnson, C. J., Atkinson, L., Young, A., Adlaf, E., et al. (2001). Fourteen-year follow-up of speech/language-impaired and control children: Psychiatric outcome. *Journal of the American Academy of Child and Adolescent Psychiatry, 40,* 75–82.

Carlsson, R., Nyman, H., Ganse, G., & Cullberg, J. (2005). Neuropsychological functions predict 1- and 3-year outcome in first-episode psychosis. *Acta Psychiatrica Scandinavica, 113,* 102–111.

Carroll, J., Maughan, B., Goodman, R., & Meltzer, H. (2005). Literacy difficulties and psychiatric disorders: Evidence for comorbidity. *Journal of Child Psychology and Psychiatry, 46,* 524–532.

Faraone, S., Biederman, J., Spencer, T., Mick, E., Murry, K., Petty, C., et al. (2006). Diagnosing adult attention deficit hyperactivity disorder: Are late onset and subthreshold diagnoses valid? *American Journal of Psychiatry, 163*(10), 1720–1729.

Folstein, M., Folstein, S., & McHugh, P. (1975). Mini-mental state: A practical method for grading the cognitive state of patients for the clinician. *Journal of Psychiatric Research, 12,* 189–198.

Friis, S., et al. (2002). Neurocognitive dimensions characterizing patients with first-episode psychosis. *British Journal of Psychiatry* (Suppl.), *43,* s85–s90.

Goldston, D. B., Walsh, A., Mayfield, A. E., Reboussin, B., Sergent, D. S., Erkanli, A., et al. (2007). Reading problems, psychiatric disorders, and functional impairment from mid- to late adolescence. *Journal of Child and Adolescent Psychiatry, 46,* 25–32.

Grawe, R. W., & Levander, S. (2001). Neuropsychological impairments in patients with schizophrenia: Stability and prediction of outcome. *Acta Psychiatrica Scandinavica, 104* (Suppl. 208), 60–64.

Green, M. F. (1996). What are the functional consequences of neurocognitive deficits in schizophrenia? *American Journal of Psychiatry, 153,* 321–330.

Green, M. F., Kern, R. S., Braff, D. L., & Mintz, J. (2000). Neurocognitive deficits and functional outcome in schizophrenia: Are we measuring the "right stuff"? *Schizophrenia Bulletin, 26,* 119–136.

Gualtieri, T., & Morgan, D. (2008). The frequency of cognitive impairment in patients with anxiety, depression, and bipolar disorder: An unaccounted source of variance in clinical trials. *Journal of Clinical Psychiatry, 69,* 1122–1130.

Hannay, H. J., Howieson, D. B., Loring, D. W., Fischer, J. S., & Lezak, M. (2004). Neuropathology for neuropsychologists. In M. Lezak, D. B. Howieson, & D.W. Loring (Eds.), *Neuropsychological assessment* (pp.157–285).

Jensen, P. S., Hinshaw, S. P., Kraemer, H. C., Lenora, N., Newcorn, J. H., Abikoff, H. B., et al. (2001). ADHD comorbidity findings from the MTA study: Comparing comorbid subgroups. *Journal of the American Academy of Child and Adolescent Psychiatry, 40,* 147–158.

Keefe, R. (1995). The contribution of neuropsychology to psychiatry. *American Journal of Psychiatry, 152,* 6–14.

Keefe, R. S. E., Poe, M., Walker, T. M., & Harvey, P. D. (2006). The relationship of the brief assessment of cognition in schizophrenia (BACS) to functional capacity and real-world functional outcome. *Journal of Clinical and Experimental Neuropsychology, 28,* 260–269.

Kieling, C., Goncalves, R. R., Tannock, R., & Castellanos, F. X. (2008). Neurobiology of attention deficit hyperactivity disorder. *Child and Adolescent Psychiatric Clinics of North America, 17,* 285–307.

Lezak, M. D., Howieson, D. B., & Loring, D. W. (2004). *Neuropsychological assessment* (4th ed.). Oxford, UK: Oxford University Press.

Malhi, G .S., Ivanovski, B., Hadzi-Pavlovic, D., Mitchell, P. B., Vieta, E., & Sachdev, P. (2007). Neuropsychological deficits and functional impairment in bipolar depression, hypomania, and euthymia. *Bipolar Disorder, 9,* 114–125.

Mandell, D. S. (2007). Psychiatric hospitalization among children with autism spectrum disorders. *Journal of Autism and Developmental Disorders, 38,* 1059–1065.

Mandell, D., Walrath, C., Manteuffel, B., Sgro, G., & Pinto-Martin, J. (2005). Characteristics of children with autistic spectrum disorders served in comprehensive community-based mental health settings. *Journal of Autism and Developmental Disorders, 35,* 113–121.

Martinez-Aran, A., Vieta, E., Torrent, C., Sanchez-Moreno, J., Goikolea, J. M., Salamero, M., et al. (2007). Functional outcome in bipolar disorder: The role of clinical and cognitive factors. *Bipolar Disorders, 9,* 103–113.

McGrath, J., Scheldt, S., Welham, J., & Clair, A. (1997). Performance on tests sensitive to impaired executive ability in schizophrenia, mania and well controls: Acute and subacute phases. *Schizophrenia Research, 26,* 127–137.

Minde, K., Eakin, L., Hectman, L., Ochs, E., Bouffard, R., Greenfield, B., & Looper, K. (2003). The psychosocial functioning of children and spouses of adults with ADHD. *Journal of Child Psychology and Psychiatry, 44,* 637–646.

Morgan, V. A., Leonard, H., Bourke, J., & Jablensky, A. (2008). Intellectual disability co-occurring with schizophrenia and other psychiatric illness: Population-based study. *British Journal of Psychiatry, 193,* 364–372.

Morice, R. (1990). Cognitive inflexibility and pre-frontal dysfunction in schizophrenia and mania. *British Journal of Psychiatry, 157,* 50–54.

Munro, J. C., et al. (2002). IQ in childhood psychiatric attendees predicts outcome of later schizophrenia at 21 year follow-up. *Acta Psychiatrica Scandinavica, 106,* 139–142.

Newschaffer, C. J., Croen, L. A., Daniels, J., Giarelli, E., Grether, J. K., Levy, S. E., et al. (2007). The epidemiology of autism spectrum disorders. *Annual Review of Public Health, 28,* 235–258.

Oscar-Berman, M., & Marinkovic, K. (2007). Alcohol: Effects on neurobehavioral functions and the brain. *Neuropsychology Review, 17,* 239–257.

Quraishi, S., & Frangou, S. (2002). Neuropsychology of bipolar disorder: A Review. *Journal of Affective Disorders, 72,* 209–226.

Renshaw, P., & Rauch, S. (1999). Neuroimaging in clinical psychiatry. In A. M. Nicholi, Jr. (Ed.), *The Harvard guide to psychiatry* (3rd ed., pp. 297–312). Cambridge, MA: Belknap Press.

Resnick, R. (2005). Attention deficit hyperactivity disorder in teens and adults: They don't all outgrow it. *Journal of Clinical Psychology, 61,* 529–533.

Savitz, J., Solms, M., & Ramesar, R. (2005). Neuropsychological dysfunction in bipolar affective disorder: A critical opinion. *Bipolar disorder, 7,* 216–235.

Semrud-Clikeman, M., Biederman, J., Sprich-Buckminster, S., Lehman, B. K., Faraone, S.V., & Norman, D. (1992). Comorbidity between ADHD and learning disability: A review and report in a clinically referred sample. *Journal of the American Academy of Child and Adolescent Psychiatry, 31,* 439–448.

Woodberry, K. A., Giuliano, A. J., & Seidman, L. J. (2008). Premorbid IQ in schizophrenia: A meta-analytic review. *American Journal of Psychiatry, 165,* 579–587.

Neuropsychology and Neurology

DARIO J. ENGLOT AND MARISA SPANN

The purpose of this chapter is to serve as a practical guide for neurologists on how to best make use of neuropsychology referrals and consultations in clinical practice. The frequency of neuropsychology consults made by neurologists in the United States differs widely by geographic location and institution, but is primarily dependent on an individual clinician's exposure to the field. This exposure is influenced both by the availability of local specialists, as well as the physician's personal awareness of the utility and suitability of neuropsychology referrals. It is our opinion that even among neurologists who have adequate resources available locally, neuropsychology referrals are sometimes under- or inappropriately utilized. Two major limitations that prevent neurologists from seeking consultations are a lack of understanding of the potential benefits of the referral, and difficulty interpreting the resultant neuropsychology report in a useful way. Thus, it is our goal to familiarize the clinical neurologist with the purpose and benefit of appropriate neuropsychology consultations, and to foster a better appreciation and understanding of the recommendations produced from these referrals. The remainder of this chapter will thus be divided into two major sections. In the first section, "The Neuropsychology Referral," we will discuss the consultation of neuropsychology, focusing on the benefits of such a referral (why?), which neurological patients should be referred (who?), the best time to refer (when?), and the important information one should include in the referral (how?). The second section of the chapter, "The Neuropsychology Report," will identify the most meaningful pieces of information in the neuropsychology report that should garner particular focus by the neurologist, and will include guidance on how to best interpret that information.

THE NEUROPSYCHOLOGY REFERRAL

Why Would a Neurologist Consult Neuropsychology?

Perhaps one of the most prominent misconceptions among neurologists who rarely seek neuropsychological input is a perceived lack of benefit from the consultations. It is our belief that this results primarily from a lack of understanding of the beneficial role that neuropsychologists hold concerning the care of a neurological patient. A clinician might wonder: "Why consult neuropsychology? If this patient has a medically treatable neurobiological disorder, neurology can manage the patient alone. If neurocognitive (cognitive functions that are associated with different brain regions) sequelae emerge, the patient should be sent to a psychologist or to a psychiatrist." In reality, however, neuropsychologists can serve to bridge the gap between the medical care provided by the neurologist and the mental health (psychological, emotional, and/ or behavioral) care provided in psychology in a way that is both useful to caretakers and beneficial to the patient. Whereas neurological care focuses primarily on "brain" disorders, and psychological treatment targets disorders of "behavior," neuropsychologists examine brain–behavior relationships in a manner beyond the scope of a general neurologist's training. We suggest that a close marriage of the care provided by the neurologist and the neuropsychologist provides the best treatment approach for neurological patients who have or may develop neurocognitive sequelae.

Although classic physical exam techniques coupled with modern laboratory and imaging methods provide for impressive diagnostic abilities among today's clinical neurologists, cases of neurocognitive dysfunction in which a clear diagnosis remains elusive often benefit from the additional insight provided by a neuropsychologist. Furthermore, even patients whose neurological diagnosis might be quite clear and symptoms seemingly typical benefit from the more comprehensive neurocognitive assessments provided by neuropsychologists, which often reveal subtle performance deficits and offer specific treatment suggestions. In addition, although consultation of a psychiatrist or psychologist in the care of a neurological patient often provides useful information about the patient, practical *integration* of the patient's neurological diagnosis with his or her psychiatric profile is not provided. It is the neuropsychologist's role to clarify this translation between brain and behavior in an individual patient: to evaluate the patient's neuropsychological profile, to relate it to the "real world" (i.e., the patient's personal and professional lives), and to suggest appropriate strategies to minimize the effects of disease on life. Synergy between neurology and neuropsychology can provide a more complete package of care for patients diagnosed with a central nervous system disorder.

How exactly does a neuropsychological evaluation compliment a neurological exam? Although the physical examination techniques available to the neurologist are vast, performing a comprehensive nervous system evaluation in the confines of a brief office visit can prove challenging. For instance, although the basic components of a neurological motor system exam provide useful assessment of the functionality of major motor neuron and muscle groups, valuable, albeit sometimes subtle, information can also be garnered from comprehensive evaluation of visuomotor integration that is rarely performed in a typical visit to neurology. Table 14.1 provides additional examples of typical components of a basic neurological exam and complementary assessments performed in a full neuropsychological evaluation.

Beyond complementing motor and sensory components of the neurological exam, the neuropsychological evaluation possesses particular strengths in the assessment of neurocognitive function. The neurologist's mental status exam evaluates alertness and orientation, and it can also be extended to include assessments of language, memory, logic, calculation, and abstraction. Nevertheless, the cognitive tests regularly employed by a neurologist, and the time he or she has to utilize them during patient visits, are limited. Conversely, neuropsychologists benefit from extensive training in administering and interpreting standardized cognitive tests. Furthermore, unlike a neurology office visit, the standard neuropsychological evaluation typically allows several hours to assess the patient's neurocognitive status. This assessment can directly comple-

Table 14.1

COMPARISON OF NEUROLOGICAL EXAM COMPONENTS TO THE NEUROPSYCHOLOGICAL EVALUATION

NEUROLOGICAL FUNCTION	DESCRIPTION OF ASSESSMENT	
	NEUROLOGICAL PHYSICAL EXAMINATION	NEUROPSYCHOLOGICAL EVALUATION
Cranial nerves	Ability to smell and taste, general visual and peripheral visual function, eyelid strength, pupillary light reflexes, oculomotor function, facial sensation, strength of facial musculature, hearing, vestibular function, palate elevation, gag reflex, strength of neck and shoulder muscles, tongue movements	Auditory comprehension, visuo-perceptual/spatial interpretation, oromotor control, identification of tactile or olfactory stimuli
Motor systems	Strength in all major muscle groups	Graphomotor speed, imitation of hand positions, manual motor sequence replication, visuomotor integration
Sensory systems	Somatosensation of pain, temperature, pressure, and position	Tactile object identification, identification of letters and numbers drawn in the hand
Deep tendon reflexes	Response of muscles to brisk tendon taps	n/a
Coordination/ cerebellar function	Finger–nose–finger repetition test, quick finger tapping, heel-to-shin test	Observation of posture, postural sway measurements, time to postural response
Gait	Forward and backward gait, heel-to-toe walking	Quantitative gait assessment, walking protocols
Mental status	see Table 14.2	see Table 14.2

ment the neurological mental status exam, as illustrated in a few examples provided in Table 14.2.

Who Should a Neurologist Refer?

Even a neurologist who appreciates the importance of neuropsychological input in patient care may sometimes be unsure whether a particular patient might or might not benefit from the consultation. The simplest answer is: *any* patient diagnosed with or suspected of central nervous system dysfunction might be an appropriate candidate for a neuropsychological evaluation. Clearly, however, limited resources may make this principle prohibitively broad. A more practical rule-of-thumb is that any patient diagnosed with or suspected of a neurological disorder *that is usually associated with cognitive or emotional sequelae* should have a neuropsychological assessment integrated into his or her care. Common examples of these disorders include dementia, brain injury, and brain tumors, although various other neurological and developmental conditions are associated with neurocognitive consequences. Table 14.3 summarizes neurological conditions in both adult and pediatric patients that are most commonly associated with neurocognitive deficits, and therefore represent diagnoses that may necessitate neuropsychological consultation. It is also important to consider referring neurological patients whose treatment plan includes medications that are commonly associated with significant neurocognitive side effects, such as many antiepileptic drugs.

It is appropriate to discuss not only which patients the neurologist should refer to neuropsychology, but also which patients should *not* be referred. A neuropsychological evaluation is time-intensive; therefore it is important to ensure that the referral is appropriate given the patient's condition. Although it is true that nearly all patients, with neurocognitive effects secondary to a neurological disease, would benefit from a neuropsychological assessment, a successful evaluation is dependent upon patient participation and responsiveness. For instance, patients who have identifiable neurological disease, yet suffer from acute psychiatric instability are often unable to effectively cooperate with an evaluation. Therefore, neurological patients with severe and acute psychiatric manifestations should be evaluated and treated by a psychiatrist prior to his or her neuropsychological assessment, to maximize

Table 14.2

COMPARISON OF THE NEUROLOGICAL MENTAL STATUS EXAM TO COGNITIVE ASSESSMENTS IN THE NEUROPSYCHOLOGICAL EVALUATION

COGNITIVE FUNCTIONS	FUNCTIONS TESTED IN EACH COGNITIVE CATEGORY	
	NEUROLOGICAL MENTAL STATUS EXAM	NEUROPSYCHOLOGICAL EVALUATION
Alertness and orientation	Level of responsiveness; orientation to person, place, and time	Cued recall of days of the week and months of the year, applied calculations and budget information
Language	Character of speech, fluency, ability to understand and follow simple and complex commands, reading and writing	Cued word retrieval, verbal fluency, vocabulary knowledge, factual knowledge, comprehension of social norms, auditory comprehension, abstract reasoning, sentence repetition
Praxis	Ability to copy a three-dimensional drawing	Ability to mimic acts such as brushing teeth and combing hair
Logic	Simple mathematical problems	Completion of a tower in a limited number of moves, sequencing and matching based on a set pattern of categories, contextual sorting of objects, interpretation of pragmatic statements, completion of word logic puzzle
Neglect	Ability to draw a clock and place the numbers and hands appropriately	Clock drawing, complex figure drawing, ability to pick up an object placed in the midline, ipsilateral space, and contralateral space
Memory	Ability to remember three words over several minutes	Spatial location, facial recognition, complex figure recall, simple shape recognition, verbal list learning, paired association, story recall, recall of pictures, recall of names of people presented visually

Table 14.3

COMMON NEUROLOGICAL DISORDERS IN PATIENTS REFERRED FOR NEUROPSYCHOLOGICAL EVALUATION

PEDIATRIC DISORDERS		ADULT DISORDERS	
Hydrocephalus	Neurotoxic exposure	Vascular disease (e.g, stroke)	Substance abuse
Epilepsy	Traumatic brain injury	Dementia	Lyme disease
Vascular disease	Childhood degenerative disorders	Pseudodementia	Brain tumors
Neurofibromatosis	Autism spectrum disorders	Alzheimer's disease	Amnesia
Down's syndrome	Premature birth/ Low birth weight	Parkinson's dsease	Epilepsy
Sickle cell disease	Brain tumors	Huntington's disease	Aphasia
Childhood cancer		Meningitis	Encephalitis

the likelihood that the neuropsychology practitioner can extract useful information from the examination. Other cases in which a referral to psychiatry or psychology would be more appropriate than a neuropsychology consultation include patients who possess a purely psychiatric disorder without any identifiable neurological underpinnings. For example, a neurologist might evaluate a patient suspected of suffering from epilepsy, only to find that the patient is actually experiencing psychogenic nonepileptic seizures (PNES), or *pseudoseizures*. Pseudoseizures represent a somatoform conversion disorder without a known neurological cause. Patients with primary psychiatric disorders absent from known neurological disease would benefit from an initial consultation with a psychiatrist or clinical psychologist.

Although it is useful to review general guidelines regarding which patients to refer, we believe it is helpful to ground these principles through the presentation and discussion of an actual case. We will continue to use this case throughout the remainder of the chapter, in our discussion of neuropsychological report interpretation. What follows is the history of Mr. X., a patient with epilepsy referred to neuropsychology by his neurologist, as written by the neuropsychologist at the time of consultation.

Case History: Mr. X.

Mr. X. is a 55-year-old, right-handed male with a longstanding history of refractory complex partial seizures. He was referred for a neuropsychological evaluation by his neurologist as part of an initial epilepsy evaluation. Mr. X. began having seizures at 18 years of age. His episodes tend to cluster seasonally or when he is stressed. They are characterized by oral automatisms, hand picking, and loss of contact, with postictal confusion. In recent years, he has fallen during seizures, suffering from two subdural hematomas (both resulting in subdural evacuations 3 years and 1 year ago, respectively). Neuroimaging and electrophysiological results are available. Recent electroencephalogram (EEG) was normal. However, a brain magnetic resonance imaging (MRI) scan in December of last year revealed ventricle enlargement, T_2 signal hyperintensity in the periventricular regions, and subcortical white matter, and left hippocampal sclerosis. His other medical history includes hypertension. Mr. X.'s current medication regimen includes anticonvulsant monotherapy (topiramate, gabapentin, and levetiracetam), metoprolol, and aspirin.

Mr. X. has noticed an increase in cognitive problems over the past few years. Specifically, he mentions having greater difficulty concentrating and focusing. He is distractible and frequently finds his mind wandering. He is also quite concerned about changes in his cognitive functioning, which can impact attention as well. Mr. X. reports increased trouble with his memory, and he specifically reports difficulty remembering supply orders that he handles over the phone at work. To address his problems with memory, Mr. X. has implemented compensatory strategies, such as using spell check on his computer and keeping a dictionary close by. He also tries to write information down soon after it is presented. Finally, Mr. X. reports increased difficulty with spelling and word finding.

Mr. X is self-employed and owns his own electrical supply company. His educational history consists of completing high school, after which he immediately joined the work force. He generally obtained adequate grades in school, with the exception of having to repeat the fifth grade.

Clearly, it was appropriate for Mr. X.'s neurologist to refer him to neuropsychology for several reasons. First, he had been diagnosed with a neurological disorder—complex-partial epilepsy—that is very commonly associated with neurocognitive sequelae. He is also currently taking three neuromodulatory medications (agents directly affecting the central nervous system), which have neurocognitive side effects. Based on his history, it is likely that Mr. X. is already suffering from neurocognitive effects secondary to his disorder, and perhaps also his treatment, including difficulties with concentration, memory, and word finding. This brings us to consider whether or not the timing of this referral is ideal. The timing of this specific referral was influenced by the consideration that Mr. X. may be a candidate for future neurosurgical intervention. However, would it have been beneficial to seek a neuropsychological evaluation earlier in the course of Mr. X.'s disease?

When Is the Right Time to Refer?

The simplest advice regarding when to refer a neurological patient to neuropsychology is that it is never too early. Too often, a neurologist will diagnose a patient with a brain disorder commonly associated with cognitive sequelae, but fail to seek neuropsychological input because cognitive effects have not yet manifested. Only after adverse neurocognitive effects of the disease become apparent will the practitioner seek a consultation. For example, a man with early-stage Parkinson's disease who had been previously functioning at a good cognitive level might only receive a referral from his neurologist after circumstances in his history—such as the loss of a job or a spouse—result in clear socioenvironmental consequences. The disadvantage of this timing is that the neuropsychologist will be unable to assess and document a cognitive *baseline* of the patient to compare to his altered mental state. Without knowing a well-defined cognitive baseline for a particular patient, determining the degree and rate of debilitation can prove challenging, and will result in suboptimal assessment and recommendations for care, to the detriment of the patient. Furthermore, when involved in patient care early, a neuropsychologist can assist in finding services for the patient and in developing an accommodation plan. Therefore, it is important to refer patients diagnosed or highly suspected of having a neurological disorder associated with cognitive sequelae *even before* those symptoms begin to manifest, to permit proper evaluation of the patient's baseline skills. In the case of Mr. X., he would have benefited from referral soon after diagnosis of his complex partial epilepsy, and the subsequent prescription of neuromodulatory agents—even before neurocognitive effects became apparent. This would have allowed the establishment of a neurocognitive baseline to which future changes might be more accurately compared.

It is important to note that although early referral to neuropsychology offers significant benefit, this should not discourage the neurologist from requesting consults for patients with neurocognitive deficits who have not yet been evaluated. When the neuropsychologist is presented with a case involving severe deficits without a documented neuropsychological baseline, he or she can still deduce important information using previous observations of the physician or the patient's own educational history. For example, a different cognitive baseline would likely be assumed for a patient without a high school diploma compared to another with a law degree. Cases referred after the onset of neurocognitive symptoms gain particular benefit from close communication between practitioners, and a more exhaustive description of the patient's neurocognitive decline than might be necessary when a baseline data are available. In short, early referral is best, but borrowing from a popular maxim—"better late than never." These strategies can also contribute positively to a continuity of care-partnership between neurology and neuropsychology.

How Should a Neuropsychology Referral Be Pursued?

A final yet important question regarding the referral is how the neurologist should prepare it in order to ensure that information gained from neuropsychology is clear, useful, and received efficiently and effectively. The neuropsychologist relies on the neurologist, as the referee, to clearly state what he or she hopes to learn from the evaluation. Typically, the referral comes in the form of a fax transmission or electronic transmission through the hospital's in-house system to the neuropsychologist's office. It includes a statement describing the patient's neurocognitive problems and any other neurological disease symptoms. Although it might seem intuitive, care should be taken in making the referral formal and thorough, including all pertinent medical background regarding the case. This will ensure that the neuropsychologist will have sufficient clinical information from the beginning, and avoid delays in evaluation caused by the backup of important documents. In addition to a clear description of the reason for the referral, essential inclusions are the patient's diagnosis, past medical history, social history, neurological exam findings, neuroimaging records and results, electrophysiology or biochemical test results, and details regarding current and past medications used in treatment. If the patient had a neuropsychological evaluation, even if it occurred at a different site, the provider should present this information. Also useful to include are the patient's insurance information and next scheduled follow-up appointment with neurology. Beyond these guidelines, a good way to assimilate all relevant information to include, while omitting extraneous information, is to understand the preparation process used by the neuropsychologist before each evaluation, discussed later in the chapter subsection entitled "How does the neuropsychologist prepare for an evaluation?"

Another decision in making a referral to neuropsychology at many institutions concerns whether to seek a *full evaluation* or simply a *brief consult*. Although a full evaluation—the most common type of assessment performed by neuropsychologists—often includes up to 6 to 8 hours of testing, a shorter 30- to 60-minute evaluation is often available through consultation for in-patients at some hospitals. These brief consultations are useful if the neurologist has a specific question about a patient's neurocognitive status, or detects acute neurocognitive changes in the patient. Albeit less exhaustive than a full evaluation, such consults typically provide the neurologist with immediate (typically in less than 24 hours) feedback from neuropsychology without enduring the lengthy delays often necessary to secure an appointment for a full evaluation and to compile a full report. For patients whose hospital stay is expected to be limited, waiting until after discharge permits a full evaluation in the more controlled setting of the neuropsychologist's outpatient facility. Nevertheless, for patients whose hospital stay is expected to be lengthy and immediate feedback is imperative, requesting a full evaluation in-house is sometimes the best option.

Finally, in preparing a patient for his or her neuropsychological evaluation, it is helpful for the neurologist to clearly communicate that the assessment is an important component of the patient's comprehensive medical care. Indeed, the neuropsychologist is part of the multidisciplinary medical team working toward the overall health and well-being of the patient. If a patient understands that his or her neurologist values the results of the neuropsychological evaluation, he or she will be more likely to put forward a strong effort during what can be a lengthy day of testing, and thus contribute positively to his or her own care.

THE NEUROPSYCHOLOGY REPORT

What Is the Purpose of the Neuropsychological Report?

Up to this point, we have discussed the reasons for and benefits of pursuing a neuropsychology consultation in the care of the neurological patient. Identifying patients who would benefit from the input of neuropsychology and arranging for a neuropsychological evaluation are important steps toward addressing acute or potential neurocognitive deficits in neurological patients. It is also important to have a clear understanding of the resultant reports produced by that evaluation, and incorporate the findings into the care of each patient.

A neuropsychological evaluation can serve a wide variety of purposes. It can be a useful tool in assisting with differential diagnosis of a medical illness, such as progressive dementia or a childhood degenerative disorder. It can also elucidate the magnitude and extent of a person's cognitive deficits in the case of static or chronic neurological disease. Data collected during neuropsychological evaluations are sometimes also used epidemiologically to evaluate the long-term consequences of medical decisions. For instance, neuropsychological data pertaining to particular sets of patients may be collected during clinical trials to parallel the medical benefits or consequences of a particular treatment with the cognitive impact of that treatment.

The neuropsychological report can also help the neurologist better understand the interaction of social-emotional factors and environmental factors that could impact a person's compliance with medication or follow-up care. Thus, the evaluation can have real-world utility for the patient. Of course, brain–behavior relationships differ in children and adults, with or without brain injury. Neuropsychologists are familiar with expected levels of skill acquisition throughout various age groups.

In the case of a child, understanding and defining his or her neurocognitive strengths and weaknesses can help determine appropriate school accommodations and services. For the young, middle-aged, or elderly adult, an evaluation can provide recommendations that can assist in determining appropriate work accommodations or transitional programming and care. Therefore, a neuropsychological report can be modified for a patient of any age to provide recommendations relevant to his or her particular stage of life.

How Does a Neuropsychologist Prepare for an Evaluation?

What happens in between the neurologist's referral and the patient's evaluation? The neuropsychologist first reviews the referral to determine the appropriateness and extent of the evaluation. He or she then collects and reviews other pieces of data available to establish the test plan and clarify the purpose of the assessment. The evaluation is hypothesis driven. To help guide the evaluation, questions and hypotheses are formulated informally based on the diagnoses that the referring neurologist is considering and any documented neurocognitive deficits. The reason for referral provides utility in developing pertinent hypotheses, as it represents the overarching question that will be answered upon completion of the evaluation. For example, if the neuropsychologist receives a referral for a man with epilepsy who is having problems with memory and attention, the physician may state, "the patient is experiencing problems with remembering new information and recalling multistep directions; he is also reporting problems with concentration." This would be informally translated to questions that ask the following, (a) "Are the patient's subjective memory (or attention) complaints evident upon formal standardized assessment?" and (b) "If areas of weakness are visible upon psychometric evaluation, are they related to the patient's medical condition?" These are the overarching questions that provide the framework or context for the evaluation. Secondary hypotheses that can be derived become much more specific, as the neuropsychologist integrates the information about the patient's history or illness. In the above mentioned situation, the neuropsychologist might then ask, "Was the onset of the patient's cognitive problems temporally related to the onset of his medical symptoms?" "Did the person's long-term use of antiepileptic medication or the specific type of antiepileptic medication have an effect on his cognitive abilities?" "Given the person's reported difficulty with memory and attention will he require accommodation or supports in his daily living environment?" "Are there other factors (e.g., emotional problems, crisis in the home) that might impact his performance or level of engagement during the neuropsychological evaluation?" "Are the patient's seizures localized, and if so, are his cognitive problems proximal to the brain regions that show epileptiform discharges?" These questions provide a directed tool to help narrow and delineate relevant areas of assessment.

The development of cognitive impairment can also be assessed by better understanding the person's medical trajectory. Initial data points include the patient's demographic information and history provided. If the patient has had neuroimaging (e.g., magnetic resonance imaging, computed tomography, electroencephalogram [EEG]), electrophysiology (e.g., EEG, EMG), or biochemical tests, these are taken into consideration. In the case of a child's evaluation, understanding the patient's developmental stage and progress is also important in assessing the implications of evaluation results.

One major challenge in evaluating a patient with acute neurocognitive symptoms is that the evaluator must estimate the patient's premorbid functioning. Typically, factors such as education, history of employment, and prior learning disability are used to provide a general estimate. If the patient ever received a previous neuropsychological assessment from another setting, this can provide a less rudimentary sense of the patient's premorbid status. Finally, once the patient is scheduled for an evaluation, a clinical interview with the patient (if lucid or of appropriate age) or a family member (e.g., spouse or parent) provides confirmatory information and sometimes yields new data that may not be available in medical notes. It also provides another data point for understanding the onset and course of the person's neuropsychological symptoms.

Once all data are collected, the neuropsychologist can then develop a hypothesis regarding the range of deficits the patient might have, based on that information. This hypothesis is valuable both preceding and following the formal evaluation, as it guides the assessment plan and interpretation of the patient's performance.

What Is in a Neuropsychology Report and What Does It Mean?

The neuropsychology report typically begins in the past tense, presenting a description of the reason for referral and a summary of the patient's history. An example of a patient history written from the neuropsychologist's perspective was offered previously in the introduction of Mr. X.'s case. Although it might be tempting for the neurologist to skip over the history—a story he or she may already know well—it is important to review it carefully. In order for the neurologist and neuropsychologist to effectively meld their treatment strategies, it is crucial to ensure that both are "on the same page." If the neuropsychologist's interpretation of the patient's history, or perhaps the exact reason for referral, differs from that of the neurologist, it is important for such discrepancies to be identified and addressed. One might interpret a neuropsychologist's recommendations in a very different light if a lack of agreement or miscommunication regarding the patient's status became apparent between the providers.

After the patient history, the neuropsychology report will typically shift into the present tense and highlight the assessment data. All evaluation data and results are broken down into categories to make it easy for both clinicians and families to locate a functional domain that might be of interest. For example, a neurologist may be most interested in the memory and intelligence portion of the assessment because he or she is concerned that the patient might have dementia. Before listing quantitative test results or discussing assessment data, however, the report will detail qualitative information about how the patient presented him or herself on the day of the evaluation. This provides a sense of the reliability and validity of the assessment results, and thus gives a greater indication about the utility of the evaluation as a whole.

To better illustrate these points, we will continue to provide excerpts of the neuropsychology report regarding Mr. X., the patient with epilepsy we introduced previously.

Mr. X. *(continued)*

Behavioral Observations: Mr. X. was well-groomed and friendly upon meeting the examiner. He expressed concern about his cognitive abilities and was anxiously anticipating the evaluation results. He participated in spontaneous and reciprocal conversation. He appeared to be in a neutral mood. Mr. X. periodically became distracted and inattentive during testing. He frequently needed information repeated to him, as he reported having trouble hearing the material. He expressed some frustration during these episodes, but was able to temper his frustration and complete the tasks. Overall, he was able to complete all of the tasks and put forth adequate effort. As such, the results of the evaluation are considered valid and reliable estimates of his current level of function.

These observations provide a description of Mr. X.'s appearance and behavior throughout the evaluation. As in the neurological examination, beginning with simple qualitative impressions can provide valuable preliminary insight into a patient's neurocognitive status. The evaluator also attempts to outline the patient's mood and social interactivity, as well as his or her effort and willingness to engage in the testing. The section usually ends with a statement about the perceived validity of and confidence in the assessment, in the opinion of the neuropsychologist, and purports whether the test results are reliable. This is important, because if a patient presents unable or unwilling to engage in the neuropsychological assessments, the validity of the results can be thrown into serious question. Although Mr. X. seems to have cooperated well with the evaluator throughout, if a patient were accommodating to certain parts of the examination, but not others, this would also be noted in the behavioral observation section of the report, providing useful guidance as to which test results might possess more validity than others.

The next section of the report details the test findings and describes each function or skill set that was being assessed. All test results are combined into sections pertinent to the functions or skills being tested. The order in which the test results are presented is typically at the discretion of the psychologist and tends to vary. In the example of Mr. X., basic functions commonly assessed in a neurological exam—fine motor coordination, speech/language function, and visual-perception—are presented first.

Mr. X. *(continued)*

Fine Motor Function: Mr. X. is right-hand dominant for most writing and drawing activities. His pencil grip is adequate, however, his visual motor skills reflect poor written production. For example, he has difficulty reliably drawing a straight line. Graphomotor speed and coordination is below average, bilaterally. He shows unexpected superiority with the nondominant hand (z-score$_{dominant}$ = -9.50; z-score$_{nondominant}$ = -3.71).

Speech and Language Function: Mr. X.'s spontaneous speech is prosodic, grammatical, and without paraphasic errors. Psychometric assessment reveals intact language function with good confrontation naming and reading. He shows below average performance on a cued verbal fluency when presented with either phonemic/orthographic or semantic cues.

Visual-Perceptual Function: Nonverbal information processing and visual perception are intact. Mr. X.'s current performance on tasks of judgment of line orientation, visual replication, and figure closure are within normal limits.

The format of each functional domain discussed, as seen in the above example, begins with simple, core functions (e.g., qualitative speech [language] and basic shape identification [visual-perception]) and gradually progresses to more complex skills (e.g., cued verbal fluency [language] and closure/integration of shape sequences [visual-perception]). Once basic functions are discussed, the report moves toward discussion of more complicated skill sets. As we see in Mr. X.'s case, although his speech and language retrieval and his visual-perceptual functions are within normal range, he displays prominent weakness in motor skills.

Characterization of *intelligence* is an often debated topic among educators, employers, and clinicians alike. Measurement of the intelligence quotient (IQ) score remains an important part of the neuropsychological evaluation, as it is used to assess and track the cognitive abilities and mental capacity of a patient. We use the term mental *capacity* rather than ability, because the intelligence tests measure both *learned* skills acquired primarily through education as well as *inherent* problem-solving skills more often attributed to core thought processes (although such distinctions are sometimes controversial). The results of Mr. X.'s intelligence tests are summarized next in his report.

Mr. X. *(continued)*

Intellectual Function: Mr. X. demonstrates overall cognitive function that falls in the low average range (Full-Scale IQ = 85; 16th percentile). Although there is no significant disparity between his low average verbal abilities (Verbal IQ = 89; 23rd percentile) and nonverbal abilities (Performance IQ = 83; 13th percentile), further breakdown of his cognitive abilities reveals specific areas of significant weakness. Mr. X. shows strength in his average verbal comprehension skills (Index score = 96; 39th percentile), but his perceptual organization skills continue to fall in the low average range (Index Score = 86; 18th percentile). Mr. X. also has significant weakness on the working memory (Index Score = 69; 2nd percentile) and processing speed (Index Score = 76; 5th percentile) indices, which impact his full-scale IQ score.

Clearly, Mr. X. is functioning broadly within the low average range. He is able to comprehend information, but displays striking weaknesses in working memory as well as processing speed—the rate at which a patient is able to understand and then react to new information appropriately. These are domains that rely heavily on executive function—higher order brain function responsible for planning, abstraction, and the initiation of appropriate actions while inhibiting inappropriate action. Thus, the neuropsychologist decides to specifically address executive function in the report.

Mr. X. (continued)

Executive Function: Assessment of executive functions reveals areas of weakness. He shows good cognitive flexibility, planning, and organization. He shows deficiency in his speed of information processing and complex working memory. Despite Mr. X.'s slow speed in processing information, he makes frequent careless errors. He has trouble maintaining focus and problems with response inhibition.

The executive system, which is typically linked neuroanatomically to the prefrontal cortex, encompasses skills that allow a person to successfully manage and maintain control over daily function. Skill sets within the executive system include organization, planning, problem solving, cognitive flexibility, working memory, processing speed, and execution (the initiation of an action). It is possible that in the case of Mr. X., deterioration of executive function precipitated a decline in measures of intellectual capacity. This example elucidates an important principle in neuropsychology and neurology: Complex skills rely on multiple systems to function effectively.

Findings suggesting executive system dysfunction will be of particular interest to the neurologist as a care-provider, as they can dramatically impact a patient's ability to manage his or her own medical condition. Other cognitive skills that hold particular relevance to the patient's capability for self care include verbal and visual memory skills—the next measurements of neurocognitive function addressed in Mr. X.'s report.

Mr. X. *(continued)*

Memory Function: Memory assessment reveals additional areas of weakness. With regard to verbal memory performance, Mr. X. performs in the low average range on a verbal list-learning task (CVLT-II Total Learning T-Score = 37) during the acquisition phase. His short- and long-term recall of information falls below average. With support, he is able to select the appropriate word from a list of target and foil items. He shows susceptibility to retroactive interference (which means that newly learned information disrupts the recall of previously learned material). He often makes repetition errors when recalling words from the list. Mr. X. has similar difficulty on a rote list-learning task, the verbal Seashore Rhythm Test (SRT) that does not contain semantically related words. He obtains a z-score of -2.93, which signifies impairment. His recall of a story read aloud is below average as well. Mr. X.'s visual memory performance suggests mixed results. His visual SRT (z-score $= -4.16$) is impaired. A measure of spatial localization, in which he is asked to recall the location of various dots, also reflects deficiency (z-score$_{\text{Short Delay}} = -1.71$; z-score$_{\text{Long Delay}} = -2.44$; z-score$_{\text{Recognition}} = -2.97$). However, Mr. X. shows strength in his ability to recall a complex figure drawing (69th percentile), performing at high average. His performance on a facial recognition task is intact following a short delay and is impaired following a long delay.

Clearly, memory appears to be a considerable area of weakness for Mr. X. The extensive testing of verbal and visual memory completed during the examination illustrates a point discussed previously: Specific aspects of the neuropsychological assessment directly complement and extend on measurements performed by the neurologist during a standard mental status exam. Although brief memory assessments used in a neurology-office visit might not have revealed the full extent of Mr. X.'s deficits, the neuropsychological report contributes novel and detailed descriptions of memory-related problems in this patient.

Emotional factors are also useful to consider when treating a neurological patient. Although the neuropsychological assessment for medical patients does not provide the *personality assessment* that a full psychological assessment might, it does include a brief screen to help the neurologist determine whether or not the patient's psychological status might require further evaluation, and additional consultations. Furthermore, symptoms of depression and emotional instability can sometimes precede more severe neurological compromise, and are thus deserving of close attention. There are differences in the behavioral and emotional assessments typically used to evaluate children versus adults. In the case of a child, more emphasis is given to psychometric or projective measures, and depending on the patient's age, parental interviews can also be useful. In contrast, self-report is the most common method of assessing an adult's emotional status. As will be seen, Mr. X. does not report any significant concern regarding his emotional status, although he does report distress about his health, which is, unfortunately, quite common among patients with serious neurological illness.

Mr. X. *(continued)*

Emotional Function: According to Mr. X.'s endorsements on a self-report measure of emotional distress (the Personality Assessment Screener) he expresses concern about his health. This is common in a medically compromised group.

In the next section of the neuropsychological report, we will discuss assessment of what is termed "adaptive living skills," and it can be incorporated into the evaluation of either a child or an adult. It provides useful information if there is concern regarding whether or not the patient can live independently without support. Among elderly adults, if a patient is rated poorly on this type of scale, or is deemed unable to comply with his or her current medical treatments, assisted living support or home bound services may be considered. In a child, this assessment can help to determine potential areas in which the patient may benefit from targeted supportive services, in an effort to address specific deficits while looking ahead. As the individual progresses in age, the focus may shift from continued improvement in a deficient skill to supportive services intended to offset the real-world consequences of the deficiency. It is not uncommon to interview other individuals close to the patient, given the patient's permission, to help compile an accurate and thorough adaptive assessment. In the case of Mr. X., both he and his wife were interviewed and completed adaptive behavioral assessments, as reported here.

Mr. X. *(continued)*

Adaptive Behavioral Function: Mr. X.'s wife rated him on adaptive living skills by completing the Vineland Adaptive Behavior Scales (second edition). Her endorsements yield average scores across all scales. Specifically, she notes that he has average skills in communication (e.g., receptive and expressive), daily living (e.g., personal care, domestic ability, and community involvement), and motor function (e.g., gross and fine motor function). In addition, Mr. X. completed components of the Independent Living Scales. He displays appropriate knowledge of specific uses of money, the importance of paying bills, and the purpose of having health insurance. He also displays an understanding of why a legal will is important and that it is imperative to read documents before signing them. He shows understanding of the reason he might receive a social security check. Mr. X. has a good sense of prices for basic grocery store items. In general, he is able to think of alternative ways to solve basic problems in everyday situations (e.g., lights shut off, heat does not work, repairs needed for the home, accidental injury).

Fortunately, Mr. X. seems adequately adapted to living at home, and benefits from additional support provided by his wife, making assisted living arrangements unnecessary at this time.

The final portion of the neuropsychology report is the impressions and recommendations section. It provides a comprehensive summary of the qualitative impressions and test results produced by the evaluation, and it may incorporate behavioral, neurocognitive, and historical factors as basis for the neuropsychologist's conclusions. It may also address diagnostic clarification if deemed necessary. Recommendations regarding future medical management and life strategies are typically offered.

Clearly, it is important for the neurologist to pay particular attention to the impressions and recommendations section. Although some practitioners prefer to read this section first, it is important to avoid the temptation to read only these conclusions and skip the rest of the report. The final section sets the framework within which assessment results should be interpreted, but it does not replace the core data points collected in the evaluation—some of which may not be addressed in the conclusions, and some of which the neurologist might interpret differently than the neuropsychologist.

The conclusion of Mr. X.'s report is shown here. We suggest comparing the impressions and recommendations that his neuropsychologist reports with those you might have formulated while reading through the various aspects of his report in order to best understand how the evaluator reached these conclusions.

Mr. X: Conclusion

Impressions and Recommendations: Overall, results of the current evaluation reflect intact cognitive functioning, with specific weakness in the memory domains. Regarding both the visual and verbal memory, Mr. X. shows good recognition when presented with cues, but he has difficulty effectively storing and retrieving new information over time. Graphomotor speed, coordination, and visual motor integration are deficient. Additionally, Mr. X. shows weakness in aspects of executive functioning including complex working memory, initiation/processing information, and attention. This neurocognitive pattern is often seen in individuals with frontotemporal dysfunction. Given his widespread weakness on memory measures, bilateral temporal dysfunction is likely.

If Mr. X. continues to have concerns about his memory, he can try behavioral strategies to assist in the recall of information. For example, when learning new information, Mr. X. should attempt to first understand the overall concepts and then work toward learning specific details. Mnemonic techniques (developing rhymes, songs, and sentences with the first letters or words of the new information) can be useful learning strategies. The method of loci may also be useful. This technique incorporates visualization or imagery by selecting a location or common path and identifying landmarks or objects along that path. The landmarks/objects are then associated with components of the new information to be remembered.

It is encouraging that Mr. X. performed adequately in the adaptive behavioral assessment, displaying a level of independence seemingly satisfactory enough to continue his current living situation with his wife. However, it is a concern that he continues to hold significant professional responsibilities in the face of his cognitive decline, and it might be suggested that he begin to relinquish these.

It will also be helpful for Mr. X. to maintain good organization and grouping of information to ensure that material is being encoded effectively, and to create an activity schedule in a logical order that enhances efficiency. There are many organizational systems (e.g., electronic organizers, computer calendars, notepads, and sticky notes) available to assist adults in recalling appointments and activities. It is important to participate in "mental exercise" throughout different stages of life to stimulate viable neural networks in the brain. Therefore, Mr. X. should be encouraged to challenge himself with activities such as reading, puzzles, games, and learning new skills. When considering any of these compensatory strategies, it is helpful to remain positive and stay motivated—a negative attitude and feelings of self-doubt can present as a barrier to cognitive improvement.

No additional follow-up has been planned at this time. However, we remain available for additional consultation as needed.

In considering the conclusions made regarding Mr. X., it is important for his neurologist to carefully consider any recommendations made. The a final goal of the summary section is not to provide a strict "to-do" list for the neurologist, but rather to convey a sense of the utility of the neuropsychological assessments performed. It is critical that results not be over-interpreted or taken out of the limited context within which they were produced. The neuropsychological evaluation is an important aspect of a patient's diagnostic framework, but should be considered alongside the neurologist's examination, neuroimaging results, electrophysiological and biochemical results, and the history of the patient and family. If a patient does have specific questions about his or her neuropsychological evaluation results, it is often beneficial to encourage him or her to contact the neuropsychologist, allowing direct communication of information with which the neuropsychologist has expertise and familiarity.

CONCLUSIONS

It is our hope that this discussion helps to foster a better understanding of the value and utility of referring a neurological patient for a neuropsychological evaluation, and serves as a useful guide for neurologists on how to better extract important information from the neuropsychological report. We believe that neuropsychologists can serve a vital role in the care of neurological patients, particularly those at high risk of developing neurocognitive sequelae related to their diagnosis, and also those within which the diagnosis remains unknown. Neuropsychological evaluations can truly complement neurological and medical treatment by providing extensive cognitive assessments, leading to recommendations that significantly improve the everyday functionality of many patients. Encouraging professional dialog between neurologists and neuropsychologists and a better understanding of their distinct but complementary roles will lead to further improvement of the medical and neurocognitive health of patients treated in the clinical neurosciences.

SUGGESTED READING

AANC. (2007). American Academy of Clinical Neuropsychology (AACN) practice guidelines for neuropsychological assessment and consultation. *Clinical Neuropsycholy, 21,* 209–231.

Baron, I. S. (2004). *Neuropsychological evaluation of the child.* New York: Oxford University Press.

Baron, I. S., Fennell, E. B., & Voeller, K. K. S. (Eds.). (1995). *Pediatric neuropsychology in the medical setting.* New York: Oxford University Press.

Cunningham, M. G., Goldstein, M., Katz, D., O'Neil, S. Q., Joseph, A., & Price, B. (2006). Coalescence of psychiatry, neurology, and neuropsychology: From theory to practice. *Harvard Review of Psychiatry, 14,* 127–140.

Goldstein, L. H., & McNeil, J. E. (Eds.). (2004). *Clinical neuropsychology: A practical guide to assessment and management for clinicians.* West Sussex, UK: Wiley.

Iverson, G. L., Brooks, B. L., White, T., & Stern, R. A. (2007). Neuropsychological assessment battery: Introduction and advanced interpretation. In A. Horton & D. Wedding (Eds.), *The neuropsychology handbook* (3rd ed., pp. 281–346). New York: Springer Publishing Company.

Lezak, M. D. (1995). *Neuropsychological assessment.* New York: Oxford University Press..

Mitrushina, M., Boone, K. B., Razanni, J., & D'Ella, L. F. (2005). *Handbook of normative data for neuropsychological assessment.* New York: Oxford University Press.

Morgan, J. E., & Ricker, J. H. (Eds.). (2008). *Textbook of clinical neuropsychology.* New York: Taylor & Francis.

Schoenberg, M. R., & Scott, J. G. (2009). *The black book of neuropsychology: A syndrome-based approach.* Heidelberg, Germany: Springer.

Spreen, O., Risser, A. H., & Edgell, D. (1995). *Developmental neuropsychology* (3rd ed.). New York: Oxford University Press.

Spreen, O., & Strauss, E. (1998). *A compendium of neuropsychological tests: Administration, norms, and commentary* (2nd ed.). New York: Oxford University Press.

Stringer, A. Y., & Nadolne, M. J. (2000). Neuropsychological assessment: Contexts for contemporary clinical practice. In G. Groth-Marnat (Ed.), *Neuropsychological assessment in clinical practice* (pp. 26–47). New York: Wiley.

Walsh, K., & Darby, D. (1999). *Neuropsychology: A clinical approach.* Edinburgh, UK: Churchhill Livingstone.

Yeates, K. O., Ris, M. D., & Taylor, H. G. (1995). Hospital referral patterns in pediatric neuropsychology. *Child Neuropsychology, 1,* 56–62.

WEB SITES

National Academy of Neuropsychology—http://www.nanonline.org/NAN/home/home.aspx

Neuropsychology Central—http://www.neuropsychologycentral.com/

The American Academy of Clinical Neuropsychology—http://www.theaacn.org/

The International Neuropsychological Society—http://www.the-ins.org/index.cfm

15 The Neurorehabilitation Psychologist

MARY R. HIBBARD, DAVID E. LAYMAN,
AND ROBERT K. STEWART, JR.

This chapter describes the roles and functions of those licensed psychologists, who by prior training and clinical experience, practice neurorehabilitation psychology, a specialty combining theoretical underpinnings of both clinical neuropsychology and rehabilitation psychology. This new specialty has emerged over the past 3 decades to address the complex treatment needs of individuals and families coping with the many cognitive (thinking), emotional, and behavioral challenges resulting from either a brain injury or other neurological conditions. Neurorehabilitation psychologists work in a wide variety of inpatient, outpatient, and community-based rehabilitation settings, which means they work closely with a multidisciplinary team of rehabilitation professionals. Neurorehabilitation psychologists administer neuropsychological, behavioral, and emotional assessments in order to determine clinical diagnosis and plan subsequent neurorehabilitation and psychological interventions. In this chapter, we introduce a conceptual model of neurorehabilitation interventions, entitled "The ABCs of Neurorehabilitation Issues and Interventions." The ABC model provides a framework that describes the repertoire of neurorehabilitation psychologists, the diversity of clinical issues that they address, and the scope of holistic interventions that they are uniquely qualified to provide. This ABC model is illustrated via a series of three fictitious case examples that describe the varied roles of the neurorehabilitation psychologist when working with individuals in both inpatient and outpatient rehabilitation settings.

NEURORHEABILITATION PSYCHOLOGY: ROLES AND FUNCTIONS

A specialty within psychology is a defined area in the practice of psychology by licensed psychologists. The specialty connotes competency acquired through an organized sequence of formal doctoral-level education, and supervised clinical training and experiences at both the internship and postdoctoral level of training. Over the past 3 decades, this new specialty has emerged from two branches of psychology, rehabilitation psychology and clinical neuropsychology, in order to address the complex treatment needs of individuals and their family members coping with the many challenges that emerge after brain injury and/or as a result of other neurological conditions. Diller (1987) used the term *neuropsychological rehabilitation* to describe the focused work of this new subspecialty. A growing literature now supports the conceptual utility of neuropsychological rehabilitation (see Leon-Carrion, 1997; Meier, Benton, & Diller, 1987; Prigatano, 1999; Prigatano, 2008; Wilson & Zangwill, 2003). In this chapter, the focused expertise of psychologists specialized in the delivery of neuropsychological rehabilitation services will be highlighted; these clinicians hereafter will be referred to as *neurorehabilitation psychologists.*

Neurorehabilitation psychologists focus on the assessment and treatment of individuals with acquired brain injury within the context of patients' lives, placing an emphasis on the multidetermined nature of their physical, cognitive, behavioral, and emotional difficulties. Diller (1987) considered this approach an *ecological* perspective in which the complex relationship between the environment and the individual is examined. Neurorehabilitation psychologists are proficient in the assessment of cognitive, behavioral *and* emotional functioning, as well as in the delivery of psychotherapeutic *and* neurocognitive interventions. Guided by a contextual model of health and illness, neurorehabilitation psychologists view identified neurological *impairments* as the injury or the illness, the functional activity limitations and participation restrictions as *disabilities*, and the resultant social and environmental barriers and disadvantages as the *handicaps* for the individuals served (World Health Organization, 2001). When seen through this ecological lens, interventions are selected to reduce disability and handicaps in personally meaningful ways.

Neurorehabilitation psychologists typically are employed within rehabilitation medicine departments of hospitals and medical centers, free standing rehabilitation facilities, and the Department of Defense or Veterans Affairs health systems. Other neurorehabilitation psychologists may be employed in community-based facilities such as assisted-living, subacute- or long-term-care facilities, as well as community agencies serving individuals with acquired cognitive disabilities. All neurorehabilitation psychologists routinely advocate for individuals with brain injury within institutional, community, and federal systems.

REFERRALS FOR NEUROPSYCHOLOGICAL SERVICES

Neurorehabilitation psychologists routinely receive referrals to treat individuals across the life span who present with new onset and/or lifelong neurological challenges that have a negative impact on the patient's everyday functioning and quality of life. Typically, these individuals present with varied neurological conditions, such as: (a) an acquired brain injury (e.g., traumatic brain injury, stroke, brain tumor, seizure disorder, hypoxia/anoxia); (b) a degenerative neurological disorder (e.g., Parkinson disease, multiple sclerosis, dementia); (c) a medical condition associated with the onset of cognitive disorder (e.g.. chemotherapy side effects, HIV, metabolic disturbances); and (d) a developmental disorder (e.g., mental retardation, autism) and/or (e) psychiatric conditions with cognitive challenges (e.g., schizophrenia).

Referral questions for neurorehabilitation psychologists across both inpatient and outpatient settings typically include: "What are the individual's cognitive, emotional and behavioral strengths and weaknesses?" and "What interventions can be provided for this individual and his/her family to enhance behavioral functioning and quality of life?"

Common diagnoses of those referred for neuropsychological services include those individuals who have experienced an acquired brain injury secondary to (a) a newly acquired neurological disorder, such as a stroke, brain tumor, or Parkinson disease, (b) a sports (e.g., contact sports, diving, skiing, biking without protective headgear) or motor vehicle accident (e.g., motor vehicle, motorcycle and all terrain accidents), or (c) a trauma to the brain secondary to falls, domestic violence, child abuse or substance-related (e.g., falls while intoxicated, cocaine-related strokes) injuries. Other referrals may include individuals who have experienced an hypoxia/anoxia event (e.g., secondary to an unsuccessful suicide attempt, near drowning, etc.) or medical and/or psychiatric conditions that may have resulted in unexpected cognitive or behavioral challenges. With the "graying" of America, neurorehabilitation psychologists are increasingly involved in assisting older individuals adjust to the cognitive challenges of normal aging. Likewise, the diverse skills of neurorehabilitation psychologists are being called upon in the treatment of veterans returning from armed conflicts overseas who present with complex neurological and emotional disabilities.

In this chapter, we limit our discussion to the roles and functions of neurorehabilitation psychologists working within either inpatient or outpatient rehabilitation settings.

■ **Inpatient neurorehabilitation psychologists** typically are referred individuals who present with a neurological injury or illness that impairs cognitive, emotional, or behavioral functioning, or are admitted with nonneurological diagnoses, but evidence cognitive or behavioral difficulties that limit their ability to profit from rehabilitation efforts. Inpatient neurorehabilitation psychologists also work within a rehabilitation team treating individuals emerging from coma or vegetative states. In contrast, individuals referred to *outpatient* neurorehabilitation psychologists typically are attempting to cope with often dramatic changes in thinking, personality, and/or behaviors secondary to neurological conditions. These individuals may be referred immediately from an acute hospital setting or from institutions that provide less intensive rehabilitation efforts (i.e., subacute rehabilitation facilities). Such referrals are made to ensure that gains made in inpatient rehabilitation are maintained while individuals transition back into the community.

■ **Outpatient neurorehabilitation psychologists** typically are referred individuals from several community-based sources. Community-based referrals to the outpatient neuropsychologist come from varied sources: (a) medical care providers (including physicians specializing in primary care, rehabilitation medicine, neurology, and psychiatry) who either identify a medical or neurological condition that has resulted in new onset cognitive/behavioral difficulties requiring further assessment and treatment and/or who seek clarification as to a specific medical diagnosis; (b) rehabilitation service providers (including occupational and physical therapists, speech–language pathologists, case managers, and social workers) who seek guidance in approaches to best provide rehabilitation services in the presence of cognitive or behavioral challenges for an individual; (c) significant others (including partners, family members, friends, and employers) who note thinking or behavioral changes that appear out of character for the individual; and (d) the individuals themselves who often times experience unexplained and distressing changes in their cognitive or behavioral functioning without a clear understanding of why these changes are occurring. Individuals may be referred months or years postonset of the neurological injury or medical condition.

NEUROREHABILITATION PSYCHOLOGICAL ASSESSMENT

Both clinical neuropsychologists and neurorehabilitation psychologists provide neuropsychological assessments. Both sets of professionals routinely administer neuropsychological tests and use data obtained from these assessments to determine an individual's cognitive abilities and limitations in multiple areas of thinking, such as attention, reasoning, problem solving, speed of verbal and motor processing, memory, visuospatial functioning, language expression and comprehension, and mood. The scope of assessment will depend on the nature and severity of the injury/medical condition, the time since injury/medical condition onset, and the specific referral question. The neurorehabilitation psychologist typically expands his or her assessment battery to include an evaluation of an individual's ability to cope, his/her overall adjustment, and his/her behavioral functioning. The impact of pre-existing personality factors that may have an impact on an individual's ability to profit from rehabilitation efforts, is also considered. Family member observations are routinely integrated into assessment. This holistic assessment allows for the development of a broader array of recommendations related to the impact of a disability on an individual, his or her family, and quality of life—paving the way for development of broad-based rehabilitation interventions to enhance overall functioning.

Neurorehabilitation psychologists' assessments will differ depending on the clinical setting where the assessment occurs:

■ **Inpatient neurorehabilitation psychology assessment**: Inpatient neurorehabilitation psychologists assess individuals early in the process of their recovery, with dramatic fluctuations in cognition and behavior, varying levels of frustration tolerance, and altered attentional capacity. Any or all of these factors preclude extensive assessments. Brief screening tools are used to evaluate cognitive, emotional, and behavioral functioning. The emphasis is placed on rapid and concise identification of cognitive and behavioral strengths and weaknesses allowing for timely, integrated treatment plans to be developed for rehabilitation interventions. This information is provided via factual and functional recommendations for individuals, their family members, and other rehabilitation professionals. Although inpatient neurorehabilitation psychology assessments may appear fairly straightforward (i.e., administration of brief tests of cognitive functions and mood to obtain clinical information about patient's current functioning), in practice objective tests are meshed with behavioral observations to determine clinical impressions and the most appropriate interventions. Neuropsychological and emotional screenings provide a "snapshot" of individual cognitive abilities and limitations as well as psychological adjustment, and serve as a baseline for retesting and treatment in inpatient, and/or subsequent outpatient, settings. Repeatable measures with alternate forms of tests are often used, thereby allowing for the tracking of functional gains over brief time intervals. For example, individuals emerging from coma are typically assessed using repeat assessments aimed at monitoring changes in level of sensory and behavioral responses, allowing for rapid shifting of treatment approaches to match changes in the mental status of these individuals.

Inpatient neurorehabilitation psychologists may also be referred individuals who present with unexpected cognitive deficits that are unrelated or unexpected given their admitting diagnosis. For example, an older individual admitted for rehabilitation after a fractured hip who presents with significant memory difficulties that interfere with the ability to learn new rehabilitation techniques. In such situations, neurorehabilitation psychologists might employ a wider range of neuropsychological tests to determine the underlying reasons for observed cognitive difficulties; they would then provide feedback to the rehabilitation team, individuals, and their families regarding potential underlying diagnoses and needed interventions. Finally, neurorehabilitation psychologists are often called upon to assess competency issues, as well as safety concerns, that may impact an individual's return to independent living in the community.

■ **Outpatient neurorehabilitation psychology assessment:** Outpatient neuropsychological evaluations will vary from focused brief assessments to comprehensive neuropsychological evaluations. Neurorehabilitation psychologists exercise judgment in test selection, being careful to consider the referral question, the nature of the presenting condition, individual tolerance and motivation, and treatment considerations and resources. For individuals roughly 6 months or less postdiagnosis, and/or those individuals recently transitioned from the inpatient to outpatient settings, brief evaluations using repeatable measures may be preferred. Brief assessments allow for rapid determination of an individual's cognitive, behavioral, and interpersonal strengths and weaknesses allowing for timely interventions. Modified batteries may be required for individuals with specific neurological syndromes that limit testing abilities, such as impaired speech, sensory and/or motor loss, or language/cultural barriers. For individuals greater than 6 months postdiagnosis, or for those who present with specific referral issues (e.g., determining the individual's ability to return to school or work), comprehensive neuropsychological evaluations may be appropriate. In-depth neuropsychological assessments focus on a greater breadth of cognitive abilities with more extensive assessment tools used; these assessments typically include intellectual and select academic abilities, review of prior medical/school records, and interview with family members.

Regardless of inpatient or outpatient referral source, neuropsychological test results establish a "blueprint" for targeted cognitive, emotional, and behavioral interventions needed as well as alternative services to be considered. Routinely, test findings are shared with examinees and their family members as "feedback" and are reported to the rehabilitation team. The cognitive, emotional, and behavioral strengths and weaknesses, resulting functional implications, and treatment recommendations are personalized and presented in a practical "consumer friendly" manner (Mateer & Sira, 2008). Recommendations usually include interventions to be rendered by neurorehabilitation psychologists and specific referrals to other professional resources.

NEUROREHABILITATION PSYCHOLOGY INTERVENTIONS

A conceptual model entitled "The ABCs of Neurorehabilitation Psychology Issues and Interventions" is presented to illustrate the diversity of issues addressed and interventions within the repertoire of neurorehabilitation psychologists. The ABCs model includes: Adjustment-based psychotherapy, Behavior-based interpersonal skills building, Compensatory skills building, Cognitive remediation, and Consultation and advocacy. Although the ABCs model is not meant to be an exhaustive list of interventions, it provides the reader with a rapid overview of key issues addressed and treatment "tools" employed by neurorehabilitation psychologists. Using a holistic approach to treatment intervention, neurorehabilitation psychologists interpret test findings within the context of a given individual's life (e.g., behavioral idiosyncrasies, family dynamics, community resources) moving flexibly in and out of a psychological and neurocognitive intervention focus. The overarching aims of interventions are to minimize the impacts of impairment, disability, and handicap upon functioning, to enhance individual quality of life and maximize community reintegration. Typically, the neurorehabilitation psychologists will opt to employ a mix of individual, family and group modalities to deliver these interventions. The ABCs model is described in detail below and is depicted in Table 15.1. The **A** of the **ABCs** model is *Adjustment-based psychotherapy*. Adjustment-based psychotherapy remains at the heart of all subsequent therapeutic processes, serving as both the umbrella and the net for the **B** and **Cs** of interventions. It is typically the starting and ending point of all clinical interventions. The process of coping with an unexpected disability or handicap is often daunting and threatening and these individuals often have little or no experience with the mental health system before the onset of their condition. Therefore, the establishment of trusting alliances with individuals is critical to the neurorehabilitation process. Initial efforts are directed at normalizing the experiences of new disability and the difficulty of sharing these experiences with professionals.

Adjustment-based psychotherapy provides the framework for openness, validation, and motivation that enables individuals to address

Table 15.1

THE ABCs MODEL OF NEUROREHABILITATION ISSUES AND INTERVENTIONS

	A	*B*	*Cs*	
MODALITIES:	ADJUSTMENT-BASED PSY-CHOTHERAPY	BEHAVIOR-BASED INTER-PERSONAL SKILLS BUILDING	COGNITIVE REMEDIATION COMPENSA-TORY SKILLS BUILDING	CONSULTATION AND ADVOCACY
Issues addressed	Loss and mourning Altered sense of self and identity Altered role Reduced awareness Body image Motivation and follow through	Emotional dysregulation Communication dysregulation Impaired social pragmatics Impulsivity Initiation problems Poor safety awareness Error-prone behavior	Arousal/ alertness Disoriented Poor attention Problem solving strategies Flexible thinking Abstract thinking skills Rigid thinking Disorganization	Multiple treatment providers Communica- tion challenges Ethical Issues Cultural considerations
Interventions provided	Disability normalization Increasing awareness Facilitation of grief and loss Facilitate home and commu- nity re- integration Validation of emotion Cognitive restructuring Reconstruction of self- identity Goal development Relaxation training	Managing emo- tional expression Enhancing com- munication Enhancing self monitoring Managing physical/ cognitive consequences Developing self- regulation Establishing structure and routine Optimizing error- detection and correction	Education about cognitive strengths and weaknesses Re-orientation Attention training Organization and Planning Skills Memory enhancing techniques Verbal fluency skills Use of compensa- tory tools	Ongoing feedback: patient/family Ongoing feed- back: rehabil- itation team Ongoing feed- back: referral source Consultation with legal/dis- ability/work or school systems Advocacy for pa- tient rights and in- dependence

new and potentially lifelong challenges. Individual psychotherapeutic approaches are variable and often integrated (Cicerone & Fraser, 1999; Coetzer, 2006; Langer, Laatsch, & Lewis, 1999; Prigatano, 2008). Emphasis may be placed on helping individuals and their families understand the cognitive underpinnings of altered mood, behavioral issues, and the process of adjustment to grief and loss. Group psychotherapy interventions are another efficient and effective Adjustment-based intervention using a semistructured process-oriented atmosphere for self-expression, emotional validation, and peer feedback. Clinical interventions addressing issues related to loss of independence, grief of former self, and adjusting to the emerging self are a core focus of treatment.

The **B** of the **ABCs** refers to *Behavior-based interventions* aimed at maladaptive actions, reduced interpersonal skills, or social pragmatics, common problems after acquired brain injury (e.g., Alderman, 2004; Morton & Wehman, 1995; Prigatano, 1999; Ylvisaker, Turkstra, & Coelho, 2005). Neuropsychological assessment findings, combined with observations of family and treating clinicians, shape both the priorities and approaches to behavioral change. Clinical interventions target maladaptive behaviors with the goal of developing adaptive behaviors and improving interpersonal skills within the context of individual, family, and group therapy settings. Behavioral and environmental modifications are major components of this approach. Group modalities are often used because they allow for peer feedback from individuals with similar challenges, thus raising an individual's awareness of his/her altered behaviors and the impact of these behaviors on others.

Several **Cs** make up the **ABCs** model of a neurorehabilitation psychology issues and interventions: *Cognitive remediation, Compensation-skills training,* and *Consultation and advocacy*. Cognitive remediation aims to bolster diminished cognitive capacities with interventions directed toward helping the individual remaster basic building blocks of thinking such as orientation, attention, memory, language skills, processing speed, organization and flexible problem solving, with the goal of promoting neurological recovery and reorganization (see Ponsford, 2004; Sohlberg & Mateer, 2001). For example, use of cognitive retraining materials, such as attention training tasks, may be used to enhance fundamental attention abilities, while at the same time the neurorehabilitation psychologist provides immediate error-correcting feedback as a way to increase an individual's awareness of newly acquired cognitive difficulty.

Compensatory-skills building involves use of strategies to help individuals "work around" their cognitive difficulties, thereby increasing functioning. For example, an individual may be taught to use a memory book[1] to compensate for known problems with memory, planning or organization, thereby permitting a greater sense of individual control about current, past, and future activities.

Consultation and advocacy are key roles for neurorehabilitation psychologists. Individuals receiving rehabilitation services typically are treated by multiple professionals who directly benefit from information obtained by neuropsychological assessment; these professionals may include rehabilitation physicians (physiatrists), speech/language pathologists, occupational therapists, physical therapists, psychiatrists, and nurses. Finally, neurorehabilitation psychologists advocate for ethically sound, culturally sensitive interventions, and needed community services. This may take the form of a presentation to a school council on section 504 of the Rehabilitation Act of 1973 emphasizing the importance of eliminating environmental handicaps for students with cognitive disabilities, or educating a business owner about the Americans with Disabilities Act (ADA; 2009) by outlining the benefits of reasonable work accommodations.

THE ABCs OF ISSUES AND INTERVENTIONS WITHIN AN INPATIENT REHABILITATION SETTING

As depicted in the *ABCs* model (see Table 15.1), primary roles for neurorehabilitation psychologists in the *inpatient* rehabilitation setting are to assist individuals and their families in their adjustment to the turbulent nature of an acute onset disability and its resultant physical, cognitive, and behavioral difficulties. Moving from a general hospital setting to an inpatient rehabilitation setting is often a period of hope and optimism for individuals and their family members; however, this transition period may also be a time of turmoil, loss, and despair as individuals and their families suddenly confront often dramatic changes in the individuals' personality, level of independence, behaviors, and cognitive abilities. Not uncommon, individuals suffer with reactive depression and anxiety, two negative emotional states that can interfere with physical and functional recovery, diminish functional independence, heighten reports of pain, slow cognitive recovery, and result in overall poorer adjustment to disability and longer hospitalizations (for example, see Hibbard et al., 2004; Paolucci et al., 1999; Seel et al., 2003). Early identification and Adjustment-based psychotherapy interventions of these negative mood states, no matter how understandable or expected, are essential roles of neurorehabilitation psychologists. Adjustment-based psychotherapy for families is a front-line intervention. Family members are provided emotional support as well as education about cognitive dysfunctions, effects on behavior and personality, and the common paths to recovery and healing.

Neurorehabilitation psychologists also play a key role in preparing both individuals and their family members for discharge to the next level of care and/or return to the community. This transition, although often anticipated by individuals and their family members as a sign of return to "normalcy," may be disruptive and difficult to manage. Family members may inadvertently undermine the adaptation process through their overoptimistic beliefs that returning home will result in restoration to prediagnosis functioning. Individual factors such as reduced awareness of deficits, loss of structure, and/or difficulty adjusting to changes in the environment often makes the transition equally difficult for the individual. Psychoeducation for individuals and their family members minimizes unrealistic expectations (often termed "magical thinking") and sets the groundwork for needed interventions in the transition phase.

A second focus of neurorehabilitation interventions in the inpatient setting involves the management of behavioral issues that frequently arise as individuals emerge from coma states. Neurorehabilitation psychologists play an important role in reducing agitation and restlessness by use of Behavior-based interventions minimizing and controlling environmental stimulation. Sensory and fatigue thresholds are identified and the immediate environment is modified to minimize effects of extraneous and unpleasant sensory stimulation. Behavioral interventions may be required when working with families in an effort to keep in check a natural tendency to overwhelm individuals with stimulation. The inpatient rehabilitation psychologist also sees many "difficult," demanding, and noncompliant individuals who frequently challenge the authority and expertise of the multidisciplinary staff. In these situations, neurorehabilitation psychologists differentiate behaviors attributable to cognitive impairment from behaviors associated with preexisting personality traits; they provide education and guidance to staff on how best to manage these elements of care.

Ameliorating cognitive challenges through use of Cognitive remediation and Compensatory strategies is the third role of neurorehabilitation psychologists. Cognitive interventions are implemented in a hierarchical manner depending upon individuals' levels of deficit, working under the theoretical assumption that lower-order cognitive proficiencies are requisite for higher-order cognitive processes (Ponsford, 2004). For individuals in coma or minimally conscious states, the neurorehabilitation psychologist provides specific sensory stimulation aimed at increasing frequency and consistency of a specific sensory response. In contrast, for an oriented individual with relatively preserved memory, but difficulties with planning and organization, interventions might focus on rebuilding these more complex executive skills through higher-level remediation.

Inpatient neurorehabilitation psychologists' use of Compensatory tools in treatment frequently involves the introduction of "work around" strategies. For example, as mentioned above, individuals with memory deficits would be introduced to the use of a "memory book" that would likely serve them throughout outpatient treatment and possibly throughout the rest of their lives. Another compensatory strategy might involve teaching individuals with left-side visual neglect to read using a visual anchor on the left-side margin of text. Neurorehabilitation psychologists routinely customize compensatory tools to ensure they are personally meaningful, and then coordinate implementation across the rehabilitation team and family members.

Group interventions represent a primary intervention tool for inpatient neurorehabilitation psychologists. Group interventions typically involve all of the **ABCs**, and are tailored to address the specific combination of emotional, behavioral, and cognitive needs of each individual. Regardless of focus, group modalities help *normalize* disability by providing psychoeducation, structure, and a reduced sense of isolation for individuals and their family members. Adjustment-based groups may address difficult emotions, either for individuals, their families, or both. Behavior-based groups can provide psychoeducation about behavioral challenges, such as impulsivity, while simultaneously modeling and reinforcing more appropriate self-regulated behaviors. Cognitive remediation groups can focus on teaching of basic skills, such as orientation, attention and memory, to more advanced skills such as complex prob-lem-solving, flexible thinking, and organization.

A final intervention role for inpatient neurorehabilitation psycholo-gists is in Consultation, Collaboration, and advocacy. Communication with other rehabilitation disciplines begins immediately upon admis-sion, reflecting the multidisciplinary philosophy of rehabilitation medi-cine. Weekly team conferences ensure clear communication across team members and provide an opportunity for neurorehabilitation psycholo-gists to coordinate, revise or expand cognitive or behavioral strategies designed to enhance individual functioning. Consultation may also take the form of organized cotreatment with another discipline. For example, neurorehabilitation psychologists may work collaboratively with physi-cal therapists, redirecting individuals to a specific physical therapy exercise, or with occupational therapists to observe—in vivo—how patients' cognitive deficits interfere with self-care. Finally, neurorehabi-litation psychologists collaborate in a consultation-liaison capacity with psychiatry to assist in the management of confused and/or agitated behaviors, on issues of medications to address mood or anxiety, and to determine an individual's capacity to make decisions about his or her health care.

THE ABCs OF INTERVENTION WITHIN AN OUTPATIENT REHABILITATION SETTING

Similar to the inpatient setting, neurorehabilitation psychologists in the outpatient setting also integrate aspects of the **ABCs** of neurorehabilita-tion issues and interventions. A primary role of these clinicians is to provide Adjustment-based psychotherapy intended to facilitate individ-uals' and family members' psychosocial adjustment to the often dis-tressing nature of "living with" subtle, or not-so-subtle, cognitive, emotional, and behavioral difficulties as they manifest in home and community settings. Equally important is the acknowledgment and facilitation of the evolving sense of self following the return to a commu-nity setting. By the time individuals are referred for outpatient services, they often have greater awareness (or have been repeatedly told) that they have difficulties with "fitting in" to former roles in the family, in the household, in the work setting, and/or in the community. It is not uncommon to hear from these individuals that they feel "back to normal," only to be devastated by unexpected failures in their lives as they attempt to resume former roles.

Outpatient neurorehabilitation psychologists are attentive to the many variables that can affect coping, such as role changes, financial stressors, cultural dynamics, and varying levels of personal awareness. These and other aspects of adjustment are in the constant "radar" of neurorehabilitation psychologists as they facilitate the gradual process of adjustment.

Unexpected, sometimes unexplained, behavioral issues surface once individuals attempt to reestablish former life roles. Subtle and overt behavioral and interpersonal issues may be revealed by others who knew the individual before the diagnosis. Additionally, behavioral and interpersonal issues may eventually emerge in treatment sessions, allowing the psychologist to witness firsthand the behavioral dysfunction. Behavioral dysregulation may present as a result of reductions in thinking speed, attention, mental flexibility, self-awareness, impulse control, planning/organization, or from emotional problems with depression, anxiety, irritability, and/or aggression. Outpatient neurorehabilitation psychologists employ a variety of Behavior-based interventions to address these issues including behavior training provided to patients and their support system. Interventions are intended to contain the dysregulated behavior while optimizing self-governance. Training includes how to establish structure and routine, communication skills, relaxation training, and environmental modifications. Neurorehabilitation psychologists might demonstrate behavioral approaches in session to educate patients and families on the use of interventions and modifications so that they may further adapt these approaches within the home, at work, and/or in the community setting.

In addition (or alternate) to specialized cognitive retraining therapies, outpatient neurorehabilitation psychologists may integrate Cognitive remediation and Compensatory-skills building approaches into psychotherapy. Interventions are tailored to the unique challenges of the individual and based on cognitive weaknesses identified, needed family and environmental supports, and the ecological relevance of the tools required for the individual. For example, the use of attention training material may improve attention abilities, but it also provides a valuable source of practical feedback to optimize detection of errors and to raise awareness of internal and environmental distractions to be managed. Other interventions may focus on the enhancement of information processing speed, mental flexibility, planning and organization, and problem solving abilities. Similar to the inpatient setting, once individuals have mastered these basic building blocks of thinking, higher order skills can be learned to increase functioning at home, at school or work, and in the community.

Among their many roles, outpatient neurorehabilitation psychologists provide Consultation and advocacy with a broad group of professionals, with the intention of optimizing communication among providers, maximizing community re-entry, and providing a voice for the consumer of brain injury resources. With individuals' permission, consultation usually involves informing other professionals about anticipated challenges, residual abilities, and cognitive/behavioral strategies found to be useful in the enhancement of functioning. Neurorehabilitation psychologists also consult with physicians to support and/or confirm medical diagnoses, provide psychological and behavioral observations after medication changes, and assist with long-term life planning and resource management. Finally, the neurorehabilitation psychologist advocates on behalf of individuals to assist them in obtaining services required to sustain a reasonable quality of life and independence of living in the community setting, with efforts ranging from local to governmental levels.

CASE STUDIES

In the final section of this chapter, clinical case examples have been created to bring to life the varied roles and approaches taken by the neurorehabiliation psychologist in both assessment and interventions. In Case One, assessment and interventions used for a prototypical individual admitted to an inpatient rehabilitation unit with a known neurological injury and complex emotional, cognitive, and behavioral challenges will be discussed. In Case Two, the inpatient neurorehabilitation psychologist identifies an underlying dementia and implements interventions to ensure the individual's safe return and functioning in his community. In Case Three, the diverse roles of an outpatient neurorehabilitation psychologist are illustrated while emphasizing maximal functioning of the patient as a mother and student within her community.

Inpatient Case Example: Angela

Angela is a 28-year-old woman who underwent elective brain surgery to decrease the frequency of recurring seizures that no longer responded to antiseizure medications. Although surgery successfully reduced the frequency of her seizures, Angela experienced an unexpected brain bleed after the surgery. Postoperatively, Angela was left with new cognitive difficulties including problems seeing things in her right visual field, difficulties expressing herself, slowed thinking, poor memory, sudden mood swings, and balance problems. Married for 10 years, Angela lives in an urban setting with her husband and 5-year-old daughter. An average student in college, Angela had completed an Associates Degree. Prior to her surgery, she worked as a paralegal in a law firm.

Within days of her admission to the inpatient rehabilitation unit, Angela was seen for a brief neurocognitive screen.[2] Testing confirmed the presence of expressive language difficulties and a right-sided visual inattention. In addition, new cognitive weaknesses in mental flexibility, attention, orientation, and memory were noted. Angela had a minimal appreciation of her physical and cognitive deficits. Emotionally, Angela was depressed, easily frustrated and discouraged, with frequent episodes of intense and disruptive tearfulness requiring interventions by specific staff.

Viewed through the lens of the **ABCs** model to guide the initial treatment plan, Angela's issues of mourning and loss, and reduced awareness of her acquired cognitive difficulties were identified. Treatment priorities included individual and family **A**djustment counseling, individual **C**ognitive remediation, and family and team **C**onsultation. During her 2-month stay on inpatient rehabilitation, Angela was seen 3–4 times a week in a combination of individual and family psychotherapy with embedded cognitive remediation. She participated in serial assessments to track her cognitive progress, allowing the neurorehabilitation psychologist to identify remaining difficulties, and to identify needed shifts in treatment focus as Angela progressed.

Individual **A**djustment-based psychotherapy addressed Angela's reduced awareness of her acquired cognitive difficulties, her frustration, her mourning of newly acquired memory and expression difficulties, her separation from her family, and her sense of "loss" in regard to her roles as a mother and provider within her family. Angela's husband, John, was seen for family **A**djustment-based psychotherapy. Psychoeducation about his wife's cognitive and emotional changes and strategies for managing these challenges were provided. The husband was helped to process his own feelings of loss. Finally, modeling of approaches to handling his daughter's reactions to her mother's illness were provided. **B**ehaviorally, Angela's explosive tearfulness and re-duced mental flexibility repeatedly interfered with her ability to engage consis-tently in rehabilitation treatment, requiring co-treatment with team members where approaches to redirection were modeled by the psychologist.

Angela presented with unsafe behaviors on the unit. For example, she insisted on walking by herself in spite of numerous reminders not to because of severe balance and visual problems. Memory problems prevented her from remembering this request. Angela was gradually able to develop an increased awareness of her memory and balance difficulties, after being introduce to a **C**ompensatory tool called a "memory book," which allowed her to remind herself of her current limitations. In addition, Angela participated in **B**ehavior-based and **C**ognitive remediation groups in which other individuals with brain injury gave her feedback about her problems with attention and memory as well as her safety issues. **C**onsultation with other team members occurred regularly in weekly case conferences and during periods of behavioral out-bursts while co-treating with other disciplines. Ongoing team communications allowed for a consistent approach to managing Angela's disruptive and unsafe behaviors, as well as the increased use of her memory book as a cueing device. Advocating on behalf of Angela, the neurorehabilitation psychologist **C**onsulted with Angela's employer (with permission of Angela and her hus-band) about how her cognitive and behavioral challenges might impact her return to work along with a discussion of retraining possibilities within her company.

At time of discharge, Angela demonstrated significant gains in her mood, memory and expressive language, although she continued to struggle with reduced awareness, and problems with complex attention, mental flexibility, and problem-solving. The team recommended 24-hour close supervision for safety at the time of discharge. Angela was referred for continued neurorehabi-litation psychology services in the outpatient setting.

Inpatient Case Example: Dr. K.

Dr. K. is a 79-year-old semiretired physician who was admitted to inpatient rehabilitation following a routine right total knee replacement. Up until his hospital admission, Dr. K. continued to treat a limited number of patients. He was widowed and lived alone with two supportive children living locally. Prior to admission, Dr. K. was independent in all activities. At time of admission to the inpatient unit, Dr. K. was sociable, oriented, and well-adjusted. Given his non-neurological admitting diagnosis, he was not initially referred for psychological services. One week later, a physical therapist requested a referral to the neurorehabilitation psychologist when she noticed that Dr. K. was having significant difficulty learning new skills required in his rehabilitation.

The neurorehabilitation psychologist saw Dr. K. for a brief neurocognitive screen. Dr. K. exhibited moderate memory impairments, problems with organization and planning, reduced verbal expression, poor judgment, and was disorientated. Behaviorally, Dr. K. frequently went off on tangents, had trouble directly answering questions, and often filled in gaps in his memory with incorrect information. When given feedback about his performance, Dr. K. denied changes in his thinking and minimized the test results. This pattern of cognitive symptoms, combined with a reduced awareness on the part of Dr. K., is consistent with the early stages of a dementing process. Using the lens of the **ABCs** model to guide the initial treatment plan, issues of individual and family adjustment, individual **A**djustment-based counseling, **B**ehavior-based interventions, **C**ognitive remediation, and ongoing family and team **C**onsultation were conceptualized as treatment priorities. During his 2-week stay on the rehabilitation unit, the patient was seen approximately 2–3 times a week.

Given that Dr. K. was denying the significance of his cognitive impairments, the primary interventions were **C**ognitive in nature with remediation aimed at raising Dr. K.'s awareness of his deficits. The neurorehabilitation psychologist created interventions that provided immediate "in the moment" feedback about his failure on personally meaningful tasks. **C**ognitive remediation also focused on approaches to optimize his attention, his memory and his mental flexibility, while providing feedback about his performance on these tasks to increase his awareness of his cognitive limitations. Family **A**djustment-based psychotherapy was provided to Dr. K.'s family to address their adjustment to the father's new diagnosis, as well as education about dementia, typical disease timelines, and the risks associated with Dr. K.'s continued independent living and continued professional activities. Concerns about independent living required ongoing **C**onsultation with the multidisciplinary team and the family to develop a safe discharge plan, as well as an ethical dialogue regarding Dr. K.'s continued work capacity. Although no specific restrictions were suggested, the team recommended that Dr. K. not return to work because of his diminished cognitive abilities.

Outpatient Case Example: Elsy

Elsy is a 19-year-old woman who suffered a stroke and underwent surgery to repair a ruptured blood vessel that left her with a right visual field loss, a marked right-side weakness, and problems with verbal expression, memory and problem solving. Prior to her stroke, Elsy was in the process of completing her last year of high school. She and her 4-year-old daughter lived with her mother. After 3 months of acute neurorehabilitation, Elsy was referred to outpatient services for continued neurorehabilitation care including referral to the neurorehabilitation psychologist and occupational therapist. At the point of referral to outpatient services, Elsy had learned to walk independently using a cane. She continued to have a right visual inattention and severe language expression difficulties. Since home, Elsy had become increasingly depressed and anxious about her loss of function and inability to care for her child. Given her profound speech limitations, a modified neuropsychological assessment was completed to clarify her residual neurocognitive strengths and weaknesses.[3] Despite her field loss, neuropsychological testing results surprisingly identified preserved intellectual, attentional, and memory abilities in visual domains of functioning. She was able to understand and follow simple instructions and could learn basic information. Severe expressive difficulties and reduced auditory attention, problem solving, and organizational abilities were identified in testing, along with depression. According to her mother, Elsy was often impatient and easily agitated, sometimes being loud and physically aggressive with her daughter. She was distressed by her limited expressive ability and used miming and gesturing to convey her sense of powerlessness and worthlessness along with her basic wants.

Viewed through the lens of the **ABCs** model, initial treatment priorities included individual and family **A**djustment-based psychotherapy to address Elsy's increasing depression, **B**ehavior-based interpersonal skills building to enhance her nonverbal expression and behavioral regulation, **C**ognitive remediation and **C**ompensatory skill building to enhance her attention to task, problem solving, organization abilities, and to optimize her communication skills. **C**onsultation with other service providers was conducted to enhance consistency in approach to treatment. Elsy was seen for 45-minute sessions twice weekly, usually once individually and once with her mother, sister, and/or daughter.

Initial **A**djustment-based psychotherapy sessions addressed Elsy's mourning and loss, her altered sense of self, her altered role as parent and family member, and her reduced self-concept and body image. Special consideration was given to the reconstruction of her identity as a young woman and mother dealing with disability. She was frequently tearful in sessions when expressing her frustrations about her communication difficulties and her inability to communicate with her daughter. Her new onset disability was processed to help her find words to express her feelings and to validate and normalize her experiences. To address her mood changes and impact on social relationships, **B**ehavior-based interpersonal skill-building interventions included role-play and relaxation strategies. Use of watercolor painting with her daughter was encouraged as an activity to establish quality time and bonding, and an alternative means of emotional expression.

Elsy's difficulties with attention, language processing and expression, information processing speed, and problem solving difficulties identified on neuropsychological testing were addressed using a variety of **C**ognitive remediation and **C**ompensatory skills-building interventions. Practical problem-solving strategies were introduced to establish her modified roles within her household. Elsy was taught to use a pocket organizer, thus allowing her greater autonomy in managing her schedule and routines. She was also taught how to advocate for her needs with others. Use of errorless learning strategies and techniques to enhance her word retrieval were practiced in session and then taught to her mother. Homework assignments designed to increase Elsy's awareness of deficiencies and "work around" strategies were facilitated by her mother. Strategies were developed to help her minimize internal and external distractions, especially during her attempts to communicate in the home setting. Assignments were broken down into discrete illustrated steps to increase compliance. **C**onsultation and co-treatment with her occupational therapist permitted sharing of communication techniques introduced in psychotherapy sessions, to ease barriers of expression with other therapists. Consultation with her medical provider resulted in Elsy initiating treatment on an antidepressant medication.

After 9 months of multidisciplinary interventions, Elsy was able to return to school in a modified capacity to complete her high school diploma. Neurorehabilitation psychology sessions continued to work on this important transition. Elsy's neuropsychological test results were shared with her school and she was identified as a student with special needs. Specific functional accommodations were recommended and put in place in the classroom. How is she doing at school? Elsy has been able to use the tools learned in treatment to minimize environmental distractions, organize her schedule, maintain her "to do" list, express her feelings and opinions, manage others' reactions to her, and to slowly rebuild her own confidence and self image. Elsy continues to be seen for weekly follow-up psychotherapy. Although her progress in her school setting continues to be monitored, the neurorehabilitation psychologist is now working with Elsy to maximize ongoing psychological adjustment to chronic disability and to expand her roles in her family. It is anticipated that Elsy will remain in treatment for a minimum of 1 additional year.

CONCLUSIONS

Neurorehabilitation psychology is an emerging subspecialty that culls professionals trained as rehabilitation psychologists and/or clinical neuropsychologists who work specifically with individuals with acquired or traumatic brain injury or neurological conditions. Neurorehabilitation psychologists view individuals holistically within the dynamic context of their lives and relationships. Neuropsychological assessment is intended to identify strengths and weaknesses in neuropsychological and social functioning, informing appropriate clinical interventions. The *ABCs Model of Neurorehabilitation Issues and Interventions* was introduced to provide a general framework from which to view the scope of interventions provided by the neurorehabilitation psychologists in both inpatient and outpatient rehabilitation settings. Neurorehabilitation psychologists remain sensitized to both the neurological and psychological factors that impact functioning and well-being as they complete assessments, conceptualize test findings, plan and implement needed interventions, and consult with other professionals to maximize an individual's functioning and well-being. Neurorehabilitation psychologists work closely with the individual, family members, and the rehabilitation team to increase empowerment through self-awareness, enhanced cognitive functioning and better emotional regulation for the individuals served. The case examples highlight the varied assessments and the **ABCs** of clinical interventions provided by these professionals.

NOTES

1. A memory book is simply a diary that aides in organization and provides a ready access to information in daily life for those with

cognitive deficits in attention, memory and/or executive functioning. It centralizes information about one's daily activities within a centralized place (such as a three-ringed binder) throughout the day and week. It helps the individual retrieve important personal information such as medication regimen and dosage, treatment schedule, personal experiences, emotions, and random thoughts. In addition to written text, a memory book may include items such as photos of people and places and other documents that will help jog or reconstruct a memory. For example, at midday the individual might write down activities completed in the morning, thoughts and feelings about the activities, future appointments, and what still needed to be done. The memory book might include a calendar or be paired with a pocket calendar to coordinate the activities. Writing down information serves as an "extension of memory" and not only documents information, but helps with storage of memory by seeing and writing to-be-remembered information. Use of memory books is a common compensatory skill developed as early as acute inpatient neurorehabilitation. It is useful in psychotherapeutic interventions by helping individuals not "lose time" in their lives; rather, they can review their early memory book entries to facilitate the integration of the earliest events during the course of their rehabilitation adjustment, events that they might have the greatest difficulty remembering.

2. Neurocognitive screening tests are typically brief (10 to 30 minutes) and are well tolerated by the individual in the acute phase of neurorehabilitation. Brief screenings target cognitive domains that are foundational to higher level cognitive functioning (e.g., arousal, orientation, attention, and memory) and that impact upon individuals' participation in other therapies such as OT, PT, and speech.

3. Neuropsychological test batteries may be modified to accommodate profound disabilities in a specific domain, allowing the examiner to evaluate other cognitive capacities while controlling for a specific deficiency. For example, if expressive speech is clearly impaired, a multiple choice modification of a vocabulary test might be given to evaluate comprehension and word knowledge. Rationale for alternate test selection or modification to a standardized test administration to accommodate an individual should be clarified in the neuropsychological report.

REFERENCES

Americans with Disabilities Act. (2009). *ADA Homepage: Information and technical assistance on the Americans with Disabilities Act.* Retrieved from http://www.ada.gov

Alderman, N. (2004). Disorders of behavior. In J. Ponsford (Ed.), *Cognitive and behavioral rehabilitation: From neurobiology to clinical practice* (pp. 269–298). New York: Guilford Press.

Cicerone, K., & Fraser, R. (1999). Counseling interactions for clients with traumatic brain injury. In R. Fraser & D. Clemmons (Eds.), *Traumatic brain injury rehabilitation: Practical vocational, neuropsychological, and psychotherapeutic interventions* (pp. 95–128). Boca Raton, FL: CRC Press.

Coetzer, R. (2006). *Traumatic brain injury rehabilitation: A psychotherapeutic approach to loss and grief.* New York: Nova Publishers.

Diller, L. (1987). Neuropsychological rehabilitation. In M. Meier, A. Benton, & L. Diller (Eds.), *Neuropyschological rehabilitation.* New York: Guilford Press.

Hibbard, M. R., Ashman, T. A., Spielman, L. A., Chun, D., Charatz, H. J., & Melvin, S. (2004). Relationship between depression and psychosocial functioning after traumatic brain injury. *Archives of Physical Medicine and Rehabilitation, 85*(4, Suppl. 2), S43–53.

Langer, K. G., Laatsch, L., & Lewis, L. (Eds.). (1999). *Psychotherapeutic interventions for adults with brain injury or stroke: A clinician's treatment resource.* Madison, CT: Psychosocial Press.

Leon-Carrion, J. (Ed.). (1997). *Neuropsychological rehabilitation: Fundamentals, innovations, and directions.* Boca Raton, FL: CRC Press.

Mateer, C., & Sira, C., (2008). The clinical neuropsychological feedback as an intervention. In J. E. Morgan & J. H. Ricker (Eds.), *Textbook of clinical neuropsychology.* New York: Taylor and Francis.

Meier, M., Benton, A., & Diller, L. (Eds.). (1987). *Neuropsychological rehabilitation.* New York: Guilford Press.

Morton, M. V., & Wehman, P. (1995). Psychosocial and emotional sequelae of individuals with traumatic brain injury: A literature review and recommendations. *Brain Injury, 9*(1), 81–92.

Paolucci, S., Antonucci, G., Pratesi, L., Traballesi, M ., Grasso, M., & Lubich, S. (1999). Poststroke depression and its role in rehabilitation of inpatients. *Archives of Physical Medicine and Rehabilitation, 80*(9), 985–990.

Ponsford, P. (Ed.). (2004). *Cognitive and behavioral rehabilitation: From neurobiology to clinical practice.* New York: Guilford Press.

Prigatano, G. P. (1999). *Principles of neuropsychological rehabilitation.* New York: Oxford University Press.

Prigatano, G. P. (2008). Neuropsychological rehabilitation and psychodynamic psychotherapy. In J. E. Morgan & J. H. Ricker (Eds.), *Textbook of clinical neuropsychology* (pp. 985–995). New York: Taylor and Francis.

Seel, R. T., Kreutzer, J. S., Rosenthal, M., Hammond, F. M., Corrigan, J. D., & Black, K. (2003). Depression after traumatic brain injury: A National Institute on Disability and Rehabilitation Research Model Systems multicenter investigation. *Archives of Physical Medicine and Rehabilitation, 84*, 177–184.

Sohlberg, M. M., & Mateer, C. A. (2001). *Cognitive rehabilitation: An integrative neuropsychological approach.* New York: Guilford Press.

Wilson, B. A., & Zangwill, O. L. (Eds). (2003). *Neuropsychological rehabilitation: Theory and practice.* New York: Taylor & Francis.

World Health Organization. (2001). *International classification of functioning, disability and health.* Geneva: Author.

Ylvisaker, M., Turkstra, L. S., & Coelho, C. (2005) Behavioral and social interventions for individuals with traumatic brain injury: A summary of the research with clinical implications. *Seminars in Speech and Language, 26*(4), 256–267.

16

Using Neuropsychological Information in Vocational Rehabilitation Planning: Perspectives for Clinical Practice

ROBERT T. FRASER, ERICA K. JOHNSON, AND JAY M. UOMOTO

The role of the neuropsychologist in vocational planning or vocational rehabilitation is not widely discussed, nor is it a formal component of clinical neuropsychology training programs. Nevertheless, as neuropsychologists begin their clinical practice, cognitive capacities in relation to work-related functions become common referral questions. Clients referred for vocational rehabilitation will often have physical disabilities (e.g., orthopedic or spinal cord injuries) or sensory disabilities, but a large segment will have cognitive issues as a result of trauma or neurological insult (e.g., traumatic brain injury, epilepsy) or disease process (e.g., multiple sclerosis). Proficiency in producing vocationally oriented neuropsychological evaluations generally exceeds the basic competencies achieved by completion of formal training in a regionally accredited university or 2 or more years of supervised experience (Hannay et al., 1998).

Neuropsychologists who develop an expertise in this area have experience not only in providing evaluations that are geared to vocational worksite recommendations, but have the experience in following the patient longitudinally, conducting serial evaluations, and providing consequent accommodation recommendations. The ideal consultant has been a member or coordinator of an outpatient rehabilitation team.

During the course of outpatient rehabilitation, salient needs emerge for the patient surrounding return to work, employment maintenance, coping and mood regulation, and family adjustment to disability. These issues commonly relate to changes in cognitive abilities and functional capacities. This allows the outpatient rehabilitation neuropsychologist the opportunity to provide both assessment and therapy services aimed at maximization of psychosocial and vocational adjustment.

PREDICTION OF WORK RETURN IN RELATION TO NEUROPSYCHOLOGICAL VARIABLES AND WORKPLACE FUNCTIONING

A number of literature reviews in traumatic brain injury (TBI) have examined factors related to employment outcome. Ownsworth and McKenna (2004) found that among numerous domains of neuropsychological performance, executive functioning has a moderate association with employment. Lesser albeit significant relationships have also been observed between employment outcomes and perceptual ability as well as global cognitive function. A more recent review in TBI by Nightingale, Soo, and Tate (2007) considered these variables as likely prognosticators, but indicated that the evidence was too limited to support a conclusive association with employment. There are a number of issues in assessing the impact of diverse factors, including neuropsychological characteristics, on work access and work return. First, longitudinal studies are the exception, with most research using a limited number of variables to predict employment status at a singular time point after injury. The study by Machamer, Temkin, Fraser, Doctor, and Dikmen (2005), however, examined the predictive value of a range of neuropsychological variables relative to total number of months employed, half-time or more, over 3 to 5 years postinjury. Using total number of months employed as a continuous outcome variable, the researchers found scores on Performance IQ, the Digit Symbol Test, the Verbal Selective Reminding Test, the Trails-Making Test Part B, and Finger Tapping (Dominant Hand) significantly predicted employment stability at a probability level less than chance of one in 1,000 ($p \leq .001$). These findings revealed a primarily positive linear relationship between these measures and work retention (i.e., better test scores were associated with greater time spent in employment during the follow-up period). Using return to work as a discrete outcome variable thus appears to be somewhat superficial as longitudinal studies demonstrate the important

relationships between cognitive capacities and employment maintenance, which is a more clinically relevant employment issue for
many patients.

In considering the predictive utility of neuropsychological performance in relationship to employment, some additional points are notable. It is likely that the neuropsychological test scores will show a
stronger relationship to employment outcome if assessed in relation
not only to employment stability (i.e., a person's ability to obtain and
maintain employment), but relative to specific sectors of work based
on requisite demands (e.g., unskilled labor, skilled labor such as com-
mercial fishing or welding, and skilled business professionals in administrative or managerial positions). Further, securing or retaining
employment may be easier for an employee returning to work in the
same job or with the same employer because of employer accommodation and existing cognitive and social cues, as opposed to an individual
needing to find new employment with a new employer. A final consideration related to the literature is that often, these neuropsychological
measures are being used to predict outcomes for a heterogeneous group
of persons with neuropsychological disability who may or may not
receive formal vocational rehabilitation intervention. Johnstone, Reid-
Arndt, Franklin, and Harper (2006) contended that provision of specific
State–Federal Vocational Rehabilitation (VR) services predicts successful vocational outcomes, whereas traditional medical and neuropsychological variables do not. It needs to be noted that neuropsychological
testing may, in fact, be guiding these successful vocational interventions
in relation to both counseling and on-the-job training. This issue is
generally in need of further investigation. In any case, the above considerations provide a number of reasons for the incongruence in findings
across studies examining neuropsychological variables in relationship
to employment outcomes. The ecological validity of neuropsychological
assessment to employability has not been decidedly established. Future
studies need to better circumscribe the vocational outcome criteria
to provide meaningful data, for example, a specific type or sector of
employment activity and include the stability variable.

NEUROPSYCHOLOGICAL ASSESSMENT
CAN PROVIDE A FRAMEWORK FOR VOCATIONAL
REHABILITATION INTERVENTION

Despite these limited research findings, quality neuropsychological assessment can provide any number of clinical advantages in the voca-

tional rehabilitation process for an individual with a disability. First, the neuropsychological assessment provides a baseline profile of the type and severity of impairments affecting the individual. This baseline can guide work access considerations as to when and at what level of activity a person might attempt pursuing employment and/or returning to work. Second, the neuropsychologist has the ability to conduct brief follow-up assessments, which may have an economic advantage for the client relative to serial comprehensive evaluations, in order to establish whether there are persisting cognitive problems related to a neurological insult or disease process. Assessment can evaluate a number of aspects relative to functional behavior including general cognitive functioning, attention, concentration, memory, and executive functioning. Emotional status is also traditionally evaluated. As indicated by Barisa and Barisa (2001), neuropsychological assessment within the vocational rehabilitation context is functionally oriented. That is, the neuropsychologist moves away from the traditional determination of basic brain–behavior relationships, or identification of pathognomonic signs, and focuses on the manner in which specific deficits are likely to interfere with daily functioning, in the realms of work (e.g., the ability to multitask, information processing speed), activities of daily living (e.g., budgeting, following recipes), and interpersonal functioning.

In conducting neuropsychological evaluations to address vocational rehabilitation concerns, Barisa and Barisa (2001) emphasized that in addition to the patient's premorbid history vis-à-vis medical background, education, psychosocial history, personality style, alcohol or drug use, and so on, there is a practical emphasis on employment performance history. This includes obtaining both a job description and a job analysis, as well as worker performance data or evaluation information. Information from a family member or relative that addresses an individual's level of personal awareness and functioning both at work and within the community is also very critical.

Without neuropsychological assessment data, the patients and significant others are left to "find their way" as to strengths and areas of deficit, which is an inexpedient and often emotionally taxing process. The neuropsychological testing at baseline also facilitates identification of cognitive changes and stability of function over time (Fuchs, 2009). Test results can inform the development of compensatory strategies with input from other members of the rehabilitation team (i.e., occupational therapy, physical therapy, speech and language pathology, rehabilitation engineering). The neuropsychologist's evaluation can also provide important recommendations surrounding approaches to behavioral management, psychotherapy, and other supportive cognitive interventions.

One of the most valuable contributions of neuropsychological assessment, as indicated by LeBlanc, Hayden, and Paulman (2000), is that it can assist in generating hypotheses about the manner in which the deficits identified on standardized testing might influence behavior in more natural environments. Such information can shape the next steps in the assessment process such as conducting a community-based vocational assessment using the federal waiver for unpaid work up to 215 hours,[1] or a situational assessment developed at a rehabilitation or vocational rehabilitation facility. As discussed by Barisa and Barisa (2001) and Uomoto (2000), neuropsychological testing can either underestimate or overestimate an individual's capability in a real work environment.

In the first case, as an individual returns to the work setting or even enters a new work setting for the first time after serious neurological insult or disease, there are often a number of environmental cues that can facilitate adequate functioning. In some cases, the actual work tasks involve overlearned behavior that the worker is able to rely upon to conduct essential tasks. For example, we observed a case in which the neuropsychological profile of a senior welder indicated moderate to severe impairment on all measures, yet the individual was able to easily pass a welding certification test. Presumably, the knowledge and skills required for performance on the certification test drew from overlearned behavior. Despite even severely occurring brain injury or disease, some individuals will have overlearned behavior that is well preserved, even as they encounter problems with new learning. Overlearned behaviors are formed over time through well-routinized repetitive learning. The ability to perform these behaviors can be widely interconnected in long-term memory. It must be remembered, however, that even these rote behaviors do not function in isolation and may be negatively impacted by impaired executive functioning or mental processing speed.

An individual may also experience certain difficulties on the day of testing to include emotional distress, medication side effects, severe pain, and so on, which can negatively affect performance. The "snapshot" in time that this testing provides relative to actual preserved abilities may be compromised to varying degrees on a particular day.

Further, it is possible that neuropsychological evaluation overestimates real-world performance as the testing occurs in a controlled environment with one test administrator. In the actual job setting there may be a number of distractions, interpersonal issues, time pressures, and other accuracy demands, that can not be comparably tapped as a function of the neuropsychological battery administered. Consequently, an individual may perform poorly on the job despite positive neuropsychological indicators of cognitive reserve or functional assets.

WHAT IS HELPFUL FOR THE NEUROPSYCHOLOGIST?

When a neuropsychological report is not helpful to the vocational rehabilitation counselor, the problem is often that the appropriate questions and information were not provided to the neuropsychologist. Uomoto (2000) has identified a number of ways in which this problem can be avoided. Information needed by the neuropsychologist is highlighted here:

1. The neuropsychologist needs to identify and obtain the records that he or she might find helpful in providing a vocationally relevant neuropsychological report. Neuropsychologists vary relative to the information that they desire. Communication with the vocational rehabilitation counselor in advance of the assessment can help determine which records can be provided, either in advance or by the client or significant other on the day of testing.
2. A clear list of the referred person's problems and specific questions to be addressed will assist the neuropsychologist in providing information that is clinically relevant to all stakeholders. These questions, provided by the vocational rehabilitation counselor, may at times be better addressed by another member of the rehabilitation team, but the neuropsychologist can redirect as appropriate.
3. It is important to underscore that all the questions that are addressed to the neuropsychologist are functional or rehabilitation oriented. By being very specific, the neuropsychologist may be deterred from a more traditional technical report in which the focus is more on the establishment of pathognomonic signs or pattern analysis.

4. It is extremely important that the neuropsychologist has a complete job description with critical tasks described and important performance criteria. In the case of an existing job, prior performance evaluation data is also of great benefit. If there is no available information, some job descriptive information may be available through the *Dictionary of Occupational Titles* (U.S. Department of Labor, 1991)—although the information may be outdated, or derived from the Department of Labor's O-NET Web site (http://online.onetcenter.org/). Some neuropsychologists have actually emphasized how much they need this information because they personally lack a range of different job experiences.

WHAT IS HELPFUL TO THE VOCATIONAL REHABILITATION COUNSELOR?

1. The neuropsychologist should to describe very carefully the client's cognitive assets and deficits. In the case of existing deficits, it would be important to describe concerns that may be amenable to change over time or remediation. For example, in the case of mild traumatic brain injury, concerns related to attention or memory may be immediately problematic, but are expected to remediate over time. In the case of deficits, specifically marked ones, it is important for the rehabilitation counselor to understand areas of function that are unlikely to change over time so that a compensatory approach can be undertaken in vocational planning. In some instances, the neuropsychologist would present hypotheses to be evaluated through situational vocational assessment.

2. It is important that potential strengths and deficits are presented within the context of the job description as it is understood. If there is no problem solving involved within a job task range, or limited speed of information processing is involved, this may not be a concern. Conversely, if an individual has impaired verbal memory and fluency, this could be a substantive concern if the individual's work involves complex people interaction.

3. It is incumbent upon the neuropsychologist to note any psychosocial issues that may affect the client's vocational performance. This can involve relationship conflicts with family and significant others, substance abuse issues, or behavioral problems that were noted throughout the testing such as impatience, impulsivity, or irritability.

4. As with the case of psychosocial problem identification, it is also of benefit to underscore positive social or religious networks, supportive social and recreational pursuits, and other aspects of an individual's background (e.g., A.A. or N.A. group involvement) that can facilitate and reinforce a more positive vocational outcome.

5. It is important to describe fatigue difficulties that are encountered over the course of the neuropsychological evaluation. This may occur over the 6 to 8 hours of interview and assessment, but also, it is important to note if the testing has to be done over several days because of difficulties with cognitive or physical fatigue and other issues such as pain. Information of this type is very important in hypothesizing performance and accommodation needs in the workplace, particularly in cognitively complex jobs.

6. Vocationally relevant recommendations are critical. The neuropsychologist might consider whether the individual could work under existing supervision at the job site or whether a paid job coach, coworker as trainer, retired professional, or other more intensive mentorship/supervision is needed. This can relate to both work-task training as well as behavioral and interpersonal difficulties that interfere with job proficiency. To that end, a mentor who can provide task supervision and behavioral management strategies or more intensive worksite social functioning mentorship is a consideration.

7. Of critical importance among a neuropsychologist's recommendations are specific guidance relative to possible procedural changes, physical modification to the work station, or assistive equipment that is critical to job site performance. These are reviewed in detail in the following section focusing on reasonable accommodation.

8. It is important that the rehabilitation counselor receive the report in an expedient manner. If this cannot be done, it is very helpful

to the counselor to have testing results in a checklist rating format within appropriate domains of functioning (see Table 16.1). This checklist with targeted notes can enable the vocational rehabilitation counselor to begin work access planning or, at minimum, construct situational assessments or community-based assessments to further clarify the cognitive and emotional/interpersonal areas of concern, while the neuropsychologist completes the formal evaluative report.

REASONABLE ACCOMMODATION

The neuropsychologist is often asked to make specific recommendations as part of the neuropsychological evaluation and report. Examples of the accommodations as provided in the Americans with Disabilities Act of 1990 (amended 2008) can be somewhat overwhelming. As previously referenced, it is helpful to think of accommodations in three categories: a change in procedure, physical modification to the work station, or some type of assistive equipment or technology. Recommendations in relation to a specific client can involve items in one category or, in some cases, two or all three. Examples of accommodations are found below to guide thinking of specific recommendations.

Procedural Accommodation

Specific neuropsychological deficits can be addressed by changes in work procedures. For example, in the case of attention/concentration deficits, recommendations can focus on ways to reduce distractions. A client may be advised to begin work earlier than co-workers and schedule uninterrupted work time (i.e., no meetings or phone contact) during specific periods of the day. Another possibility is to recommend the client receive assistance in dividing multistep procedures or large work segments into smaller tasks and steps, emphasizing routine repetition as much as possible.

Work Station Modification

Continuing with the same example of individual deficits in attention and concentration, work site modification may be considered. For instance, a

Table 16.1

COGNITIVE RATING CAPACITIES FORM

Client Name:
Date of Birth:
Date of Testing:
Referring Party:
Neuropsychologist:

The rating codes for the cognitive areas of functioning are as follows. Please circle as appropriate: **E = excellent; G = good; F = fair; P = poor; NA = not accessed.**

Attention/Concentration

1a) Ability to attend and concentrate at a basic level
    Immediate   E G F P NA
    On Delay   E G F P NA

Comment _____

1b) Ability to function with divided attention/complex concentration
    Immediate   E G F P NA
    On Delay   E G F P NA

Comment _____

Memory

2a) Ability to remember written instructions
    Immediate   E G F P NA
    On Delay   E G F P NA

Comment _____

2b) Ability to remember spoken instructions
    Immediate   E G F P NA
    On Delay   E G F P NA

Comment _____

2c) Ability to remember visual material
    Immediate   E G F P NA
    On Delay   E G F P NA

Comment _____

2d) Ability to remember incidental information
    Immediate   E G F P NA
    On Delay   E G F P NA

Comment _____

Language

3a) Ability to articulate information in conversation
    Basic Level   E G F P NA
    Complex Level   E G F P NA

Comment _____

3b) Ability to articulate information in writing
    Basic Level   E G F P NA
    Complex Level   E G F P NA

Comment _____

Table 16.1 *(continued)*

3c) Read, comprehend, and utilize written material
     Basic Level   E G F P NA
     Complex Level   E G F P NA
Comment _____

3d) Communicate & solicit information from others in a professional manner
     Basic Level   E G F P NA
     Complex Level   E G F P NA
Comment _____

3e) Ability to train others in relation to job-site responsibilities: Performing:
     Basic Tasks   E G F P NA
Comment _____
     Complex Tasks   E G F P NA
Comment _____

3f) Ability to present information to others, utilizing media
     Basic   E G F P NA
Comment _____
     Complex   E G F P NA
Comment _____

Spatial Abilities

4a) Ability to deal with two- and three-dimension formats
     E G F P NA
Comment _____

4b) Ability to deal with part-to-whole relationships, manipulate material in design, etc.
     E G F P NA
Comment _____

Cognitive Efficiency

5a) Ability to perform repetitive or simple task sequences within reasonable timelines
     E G F P NA
Comment _____

5b) Ability to perform complex activities in an expedient manner
     E G F P NA
Comment _____

5c) Ability to use technology, tools/instruments, or systems in completing work activity efficiently
     E G F P NA
Comment _____

(continued)

Table 16.1 *(continued)*

5d) Ability to collect and compile data from several sources
     E G F P NA

Comment _____

Problem Solving—Executive Functioning/Learning

6a) Ability to synthesize/integrate and analyze data/ideas
     Basic   E G F P NA

Comment _____
     Intermediate   E G F P NA

Comment _____
     Complex   E G F P NA

Comment _____

6b) Ability to carefully assess needs and potential consequences before implementing a plan
     Basic   E G F P NA

Comment _____
     Intermediate   E G F P NA

Comment _____
     Complex   E G F P NA

Comment _____

6c) Ability to plan, implement, and modify activities as necessary in relation to:
     A Basic Level of Difficulty
     E G F P NA

Comment _____
     Intermediate Level of Difficulty
     E G F P NA

Comment _____
     Complex Level of Difficulty
     E G F P NA

Comment _____

6d) Ability to direct and supervise others as necessary in relation to:
     Basic Level of Difficulty
     E G F P NA

Comment _____
     Intermediate Level of Difficulty
     E G F P NA

Comment _____
     Complex Level of Difficulty
     E G F P NA

Comment _____

Table 16.1 *(continued)*

6e) Ability to effectively learn and master new materials as a function of:
Academic
Instruction
E G F P NA

Comment _____

Job-Site Instructions/Work Setting Experience
E G F P NA

Comment _____

Cognitively Related Emotional, Interpersonal, and Work Behaviors

7a) Ability to sustain energy level/appropriate pace over work day
E G F P NA

Comment _____

7b)
(1) Ability to work independently without supervision
E G F P NA

Comment _____

(2) Ability to work physically separated from group
E G F P NA

Comment _____

(3) Ability to function as part of integrated team
E G F P NA

Comment _____

7c) Ability to maintain emotional/social control and deal with others during
work day
E G F P NA

Comment _____

7d) Ability to respond to stress and emotionally weighted situations
E G F P NA

Comment _____

7e) Ability to profit from interpersonal interactions and accept/appropriately
respond to criticism
E G F P NA

Comment _____

7f) Ability to maintain an appropriate level of personal and social awareness
in order to function on the job
E G F P NA

Comment _____

7g) Ability to assertively and appropriately express positive and negative
perceptions/feelings relative to work-related products and issues
E G F P NA

Comment _____

private office or work module away from the center of activity and office traffic may facilitate more focused work. Increasing natural or full spectrum lighting might be helpful to concentration efforts. Appropriate equipment or materials should be provided whenever possible at the employee's work station in order to reduce the need for extraneous movement within the office in completing work functions.

Assistive Technology

The use of assistive technology can have pronounced effects in cases involving memory deficit. Often, such technologies are ones that are readily available in the marketplace, such as cell phones, personal data assistants (PDAs), pagers, and electronic mail (e-mail). Recommendations from the neuropsychologist in this instance could focus on the ways in which technology can provide behavioral and cognitive cues, such as a watch alarm signal to cue consumption of prescribed medications, an e-mail account to send oneself notes or reminders, and electronic calendar functions to facilitate structure and scheduling. Digital cameras, computer software, and color printers provide powerful visuals as memory aides. Current cell phones (smart phones) provide a variety of options for completing many of the previously mentioned solutions. For some individuals having e-mailed or faxed instructions on the day before scheduled activities is very helpful in order that the activities can be reviewed before the day's planned events.

   Other resources relating to accommodation are available through the Job Accommodation Network (JAN), which is a service provided by the U.S. Department of Labor's Office of Disability Employment Policy (ODEP) and housed at West Virginia University. The service is available by both internet (www.jan.wvu.edu) and telephone (toll free at 1-800-526-7234). The JAN service has recently been expanded to provide more specific information on the Americans with Disabilities Act Amendments of 2008. JAN consultants have specialized training in domains such as engineering and rehabilitation counseling. The Searchable Online Accommodation Resource (SOAR) has recently been added to JAN and includes information on accommodations as well as searchable resources for assistive technology. Another extremely helpful international resource that provides objective information on rehabilitation equipment and assistive technology is ABLEDATA at www.abledata.

com—a searchable database of 19,000 assistive technology products maintained under contract from the U.S. National Institute for Disability and Rehabilitation Research.

INTERPRETING FINDINGS FOR THE CLIENT AND REHABILITATION COUNSELOR

It is very important that the client receives the results of the neuropsychological evaluation and recommendations in a clear, concise, and retrievable fashion. It is quite common that clients who have received a full assessment and interpretation of findings from a neuropsychologist, particularly those clients with more severe brain impairment, recall none of the information after the fact. Clients with more severe impairment or specific deficits that affect encoding and storage (e.g., short-term memory concerns) deserve special consideration in the interpretation process. The following recommendations are offered to provide meaningful and relevant feedback:

1. The neuropsychologist should provide a clear verbal summary of the individual's assets and limitations based upon clinical interview, record review, and test results. Whenever possible, it can be helpful to emphasize a particular asset or deficit as linked to information about real life functioning provided by the client or significant other. After review with the client, these results might be provided in a one to two page summary using bullet points to outline each important finding. Another consideration is audio recording the feedback session, so that the client can listen to the information again as needed in order to refine vocational pursuits and address accommodation needs.

2. The neuropsychologist should emphasize to the client and family or significant other that neuropsychological evaluation can be an under- or overestimate of actual everyday abilities. Areas of concern are certainly presented, but at times, it can be emphasized that actual competency is often best assessed in a situational non-paid assessment or tryout at the workplace (U.S. Department of Labor, 1993), or a situational assessment established by vocational rehabilitation staff.

3. A special effort might be made to review recommendations relative to accommodation (e.g., procedural, work station modification, or assistive equipment). The client might also be provided with the JAN and ABLEDATA Web sites (www.jan.wvu.edu/; www.abledata.com/) for further information. In cases of more severe cognitive impairment, the client should be referred to work with his or her rehabilitation counselor, speech and language pathologist, and assistive technologist or rehabilitation engineer in reviewing and implementing the recommended accommodations.

4. In terms of reported assets and deficits, potential strengths or concerns might be presented within the context of the client's job duties whenever possible. Linking the assessment information to subjective experience will aid in storage and retrieval of this information. A similar approach might be highlighting a specific aspect of functioning for further investigation. For example, stating to a client, "Your visual-spatial problem solving is superb and could be very valuable in the right type of job."

5. Whenever possible, it is best to recommend other rehabilitation personnel (e.g., speech and language pathologist, assistive technologist, rehabilitation engineer, rehabilitation counselor) in order to maximize potential for vocational intervention or accommodation that will not be done by the neuropsychologist.

In closing, summaries of the functionally pertinent information might be provided in a brief one to few-page format that is more readily accessible to the client. This information can be e-mailed to the client, or the entire feedback session can be audio recorded for the client. In this manner, the client has a user-friendly record of the neuropsychological assessment, interpretation of findings, and recommendations that can be accessed as needed in the future. Storage of this information in multiple places is also important in report loss prevention.

DIALOGUE WITH THE VOCATIONAL REHABILITATION COMMUNITY

It often behooves the neuropsychologist who is involved in serving the needs of vocational rehabilitation counselors to have consultation meetings with these personnel. One or more of these meetings can involve basic training, education, and review of neuropsychological testing. Part of these meetings can also focus on open dialogue as to what each party needs in order to enhance the vocational rehabilitation assessment and intervention process. This training and dialogue can be conducted at the neuropsychologist's or vocational rehabilitation agency's office. Some neuropsychologists are involved in community- or state-level training meetings for vocational rehabilitation personnel. Neuropsychologists who take this extra step can benefit greatly from an enhanced practice and an increased professional level of satisfaction.

CONCLUSION

This chapter has provided a basic review of considerations for the neuropsychologist practicing in the vocational rehabilitation arena. Two essential ways in which the neuropsychologist enhances the return to work effort are by conveying a clear understanding of the findings from a neuropsychological assessment and specific recommendations that are tailored to the individual patient's work functions. Such efforts are facilitated by clear communication between the neuropsychologist and referral source in terms of referral questions, and between the neuropsychologist, patient/family, and referral source in terms of results and recommendations. Practical, reasonable accommodation recommendations can prove invaluable in the evaluation summary and the reader is encouraged to explore the resources provided in this chapter.

Employment is very important to people with disabilities for purposes of financial support, social connectedness, mental and physical health, and self-empowerment/actualization, as recently reported in a multistate qualitative study (Yeager, Donnelly, Copeland, & Fraser, 2010). Expanding one's neuropsychology practice to include consultation with vocational rehabilitation systems and providers will not only contribute to a diversity of practice, but provide the neuropsychologist with the professional fulfillment of having the most practical of effects on people's lives: successful employment.

ACKNOWLEDGMENT

Support of the University of Washington TBI Model Systems grant #113A980023 is provided by the National Institute of Disability and

Rehabilitation (NIDRR), U.S. Department of Education. Support is also provided by resources from the VA Puget Sound Health Care System, Seattle, Washington.

NOTE

1. The unpaid work of up to 215 hours is to be used for purposes of vocational exploration, vocational assessment, and job training within a private-sector job, but not to displace a paid employee (U.S. Department of Labor, 1993).

REFERENCES

Barisa, M. T., & Barisa, M. W. (2001). Neuropsychological evaluation applied to vocational rehabilitation. *NeuroRehabilitation, 16*, 289–293.

Fuchs, K. L. (2009). Neuropsychologist. *International Journal of MS Care, 11*, 32–37.

Hannay, H. J., Bieliauskas, L., Crosson, B. A., Hammeke, T. A., Hamsher, K. deS., & Koffler, S. (1998). Proceedings of the Houston conference on specialty education and training in clinical neuropsychology. *Archives of Clinical Neuropsychology* (Special Issue) *13*, 157–250.

Johnstone, B., Reid-Arndt, S., Franklin, K. L., & Harper, J. (2006). Vocational outcomes of state vocational rehabilitation clients with traumatic brain injury: A review of the Missouri model brain injury studies. *NeuroRehabilitation, 21*, 335–347.

LeBlanc, J. M., Hayden, M. E., & Paulman, R. G. (2000). A comparison of neuropsychological and situational assessment for predicting employability after closed head injury. *Journal of Head Trauma Rehabilitation, 15*, 1022–1040.

Machamer, J., Temkin, N., Fraser, R., Doctor, J. N., & Dikmen, S. (2005). Stability of employment after traumatic brain injury. *Journal of the International Neuropsychological Society, 11*, 807–816.

Nightingale, E. J., Soo, C. A., & Tate, R. L. (2007). A systematic review of early prognostic factors for return to work after traumatic brain injury. *Brain Impairment, 8*(2), 101–142.

Ownsworth, T., & McKenna, K. (2004). Investigation of factors related to employment outcome following traumatic brain injury: A critical review and conceptual model. *Disability and Rehabilitation, 26*, 765–783.

Uomoto, J. M. (2000). Application of the neuropsychological evaluation in vocational planning after brain injury. In R. T. Fraser & D. C. Clemmons (Eds.), *Traumatic brain injury rehabilitation: Practical vocational, neuropsychological, and psychotherapy interventions*. Boca Raton, FL: CRC Press.

U. S. Department of Labor. (1991). *Dictionary of occupational titles* (4th ed.). Washington, DC: Author.

U. S. Department of Labor. (1993). *Individual vocational rehabilitation programs: Transition of persons with disability into employment.* Washington, DC: Author.

Yeager, P., Donnelly, M., Copeland, J., & Fraser, R. (2010). *Because I work: A phenomenological inquiry of people with disabilities.* Manuscript submitted for publication.

17 Neuropsychological Testing in the Geriatric Patient

KRISTINA F. ZDANYS AND RAJESH R. TAMPI

Practitioners with elderly patients often face the question, "What is normal aging?" If a family member or other caregiver raises the concern that a patient is more forgetful, when does "forgetfulness" become "mild cognitive impairment (MCI)" and finally "dementia"? This chapter examines the role of neuropsychology in answering such questions in the care of a geriatric patient. Specifically, it will address why, when, and how a clinician should refer a patient to a neuropsychologist, what tests are frequently done to evaluate common neuropsychological complaints in the geriatric patient, and how to interpret those tests. The goal is for the practitioner to incorporate neuropsychological testing into an integrated model of patient care involving medicine, psychiatry, radiology, other subspecialties, family resource specialists, and social workers to classify the neuropsychological deficits, to develop treatment plans, and to involve the patient and family in management strategies to improve quality of life and to maximize the patient's independence throughout the course of his or her illness.

NEUROPSYCHOLOGICAL REFERRAL

Why Should Clinicians Refer Geriatric Patients to Neuropsychologists?

Discriminating between normal and pathological changes of aging is difficult without standardized methods of evaluating these symptoms.

The role of neuropsychology in a geriatric patient population is to provide the primary physician with:

1. Characterization of the symptoms:
   In a patient with memory problems, do the deficits point to a frontal dementia such as Pick's disease, a subcortical dementia such as AIDS or Parkinson's, or perhaps a pseudodementia associated with depression? Neuropsychological testing detects subtle differences that help distinguish among the types of dementia. A specific diagnosis is often the key to appropriate treatment of both cognitive and behavioral symptoms.

2. Quantification of the symptoms:
   It is important to establish a baseline for comparison in patients suffering from cognitive deficits or other neuropsychological conditions in late life. Neuropsychological tests often assign specific values of severity that can then be tracked over time. These patterns help a practitioner to distinguish among types of neuropsychological illness; for example, a step-wise cognitive decline is consistent with vascular dementia, a gradual and progressive cognitive decline is typical of Alzheimer's disease (AD), and waxing and waning performance on cognitive testing is indicative of delirium. Certain medications for AD are indicated for specific severities of the disease; thus, distinguishing among mild, moderate, and severe stages allows the practitioner to provide the most effective medication for the patient at that point.

3. Recommendations for management:
   By identifying specific strengths and weaknesses in a patient's neuropsychological profile, the practitioner can work together with the family to assess safety in the home environment and community. Does the patient require a companion for shopping and other activities outside the home? Is the patient a danger to herself within the home, requiring 24-hour supervision, or might she need help preparing meals and bathing? Using neuropsychological testing to follow a patient over time is valuable in assessing the appropriate level of care as cognitive deficits progress.

When Is a Good Time to Refer?

In cases of suspected dementia, referral to a neuropsychologist is valuable soon after a patient presents with a complaint of memory deficit or after abnormal mental status assessment is detected on a routine visit (e.g., disorientation to place or time). It is important, however, for the practitioner to first rule out medical causes of dementia. A standard outpatient dementia workup includes vitamin B_{12}, folate, and thyroid stimulating hormone (TSH), as well as rapid plasma reagin (RPR) or venereal disease research laboratory (VDRL) to assess for syphilis. Additional labs that may be useful include erythrocyte sedimentation rate (ESR), chemistries, glucose, and other thyroid function tests. The patient should be evaluated for signs of infection, and a complete blood count is appropriate to assess white blood cell count with differential. It is important to rule out iatrogenic causes of cognitive impairment, and so the practitioner should review fully the patient's medication list for possible interactions or toxicities. Noncontrast computerized tomography (CT) scan or magnetic resonance imaging (MRI) of the brain may be useful, particularly in patients presenting with focal neurological deficits, but most forms of dementia will show no radiologic abnormality. Once these studies are determined to be within normal limits, a neuropsychological evaluation should be scheduled, as often patients and their caregivers do not notice the subtle signs of early dementia until they have progressed to interfere with the patient's daily activities. The sooner a diagnosis is made, the more effective will be a treatment plan devised to provide symptomatic relief and to maintain an independent and higher quality of life for the patient, as well as to alleviate the stress of caregivers.

What Sort of Information or Questions Should Be Presented With the Referral?

The referral to a neuropsychologist should start with the patient's name, age, and chief complaint. A history of present illness may include estimated onset and time course of symptoms, any exacerbating events, and how symptoms have been interfering with the patient's daily activities. Other relevant information includes past medical and psychiatric history, history of traumatic head injury with loss of consciousness, list of medications, family history of neuropsychiatric illness, handedness, and level of education. Additionally, in a geriatric population it is important to note any physical handicap that the patient may have, including auditory or visual deficits, as these are often mistaken for cognitive deficits if they remain unrecognized. This basic information will help the neuropsychologist to tailor the battery of tests to the patient's specific needs.

INTERPRETING A NEUROPSYCHOLOGICAL REPORT

Geriatric patients commonly undergo neuropsychological testing for assessment of cognitive deficits. This chief complaint may be part of a patient's presentation to a primary care provider, a neurologist, a psychiatrist, or other professional. To illustrate how neuropsychological testing of such a patient may be employed and interpreted, we provide the following clinical scenario of a 90-year-old woman who was referred for testing after her daughter raised concern that the patient was exhibiting progressive cognitive decline. Elements of the neuropsychological battery are explained with practical application for the health care provider.

Case Example: Identifying Information and Reason for Referral

The following information was obtained via patient report during the clinical interview and from Ms. X.'s medical record. Ms. X. is a 90-year-old, widowed, Caucasian woman who was referred because of cognitive difficulties. Neuro-psychological testing was requested to investigate changes in her cognitive functioning. According to Ms. X.'s daughter, concern about her mother's cognitive functioning arose last fall. At that time, Ms. X. and her daughter were on a short cruise and Ms. X. became disoriented and confused. Once back home in a familiar environment, Ms. X. returned to baseline. However, since Mother's Day 2007, Ms. X.'s daughter has observed a progressive decline in functioning; Ms. X. has been forgetting to take her medication, forgetting dates and plans she has made, and has overpaid her bills. Ms. X. reports mild difficulty with her memory and reports that she has difficulty finding words.

The preceding identifying information and reason for referral exemplify the value of providing a detailed referral to the neuropsychologist. Important elements include the patient's name, age, and reason for referral ("cognitive difficulties"), along with specific details regarding onset, progression, and impact of symptoms on daily activities. Often in assessing time of onset of cognitive symptoms it is helpful to use specific events in the patient's life that the patient and caregiver will remember (in this case, a cruise and Mother's Day) to pinpoint when the symptoms started. Families will frequently remember if patients were showing deficits at weddings of grandchildren, at the time of the death of a spouse, or on vacations.

Ms. X.'s Social and Family History

Ms. X. is widowed and is living independently. She does not drive. She is taking care of her basic activities of daily living and has some assistance with instrumental activities of daily living from her brother. Her brother helps with transportation and shopping. She has help with housework once a week. Her daughter has recently assumed responsibility of her finances.

The patient's social and family history may be known to the practitioner already, but elements of this history are important in the context of neuropsychological testing because they provide clues to how severely the cognitive deficit is impacting the patient's daily life. A distinction not familiar to many practitioners is between "basic activities of daily living" and "instrumental activities of daily living." *Basic* activities refer to the Katz Basic Activities of Daily Living Scale (Katz, 1983) and include bathing, dressing, toileting, transferring, continence, and feeding. *Instrumental* activities refer to the Lawton-Brody Instrumental Activities of Daily Living Scale (Lawton & Brody, 1969) and include the degree of independence the patient maintains using the telephone, shopping, preparing food, housekeeping, doing laundry, using modes of transportation, maintaining responsibility for medications, and handling her own finances.

Ms X.'s Educational and Occupational History

Ms. X. attended 2 years of high school. She had been a dietary aide at a local hospital and has been retired for the past 20 years.

As previously stated, a patient's educational attainment is important to put neuropsychological testing into context. A patient with higher educational attainment may perform better on particular sections of a neuropsychological examination, such as verbal or computational tasks, simply because she may start at a higher baseline of ability. The Cognitive Reserve Hypothesis (Roe, Xiong, Miller, & Morris, 2007) suggests that patients who have achieved a higher level of education may manifest signs and symptoms of Alzheimer's disease and other progressive dementias at later neuropathological stages than counterparts with less education, presumably because the brain has established more complex neuronal networks that may compensate for neuropathological insult. Although education alone may not determine a patient's resilience to incipient dementia, as patients with high IQ may not have pursued higher education for a variety of psychosocial reasons, considered together with occupation (what were the cognitive demands of the patient's job, and until how recently was the patient working?), childhood cognition, and lifestyle, education serves as a practical marker for generalizing the patient's expected cognitive function. Additionally, patients with high educational attainment who show minimal deficits on neuropsychological testing should be examined more closely than counterparts with less education simply because their compensatory networks may be masking a more serious dementia.

Ms. X.'s Medical and Psychiatric History

Ms. X. has a history of multinodular goiter, tachycardia, hypercalcemia, hypertension, insulin-dependent diabetes mellitus, spinal stenosis, and syncope. Ms. X. also has a history of falls because of mechanical problems. She reports that her motor functioning in her legs has slowed because of osteoarthritis and denies problems with her hands. A neurological examination 2 months prior to this assessment was grossly normal. No psychiatric history is noted.

As mentioned, multiple medical problems may contribute to symptoms of dementia. It is important for the primary physician to evaluate patients for these illnesses as part of the workup for dementia as the associated cognitive deficits are often reversible. Common conditions include:

Depression: Depression and dementia frequently coexist, and depression is often the earliest symptom in patients with dementia. Symptoms such as mood change, apathy, changes in sleep pattern, psychomotor slowing, and decreased attention and concentration are often characteristic of patients with either condition. *Depressive pseudo-dementia* is a term used to describe a patient with depression who complains of symptoms of dementia such as confusion and poor concentration in the context of an affective disorder (Fischer, 1996). Such patients often respond to treatment with antidepressants.

Hypothyroidism: Symptoms of hypothyroidism such as slowed thinking, lethargy, and apathy may be mistaken for both depression and dementia. As part of a dementia workup a TSH level should always be checked; if the patient does have hypothyroidism, symptoms may be reversed with thyroid supplementation.

HIV/AIDS: Patients with the HIV/AIDS virus may develop signs and symptoms of the *AIDS dementia complex*, which is characterized by psychomotor slowing and deficits in the domains of memory and concentration (McArthur, Sacktor, & Selnes, 1999). Severity correlates with CD4 count, and patients at highest risk of this disorder are those with CD4 counts less than 200 cells per microliter (McArthur et al., 1999). Antiretroviral therapy may reduce risk (McArthur et al., 1999). HIV testing is not normally included in a routine dementia workup, and AIDS dementia is rarely a presenting symptom of the virus, but if a patient has risk factors and other possible causes of cognitive impairment have been ruled out, it may be valuable to obtain the patient's HIV status.

Syphilis: Syphilis infection of the central nervous system may cause symptoms of dementia such as progressive memory impairment and personality change. Although this form of dementia is much less common since antibiotic treatment of syphilis became available, it is still seen among untreated and immunocompromised patients including those with HIV coinfection. As previously stated, RPR and/or VDRL blood testing is frequently included in a dementia workup.

Brain tumors: Many types of brain tumors may cause symptoms that may be mistaken for dementia, including impaired concentration, confusion, personality change, and depressed mood. Patients who have focal deficits on a neurological exam, new-onset seizures, or complaints of a persistent headache that is worse in the morning should be evaluated with CT or MRI of the brain to rule out tumor.

Subdural hematoma: Chronic subdural hematoma, often but not always associated with a history of trauma, can present with progressively worsening cognitive symptoms depending on the location of the hematoma. Symptoms may include memory loss and aphasia and may occur days to weeks following a trauma. As with evaluation for brain tumor, patients with focal neurological deficits, seizures, or headache should be evaluated with neuroimaging, and immediate surgical intervention may be indicated.

Normal pressure hydrocephalus: Memory problems are characteristic of patients with normal pressure hydrocephalus. Other associated cognitive deficits include decreased attention, aphasia, and behavioral changes. Patients with concomitant gait abnormality and urinary incontinence should be assessed with neuroimaging for hydrocephalus and undergo lumbar puncture. Patients often experience symptomatic improvement following therapeutic lumbar puncture and / or shunt placement.

Lyme disease: Chronic encephalomyelitis associated with Lyme disease may cause progressive cognitive impairment. It may be valuable to obtain Lyme titers for patients who live in endemic areas or have a history of tick bite.

B_{12} deficiency: Patients who are deficient in vitamin B_{12} may present with complaints of memory impairment, decreased concentration, and mood changes. Although B_{12} deficiency is considered a reversible cause of dementia, a Cochrane review showed no statistically significant benefit of B_{12} supplementation among patients with low B_{12} levels and dementia (Malouf & Areosa Sastre, 2003).

Alcoholism: Diminished thiamine levels among patients with alcoholism lead to Wernicke's encephalopathy and Korsakoff's syndrome. Cognitive symptoms of Wernicke's encephalopathy include short term memory impairment and confabulation. Korsakoff's syndrome is characterized by confabulation as well as significant anterograde and retrograde amnesia, poor insight, and apathy. These symptoms may be mistaken for an Alzheimer's type dementia. Patients may benefit from thiamine repletion, particularly at earlier stages, and therefore practitioners who suspect a patient may have a history of alcoholism should consider thiamine supplementation even before cognitive deficits develop.

Drug use: Use of illicit substances is more common among the elderly population than might be expected. Although a full outline of effects of drug use on cognition is beyond the scope of this chapter, it is valuable to perform a urine toxicology screen for any patient who presents with a change in mental status to assess whether these symptoms may be substance-induced.

Ms. X.'s Evaluations to Date

The patient was seen 2 months ago because of concerns regarding cognitive functioning. At that time, she scored 29/30 on the Folstein Mini-Mental Status Exam (Folstein, Folstein, & McHugh, 1975). She lost one point on orientation to place. She scored 8/50 on the Executive Interview and was able to draw a clock spontaneously.

Common Neuropsychological Tests

The Folstein Mini-Mental Status Exam (MMSE), the Executive Interview (EXIT), and clock drawing are among some of the most common neuropsychological tests employed as part of a geriatric assessment.

MMSE

This assessment is a 10-minute, 30-point exam with a series of questions to assess orientation, registration, recall, calculation, concentration, verbal skills, and visuo-spatial skills (Folstein, Folstein, & McHugh, 1975). Higher scores indicate more "normal" functioning. Consideration must be given to a patient's baseline educational level, fluency in English, and physical disabilities that may interfere with the patient's ability to perform the tasks requested. This is a useful test for tracking the progression of cognitive decline, which can help to distinguish between the step-wise decline of vascular dementia and the progressive decline of Alzheimer's disease. It can be performed at a general practitioner's office as part of routine geriatric patient evaluation.

EXIT

This assessment, also approximately 10 minutes, is a 25-item 50-point examination that measures executive function (Royall, Mahurin, &

Gray, 1992). Higher scores indicate greater deficits. The term *executive* refers to higher cortical functions required for organization, planning, and goal-directed behavior. Impairments with executive function are seen in illnesses that affect the frontal lobe, such as Pick's disease (frontotemporal dementia) and frontal lobe tumors. Patients who present with personality change, decreased concentration, and difficulty reasoning should be assessed for executive performance, as these results aid in diagnosis. Performance on executive function tasks also may reflect a patient's functional status (i.e., impaired ability to reason and concentrate may translate to the patient's inability to care for herself independently).

Clock Drawing Test

In this test, patients are instructed to draw a clock to show a particular time. The clock drawing test has been found to be highly specific for assessing executive dysfunction (Juby, Tench, & Baker, 2002). There are multiple scoring systems for clock drawing (e.g., Rouleau, Salmon, Butters, Kennedy, & McGuire, 1992; Sunderland et al., 1989; Watson, Arfken, & Birge, 1993). Refer to the neuropsychological report for the specific scoring system employed.

Ms. X.'s Medications

Ms. X. is maintained on the following medications and supplements: tramadol 50 mg as needed, amlodipine 10 mg daily, gabapentin 300 mg daily, aspirin 81 mg daily, acetaminophen extra strength 500 mg as needed, NPH insulin 26 units in the morning and 22 units in the evening, and regular insulin 6 units in the morning and 2 units in the evening.

A discussion of medications that may affect cognition in the elderly is too broad a topic for the purposes of this chapter; however, in the initial assessment for cognitive impairment the medication list is a valuable tool when the practitioner is aware of drugs that commonly are associated with cognitive side effects. Review of medications involves first identifying the drugs that are psychoactive (opioids, anxiolytics, antidepressants, antipsychotics, anticonvulsants, etc.) and whether the dosing is appropriate for the patient, as the elderly often require lower doses of psychoactive medications than younger patients. In this case, the patient is maintained on an opioid (tramadol) and an anticonvulsant (gabapentin), both at low doses for pain associated with her spinal stenosis. It would be helpful to know when the patient started these medications and how often she uses the opioid medication for pain control. She also takes insulin, and it would be important to know her typical blood sugars measured by finger sticks at home, as hypoglycemia may induce change in mental status. Other drug classes important to review include cardiac medications, antihistamines, steroids, diabetic medications, and nonopioid pain medications including nonsteroidal antiinflammatory drugs.

Ms. X: Behavioral Observations

Ms. X. arrived for her scheduled appointment appropriately groomed and appearing younger than her chronological age. She participated cooperatively during the assessment and was very pleasant to work with. She ambulated slowly and required a walker. She had difficulty sitting down and getting out of her chair. Rate of speech, rhythm, and prosody were unremarkable in casual conversation. Her affect was full-range and her mood was "good." There were no indications of hallucinations or delusional thinking at the time of the evaluation. The results of this evaluation are thought to be an accurate assessment of Ms. X.'s cognitive functioning from the point of effort.

These behavioral observations comprise much of a typical psychiatric mental status examination. They are relevant to the neuropsychological assessment as they provide clues to underlying medical or psychiatric disorder as well as to the patient's ability for self-care. For example, in this case Ms. X. was appropriately groomed and appeared younger than her stated age; however, if the patient appeared disheveled or possibly older than stated age there is a higher likelihood that she has trouble performing her activities of daily living and may indicate more significant cognitive impairment or underlying psychiatric affective or psychotic disorder. Observations of gait and overall movements are important to assess whether underlying Parkinson's disease or normal pressure hydrocephalus may contribute to declining cognitive function. In this case, although the patient was slow, there is no mention of shuffling gait, tremor, or ataxia. Rate, rhythm, and prosody of speech are important to note, as abnormalities of speech may suggest a focal neurological insult involving Broca's or Wernicke's areas, or possibly an underlying psychiatric mood disorder such as depression or mania. Psychotic symptoms (hallucinations, delusions) are relevant to behavioral observation, as patients with dementia often demonstrate delusional thinking (particularly persecutory delusions, suspicion that others are stealing from them, etc.) and patients with Lewy Body Dementia frequently experience visual hallucinations. Additionally, elderly patients may experience psychosis while taking certain medications, such as steroids, suggesting cognitive impairment may also be associated with drugs. Finally, with respect to effort, some patients' neuropsychological test results may be biased by lack of effort to participate in tasks. Often this may be reflective of underlying affective disorder, such as depression, and may cause results to demonstrate more significant cognitive impairment than the actual deficit; therefore, it is important to observe patient effort during assessment.

Ms. X.'s Orientation

Ms. X. was alert with no complaints of fatigue during the testing session. She scored a 25/30 on the MMSE using serial sevens criteria and a 26/30 using WORLD. Ms. X. did not know the county she was in, did not know the date, lost 1 point on serial sevens, and lost 2 points on the 3-item delayed recall section.

The MMSE, as discussed previously, is one of the standard methods to assess degree of dementia. In this case, the patient demonstrates mild dementia. Of note, the patient has declined 3 to 4 points in 2 months. Abrupt declines in cognitive ability are more often associated with vascular dementia than AD. It would be valuable to track serial MMSE scores over time with this patient to observe better this pattern of decline—will the scores plateau and then acutely drop (vascular dementia) or will she progressively decline over the course of several months and years? Of note, 5 points of the MMSE may be measured in two ways, either via serial sevens or WORLD. Either is appropriate when performing the MMSE, but it is often helpful to have both as a point of comparison if a patient, for example, has "always been bad at math," as well as for inter-rater consistency. Individuals qualified, by virtue of their education and training, to administer the MMSE should consult the MMSE for further information.

Ms. X.'s Sensory-Perceptual Processes

No evidence of hemi-spatial neglect or inattention emerged from the line bisections. On a visually challenging symbol cancellation task, Ms. X. exhibited two errors of omission, which is within normal limits.

The line bisection task is a pencil-and-paper task measuring visual-spatial neglect in some portion of the examinee's visual field. (Heilman & Valenstein, 1979). Hemi-neglect is suggestive of a focal lesion in the contralateral inferior parietal lobe and is most frequently seen with right-sided lesions and left neglect (Hodgson & Kennard, 2000).

There are several types of symbol cancellation tasks that also assess for spatial neglect: The Star Cancellation Test (Halligan, Marshall, & Wade, 1989), The Letter Cancellation Test (Weintraub & Mesulam, 1985), and The Bells Test (Gauthier, Dehaut, & Joanette, 1989). For any of these tasks, a patient with hemi-neglect will identify the targets accurately on the side of the lesion, but not on the side of neglect. Ferber and Karnath (2001) investigated the accuracy of line bisection and cancellation tasks and found that the cancellation tasks, particularly the Bells Test and Letter Cancellation Test, were superior to line bisection for identifying patients with spatial neglect.

Ms. X.'s Attention, Concentration, and Working Memory

Ms. X.'s basic auditory attention was below average, as she recited 5 digits forward and on digits backwards, a more demanding task, she was only able to recite 3 digits.

Miller (1956) first suggested that working memory has the capacity to hold seven items, such as numbers, plus or minus two other items. The digit span is a measure of working memory that asks patients to repeat a series of digits forward and backward. In an elderly population age 75 and older, research suggests that the digit span might be smaller than 7, with mean digits forward around 5.8 and mean digits backwards around 4.2 (Ryan, Lopez, & Paolo, 1996). Of note, performance appears to be associated with educational level (Ryan et al., 1996). Backward recitation is thought to involve more frontal lobe and executive function than forward recitation (Hoshi et al., 2000). It has been suggested that patients with vascular dementia have significantly poorer performance on backwards digit span than patients with AD, reflective of impaired executive function (Oosterman & Scherder, 2006). However, deficits in attention also have been observed in patients with mild AD compared with age-matched controls (Gorus, De Raedt, Lambert, Lemper, & Mets, 2006). If Ms. X. had been able to perform the backwards digit span more accurately, she may have been invited to perform more complicated dual attention tasks with simultaneous digit span and visual tasks.

Ms. X.'s Processing Speed

Performance on a test of visual tracking and psychomotor speed was severely impaired on one task in which Ms. X. was required to connect numbers and letters serially and discontinued on a second task where she was required to switch between numbers serially, as she was working extremely slowly (although she was able to generally perform the task correctly). Ms. X.'s WAIS-III Processing Speed index score (96) was in the average range for age. She performed in the average range on a task of coding and in the average range on a task of scanning, making one error on the latter task.

Processing speed pertains to how quickly a patient can perform a cognitive task. As described, measures of processing speed include tasks in which patients are asked to connect numbers serially and connect letters and numbers alternately. A coding task such as Digit-Symbol found on the WAIS-III is one example (Wechsler, 1997). Scanning tasks include the Symbol Search found on the WAIS-III (Wechsler, 1997). Poor performance in processing speed has been associated with greater impairment among patients with vascular dementia than with Alzheimer's disease (de Jager, 2004).

Ms. X.'s Motor Functions

Finger Tapping: Dominant mildly impaired, nondominant mildly impaired. Grooved Pegboard: Dominant severely impaired, nondominant severely impaired.

Ms. X. reports left-hand dominance. Measures of gross motor dexterity were mildly improved bilaterally. A measure of fine motor dexterity was severely impaired bilaterally for slowness and incoordination.

Although impaired motor function is not diagnostic in assessing for dementia, it has been observed that patients with Alzheimer's disease demonstrate significant bradykinesia on finger tapping when compared with age-matched controls (Ott, Ellias, & Lannon, 1995). A grooved pegboard task assesses visuo-motor coordination. Hand motor function has been associated with decline in ADLs and IADLs and therefore may offer the practitioner insight into the patient's ability to take care of himself (for review, see Scherder, Dekker, & Eggermont, 2008).

Ms. X.'s Language Functions

Spontaneous speech was fluent, grammatically adequate, and conveyed information satisfactorily.

Confrontational naming was severely impaired (Raw score: 17 of 60). Ms. X. was able to correct 10/21 errors following a phonemic cue. Execution of serial commands requiring precise syntactical comprehension was generally intact. Ms. X. made no errors when asked to repeat both high and low frequency phrases.

The Boston Naming Test (Kaplan, Goodglass, & Weintraub, 1983) is a 60-item test in which patients are presented with line drawings of various objects and are required to name the objects. If the patient is unable to spontaneously provide the name, the tester provides one or more cues. It has been shown that patients with AD demonstrate significantly more errors relative to patients with MCI or normal controls on this test, even after a semantic cue is given. However, after a phonemic cue is given there is no difference statistically among AD, MCI, and control groups (Balthazar, Cendes, & Damasceno, 2008). This is exemplified by Ms. X. who was able to correct 10/21 errors after phonemic cuing. As AD progresses, patients have difficulty holding serial commands in working memory as well as interpreting more complex syntax, such as a simple, auditory three-step command. Errors in repetition are observed in later stages of Alzheimer's disease (Weiner, Neubecker, Bret, & Hynan, 2008).

Ms. X.'s Spatial Functions

When Ms. X was asked to produce a clock drawing, the placement of her numbers was slightly off and she incorrectly drew the lengths of the hands. The hands were pointed to the correct numbers.

Please refer to prior discussion of clock drawing for details of analysis.

Ms. X.'s Educational Attainment

Word reading was average, equivalent to a high school grade level.

Although there will be variability in each patient's performance, the key for understanding educational attainment is to assess whether the patient's performance is appropriate for her own known educational level.

Ms. X.'s Verbal Intellectual Functioning

Ms. X. displayed below-average performances on a test of vocabulary.

The WAIS-III vocabulary subtest (Wechsler, 1997) is a test of verbal comprehension. Word-finding difficulty is a presenting symptom in both vascular dementia and AD, and studies suggest that there is no difference in performance on this subtest between the two groups (Oosterman & Scherder, 2006). Time to onset of word-finding difficulty may be an indicator of underlying pathology; acute onset of impairment is more likely associated with aphasic stroke and slowly worsening impairment is more likely associated with a progressive disease.

Ms. X.'s New Learning and Memory for Verbal Information

Ms. X. obtained below-average scores for both immediate memory for paragraph length stories and mildly impaired scores for free recall of the information following a 30-minute delay. Her ability to learn the stories was in the below-average range.

During a paragraph recall task the patient listens to the examiner read a passage and recalls as much of the paragraph as possible both immediately and after a delay. Impaired performance on delayed paragraph recall has been demonstrated to be a significant predictor of decline from MCI to dementia, and more specifically to AD (Fleisher et al. 2007; Kluger, Ferris, Golomb, Mittelman, & Reisberg, 1999). Performance in this patient is consistent with such a pattern of decline.

Ms. X.'s New Learning and Memory for Visual Information

Memory for visual information was average for immediate recall and delayed recall was below average.

In tasks of visual memory such as the delayed matching to sample task (DMS 48), patients are presented with images of novel items and after a distractor task they must identify which item of a series of pairs is the object previously displayed. This is then repeated after a delay (Barbeau et al., 2004). Research indicates that deficits in this domain occur in early MCI and progressively worsen until patients with moderate AD answer at random (Barbeau et al., 2004). SPECT imaging suggests that temporomesial and temporoparietal hypoperfusion observed in patients with MCI who perform poorly on this task is similar to that observed in patients with AD (Guedj et al., 2006). Tests of visual memory also help to distinguish among other types of dementias; for example, patients with Lewy Body Dementia demonstrate significantly impaired performance on the DMS 48 compared with patients with Parkinson's disease dementia (Mondon et al., 2007). Therefore, it is important to consider visual memory as one component of a full neuropsychological profile in considering possible diagnoses for a patient. This patient's performance on this visual memory task, in combination with performance on other neuropsychological tasks, is suggestive of dementia on the AD spectrum.

Ms. X.'s Self-Regulation / Executive Functions

Ms. X.'s performance on controlled phonemic fluency was average. Her performance on semantic fluency was moderately to severely impaired. Complex

motor programming was performed with difficulty. Ms. X. was able to spontaneously mimic the Lurian pronation/supination task, but made two errors.
She was unable to perform the clenching/extending task even after several
attempts. On a verbal regulation task, there was one error on a go/no-go
during the habitual meaning trial and one error on the reverse meaning trial.
Graphic sequencing was within normal limits. On a planning task in which Ms.
X. was asked to solve WISC mazes she performed in the low average range.

The above tasks are means of testing executive function, governed
by the frontal lobe. Semantic fluency is one such type of test. Lurian
motor sequencing tasks were developed to assess frontal lobe function
through imitation of specific gestures (Luria, 1966), as in go/no-go
testing involving motor tapping (Hodges, 1994). The Wechsler Intelligence Scale for Children (WISC) maze task (Wechsler, 1949) is a maze
task with points given increasingly for errors in following the established
rules. Although traditionally executive function impairment has been
considered a factor distinguishing frontotemporal dementia from AD, at
least one study has shown no statistically significant difference between
these two conditions with respect to semantic fluency, Lurian motor
sequencing, go/no-go testing, and the WISC maze task, although patients in both groups were on average in early stages of disease (Gregory,
Orrell, Sahakian, & Hodges, 1997). Therefore, as in the case with this
patient, it is important to consider the full clinical picture before selecting a diagnosis based on testing of executive functions alone.

Conclusions

Overall Ms. X. demonstrates cognitive decline consistent with mild cognitive
impairment through to early phase dementia. Although her visual memory
was average to below average, her verbal memory was mildly impaired to
low average. Additionally, her complex mental tracking, semantic fluency,
and confrontation naming were severely impaired. Given her multiple medical
problems, a multifactorial etiology seems likely. Her impaired performances
on semantic fluency and naming tasks suggest that Alzheimer's pathology is
likely contributory. Ms. X. demonstrated severe deficits on motor tasks, and

it is unclear whether these deficits are related to her osteoarthritis or to another cause.

Although the neuropsychological assessment taken as a whole suggests that this patient has MCI progressing to early AD, it is important
to note that some inconsistencies with this diagnosis may be observed
in the report (such as deficits on motor tasks). It is therefore necessary
to take other comorbid etiologies, such as the patient's chronic medical
conditions, into consideration when considering these results.

AFTER REVIEWING THE REPORT

How Should the Neuropsychological
Report Affect Clinical Management?

After a full medical workup, the neuropsychological report can prompt
the next steps for patient care. The patient discussed in this chapter
appears to have MCI progressing to AD, and therefore might benefit
from psychopharmacological treatment appropriate for early stage AD.
A home safety assessment should be considered in any patient with
progressive cognitive decline to identify environmental hazards. Additionally, planning for future care including discussion of advanced
directives and health care proxy is wise to consider while the patient
maintains capacity for decision-making. It is helpful to establish a treatment team whenever possible, including a general practitioner, psychiatrist, neuropsychologist, and social worker, who can work together with
the patient and her family in a holistic approach to patient management.

When Should the Patient Obtain
Follow-Up Neuropsychological Evaluation?

In general, the neuropsychological assessment should be considered
part of a continuing process of evaluating patients' abilities to care for
themselves safely and independently. Therefore, follow-up assessments
are useful to monitor the rate and pattern of cognitive decline. Specific
time frame for repeat assessment is individual and may be dictated by

subjective report by the patient or caregiver of worsening performance with ADLs and IADLs. Generally, with slow progressive decline a patient may be re-evaluated with full neuropsychological assessment in 12 to 24 months, with MMSE evaluations done at the practitioner's office at scheduled visits in the interim. Acute change in mental status, however, always should be assessed medically before proceeding to neuropsychological evaluation.

CONCLUSION

In summary, neuropsychological testing is beneficial in the assessment of geriatric patients who exhibit symptoms of cognitive decline. As the preceding case demonstrates, determination of a specific diagnosis of cognitive impairment in the elderly is often complicated by comorbid medical conditions, medications, affective symptoms, and demographic features. Additionally, a patient may suffer from more than one type of dementia (e.g., AD with superimposed vascular dementia and depression). As part of a comprehensive evaluation by psychiatrists, psychologists, medical doctors, radiologists, family resource specialists, and social workers, neuropsychological evaluation is helpful to establish a baseline, monitor pattern of decline, aid in diagnosis, assess for safety, and provide a basis to determine appropriate management.

ACKNOWLEDGMENT

The authors are indebted to Keith Hawkins, PsyD, Yale University Department of Psychiatry, for excerpts from the neuropsychological report used in this chapter.

REFERENCES

Balthazar, M. L., Cendes, F., & Damasceno, B. P. (2008). Semantic error patterns on the Boston Naming Test in normal aging, amnestic mild cognitive impairment, and mild Alzheimer's disease: Is there semantic disruption? *Neuropsychology, 22,* 703–709.

Barbeau, E., Didic, M., Tramoni, E., Felician, O., Joubert, S., Sontheimer, A., et al. (2004). Evaluation of visual recognition memory in MCI patients. *Neurology, 62,* 1317–1322.

de Jager, C. A. (2004). Changes over time in memory, processing speed, and clock drawing tests help to discriminate between vascular cognitive impairment, mild cognitive impairment, and Alzheimer's disease. *Neurological Research, 26,* 481–487.

Ferber, S., & Karnath, H. O. (2001). How to assess spatial neglect—Line bisection or cancellation tasks? *Journal of Clinical and Experimental Neuropsychology, 23,* 599–607.

Fischer, P. (1996). The spectrum of depressive pseudo-dementia. *Journal of Neural Transmission. Supplementum, 47,* 193–203.

Fleisher, A. S., Sowell, B. B., Taylor, C., Gamst, A. C., Petersen, R. C., Thal, L. J., & Alzheimer's Disease Cooperative Study. (2007). Clinical predictors of progression to Alzheimer's disease in amnestic mild cognitive impairment. *Neurology, 68,* 1588–1595.

Folstein, M. F., Folstein, S. E., & McHugh, P. R. (1975). "Mini-mental state." A practical method for grading the cognitive state of patients for the clinician. *Journal of Psychiatric Research, 12,* 189–198.

Gauthier, L., Dehaut, F., & Joanette, Y. (1989). The bells test: A quantitative and qualitative test for visual neglect. *International Journal of Clinical Neuropsychology, 11,* 49–54.

Gorus, E., De Raedt, R., Lambert, M., Lemper, J. C., & Mets, T. (2006). Attentional processes discriminate between patients with mild Alzheimer's disease and cognitively healthy elderly. *International Psychogeriatrics, 18,* 539–549.

Gregory, C. A., Orrell, M., Sahakian, B., & Hodges, J. R. (1997). Can frontotemporal dementia and Alzheimer's disease be differentiated using a brief battery of tests? *International Journal of Geriatric Psychiatry, 12,* 375–383.

Guedj, E., Barbeau, E. J., Didic, M., Felician, O., de Laforte, C., Ceccaldi, M., et al. (2006). Identification of subgroups in amnestic mild cognitive impairment. *Neurology, 67,* 356–358.

Halligan, P. W., Marshall J. C., & Wade, D. T. (1989). Visuospatial neglect: Underlying factors and test sensitivity. *Lancet, 14,* 908–911.

Heilman, K. M., & Valenstein, E. (1979). Mechanisms underlying hemispatial neglect. *Annals of Neurology, 5,* 166–170.

Hodges, J. R. (1994). *Cognitive assessment for clinicians: A practical guide.* Oxford, UK: Oxford University Press.

Hodgson, T. L., & Kennard, C. (2000). Disorders of higher visual function and hemispatial neglect. *Current Opinion in Neurology 13,* 7–12.

Hoshi, Y., Oda, I., Wada, Y., Ito, Y., Yutaka, Y., Oda, M., et al. (2000). Visuospatial imagery is a fruitful strategy for the digit span backward task: A study with near-infrared optical tomography. *Brain Research. Cognitive Brain Research, 9,* 339–342.

Juby, A., Tench S., & Baker, V. (2002). The value of clock drawing in identifying executive cognitive dysfunction in people with a normal Mini-Mental State Examination score. *Canadian Medical Association Journal, 167,* 859–864.

Kaplan, E. F., Goodglass, H., & Weintraub, S. (1983). *Boston Naming Test.* Philadelphia: Lea & Febiger.

Katz, S. (1983). Assessing self-maintenance: Activities of daily living, mobility, and instrumental activities of daily living. *Journal of the American Geriatrics Society, 31,* 721–727.

Kluger, A., Ferris, S. H., Golomb, J., Mittelman, M. S., & Reisberg, B. (1999). Neuropsychological prediction of decline to dementia in nondemented elderly. *Journal of Geriatric Psychiatry and Neurology, 12,* 168–179.

Lawton, M. P., & Brody, E. M. (1969). Assessment of older people: Self-maintaining and instrumental activities of daily living. *The Gerontologist, 9,* 179–186.

Luria, A. R. (1966). *Higher cortical functions in man.* New York: Basic Books.

Malouf, R., & Areosa Sastre, A. (2003). Vitamin B12 for cognition. *Cochrane Database of Systematic Reviews, 3,* CD004326.

McArthur, J. C., Sacktor, N., & Selnes, O. (1999). Human immunodeficiency virus associated dementia. *Seminars in Neurology, 19,* 129–150.

Miller, G. A. (1956). The magical number seven, plus or minus two: Some limits on our capacity for processing information. *Psychological Review, 63,* 81–97.

Mondon, K., Gochard, A., Marqué, A., Armand, A., Beauchamp, D., Prunier, C., et al. (2007). Visual recognition memory differentiates dementia with Lewy bodies and Parkinson's disease dementia. *Journal of Neurology, Neurosurgery, and Psychiatry, 78,* 738–741.

Oosterman, J. M., & Scherder, E. J. (2006). Distinguishing between vascular dementia and Alzheimer's disease by means of the WAIS: A meta-analysis. *Journal of Clinical and Experimental Neuropsychology, 28,* 1158–1175.

Ott, B. R., Ellias, S. A., & Lannon, M. C. (1995). Quantitative assessment of movement in Alzheimer's disease. *Journal of Geriatric Psychiatry and Neurology, 8,* 71–75.

Roe, C. M., Xiong, C., Miller, P., & Morris, J. C. (2007). Education and Alzheimer's disease without dementia: Support for the cognitive reserve hypothesis. *Neurology, 68,* 223–228.

Rouleau, I., Salmon, D. P., Butters, N., Kennedy, C., & McGuire, K. (1992). Quantitative and qualitative analyses of clock drawings in Alzheimer's and Huntington's disease. *Brain and Cognition, 18,* 70–87.

Royall, D. R., Mahurin, R. K., & Gray, K. F. (1992). Bedside assessment of executive cognitive impairment: The executive interview. *Journal of the American Geriatrics Society, 40,* 1221–1226.

Ryan, J. J., Lopez, S. J., & Paolo, A. M. (1996). Digit span performance of persons 75–96 years of age: Base rates and associations with selected demographic variables. *Psychological Assessment, 8,* 324–327.

Scherder, E., Dekker, W., & Eggermont, L. (2008). Higher-level hand motor function in aging and (preclinical) dementia: Its relationship with (instrumental) activities of daily life—a mini-review. *Gerontology, 54,* 333–341.

Sunderland, T., Hill, J. L., Mellow, A. M., Lawlor, B. A., Gundersheimer, J., Newhouse, P. A., et al. (1989). Clock drawing in Alzheimer's disease. A novel measure of dementia severity. *Journal of the American Geriatrics Society, 37,* 725–729.

Watson, Y. I., Arfken, C. L., & Birge, S. J. (1993). Clock completion: An objective screening test for dementia. *Journal of the American Geriatrics Society, 41,* 1235–1240.

Wechsler, D. (1949). *Weschler Intelligence Scale for Children. Manual.* New York: Psychological Corporation.

Wechsler, D. (1997).*Wechsler Adult Intelligence Scale—Third edition (WAIS-III).* San Antonio, TX: Psychological Corporation.

Weiner, M. F., Neubecker, K. E., Bret, M. E., & Hynan, L. S. (2008). Language in Alzheimer's disease. *The Journal of Clinical Psychiatry, 69,* 1223–1227.

Weintraub, S., & Mesulam, M. M. (1985). Mental state assessment of young and elderly adults in behavioral neurology. In M. M. Mesulam (Ed.), *Principles of behavioral neurology* (pp. 71–123). Philadelphia: F. A. Davis.

Index